The Complete Time Waster

...gpie Books, London

Constable & Robinson Ltd
3 The Lanchesters
162 Fulham Palace Road
London W6 9ER
www.constablerobinson.com

This edition published by Magpie Books,
an imprint of Constable and Robinson Ltd 2005

A copy of the British Library Cataloguing in Publication Data
is available from the British Library

ISBN 1 84529 014 3

Printed and bound in India

3 5 7 9 10 8 6 4

Puzzle compilation, typesetting and design by:

Puzzle Press Ltd
http://www.puzzlepress.co.uk

with additional material by Diane Law

PICK 'N' MIX

Choose three words to make your new musical style:

Fusion	Indie
Syncopation	Alien
Mega	Wave
Roots	Blue
Delinquent	Casual

PRE-FAME NAME GAME

By what name do we know this famous person?

Richard Jenkins

_____

TODAY'S GREATEST ACHIEVEMENT

Getting out of bed ☐

Act of random kindness ☐

Nobel nomination ☐

WHATEVER YOU DO, don't even THINK about...

Any of the following songs:

Tie A Yellow Ribbon
Danny Boy
Popcorn
Chirpy Chirpy Cheep Cheep
Hurdy Gurdy Man

COUPLINGS

Apart from two, every word listed below can be coupled with one of the others to make another word or phrase. Rearrange the letters of the two which can't be paired together, to form one word, the name of a fictional character.

1 BIRTHDAY	2 GOOD
3 PEN	4 BROKEN
5 STORM	6 HAPPY
7 BONNET	8 LINED
9 LUCK	10 RAIN
11 CLEAR	12 FRIEND
13 EASTER	14 HEART

Answer: _____

WORK BOUND

What's the best route to work – and the best route home?

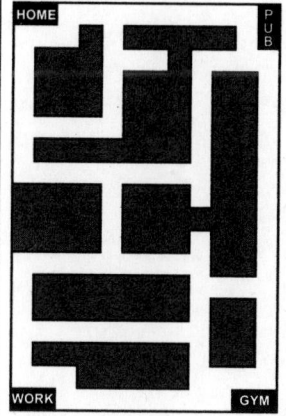

MISSING LETTERS

One letter of the alphabet is missing from each box. Find them all and place them in the order of the numbered boxes to reveal a six-letter word.

Word: _____

1	2	3
QYVMF RLNGS HOWKT XIUPC EJZAB	YITAN SBJFM PUCZD QHVGL REWXK	ATXOI HUWBP MCVJQ ZRDFK LSYGE

4	5	6
AZRVG SLQFB JMECP DUNXH YTIWO	RAOFZ KSPLX GNTJB HCIVD YMUQW	OVCGJ BPKRS LAUZE HMDIR NWTXQ

DICEY ARITHMETIC

Using three of the arithmetical signs ÷, −, x and +, can you achieve the correct total?

    =

STARTING LINE

Which three letter word can be placed at the start, to form three seven-letter words?

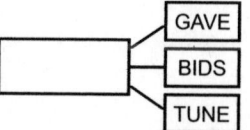

GAVE
BIDS
TUNE

TWO DOWN

Fit five of the seven listed words into the Across rows in the grid, so that the other two words read down the shaded columns numbered 2 and 3.

BELLY	EDGES
EIGHT	HIRED
SHOWS	TRAIL
WHILE	

1	2		3	
4				
5				
6				
7				

1

BROKEN-HEARTED

Don't be half-hearted in your attempts to get these couples back together again! Match both sides of each heart, to reveal their names.

___ & ___   ___ & ___   ___ & ___

___ & ___   ___ & ___   ___ & ___

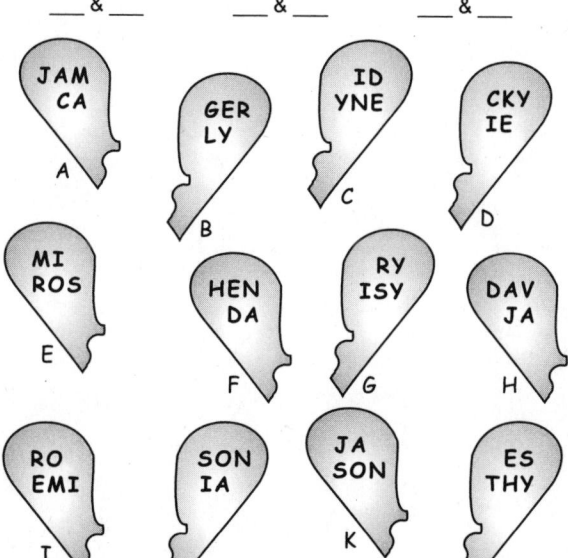

JAM CA — A

GER LY — B

ID YNE — C

CKY IE — D

MI ROS — E

HEN DA — F

RY ISY — G

DAV JA — H

RO EMI — I

SON IA — J

JA SON — K

ES THY — L

JOIN THE DOTS

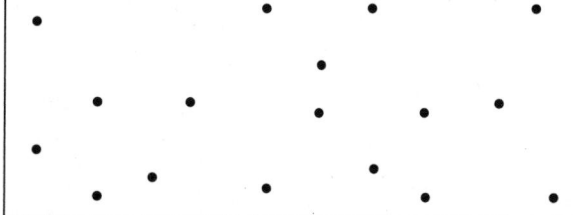

JIGSAW CROSSWORD

Fit the blocks into the empty grid to form a complete crossword which, when finished, will be symmetrical, similar to the example seen here:

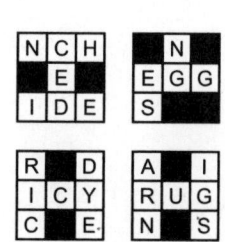
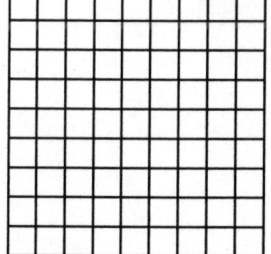

BRIEF SURVIVAL GUIDE

ALIEN INVASION:

1 Mutate and mingle

2 Identify crucial weaknesses

3 Run for the hills

WHERE ON EARTH?

Where on earth is Bastard?

Answer: _____

ODD ONE OUT

Which one is different to the rest?

A   B

C   D

E   F

GET THE LOOK

Make the face:

CONFUSED

PLACE YOUR BETS

State of bank account:

Pleasantly full ☐

Nerve-wrackingly empty ☐

Frozen months ago ☐

LOOSE VOWELS

Someone has taken all the vowels out of what was once a completed crossword. Can you put them all back in again? You should use only those letters beneath the grid.

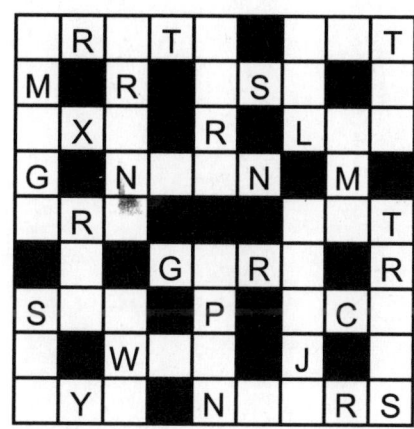

A A A A A A A

E E E E E E E E E E E E E E E

I I

O O O O

U U U U U U

NAME THAT SONG

We give you the first line, you name the song: ♪

Oh yeah, I'll tell you something, I think you'll understand …

Song: _____

IN YOUR OWN LANGUAGE

Devise an Oriental-looking sign for your place of work.

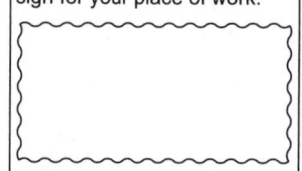

BERMUDA TRIANGLE

Travel through the 'Bermuda Triangle' by visiting one room at a time and collecting a letter from each. You can enter the outside passageway as often as you like, but can only visit each room once. When you've completed your tour, rearrange the fifteen letters to spell out a word.

DOMINOLOGICAL

What is the value of the question mark?

= 18

= 20

= 25

= ?

PAIR SHAPES

In the box below there are shapes in three different colours, black, white and grey. Any shape may have been rotated, but can you see which is the only shape to appear exactly twice in exactly the same colour?

WEATHER for OPTIMISTS

Today the weather will be:

Full of glorious sunshine, despite the clouds!

CODEWORD

This is a crossword puzzle in code. Every number represents a different letter of the alphabet and this number remains the same throughout the puzzle. Use the check-box to keep a track on your progress.

23	4	26	17		2	22	3	18	19	7
1		1			1		7			12
21	22	19	10	1	15		1	19	13	7
7		21		25			25		16	
26	3	13	9	8		26	5	1	4	14
	1			19	7	5			14	
6	4	11	22	7		22	6	26	7	5
	24		25			20		17		1
26 S	7	19	20		1	20	20	1	4	15
7 E			4		25			14		14
1 A	6	1	5	17	12		21	7	15	12

1	2	3	4	5	6	7	8	9	10	11	12	13

14	15	16	17	18	19	20	21	22	23	24	25	26

NAMED AND SHAMED

Least eligible bachelor

_____

Harbouring dark secrets

_____

Possible alien clone

_____

WHAT DOES IT MEAN?

What is the meaning of the word

SOTTAGE

Answer: _____

Answers to puzzles on the previous page

Name That Song: *I Want To Hold Your Hand*, The Beatles.
Bermuda Triangle: The word is RECONSIDERATION.
Odd One Out: C – It is the only one with a mirror image on the right.

Loose Vowels:

I	R	A	T	E		E	A	T
M		R		U	S	E		E
A	X	E		R		L	E	A
G		N	E	O	N			M
E	R	A				O	U	T
		U		G	U	R	U	
S	E	A		P		I	C	E
U		W	O	O		J		E
E	Y	E			N	E	A	R	S

4

MASS HYSTERIAS

Today we are all going to:

> Panic and faint because the Martians are coming.

MIRROR WRITING

Write this word upside down:

GHASTLY

_____

LETTER TRACKER

Begin in the central shaded square and follow a continuous path which will track from square to square, up, down and sideways, but never diagonally.

Your trail should cover every letter once only, in order to find:

Eighteen sports, hobbies and pastimes.

D	I	R	G	N	I	F	O	O	L	C
I	N	G	D	I	V	Y	E	T	L	R
I	L	C	G	N	I	C	K	B	A	I
M	N	G	B	O	X	O	A	B	T	C
B	I	L	N	I	S	H	S	E	E	K
I	S	T	N	E	T	C	G	B	A	L
N	E	Y	R	E	H	Y	N	I	M	L
G	R	W	N	G	C	C	N	G	M	S
S	K	I	I	Y	R	L	I	J	I	W
I	T	H	C	A	A	O	D	U	O	L
N	G	J	O	G	G	I	N	G	P	O

CHARACTER ASSIGNATION

Fill in the answers to the clues, across the grid. Then read down the diagonal line of eight squares, to reveal:
A character from John Bunyan's _The Holy War_.

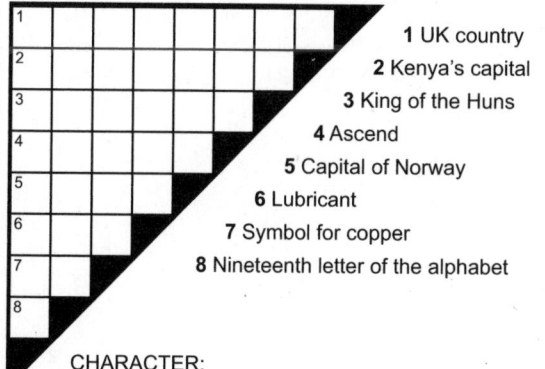

1 UK country
2 Kenya's capital
3 King of the Huns
4 Ascend
5 Capital of Norway
6 Lubricant
7 Symbol for copper
8 Nineteenth letter of the alphabet

CHARACTER: _____

SECRET MISSION

Your secret mission (should you choose to accept it) is:

To make as many comedy belching noises as possible without detection.

DO YOU KNOW...

...what happened on this date?

26 April 1986

ARRANGING THINGS

If you fit six of these seven words into the grid below, the word left over will appear reading down the shaded squares.

ABACUS   ACCRUE
CHANGE   CHEQUE
COUNTS   FISCAL
        OBTAIN

A MATCHING PAIR

Miss Washet would like a matching pair of bowls and pitchers for her bedroom. Which two should she buy?

A   B

C   D

E   F

DOMINADDITION

Can you place the remaining dominoes in their correct positions, so that the total number of spots in each of the four rows and five columns equals the sum at the end of that row or column?

? = 17
= 15
= 20
= 11

= 13   = 17   = 14   = 6   = 13

TOP TEN

CARROTS ☐
POTATOES ☐
CABBAGES ☐
SPROUTS ☐
ONIONS ☐
BROCCOLI ☐
MUSHROOMS ☐
PEPPERS ☐
AUBERGINES ☐
ASPARAGUS ☐

THIS WEEK'S PHOBIAS

Ablutophobia – fear of washing or bathing
Dextrophobia – Fear of objects at the right side of the body
Metrophobia – Fear of poetry

GET THE LEADER

Can you unscramble the anagram to reveal the leader?

He bugs Gore

Answer: _____

COMPLETE THIS LIMERICK:

There was a young lady from Ealing

Who had a peculiar feeling

She took off her mac

Then lay on her back

And _____

Answers to puzzles on the previous page

Do You Know… There was a nuclear disaster at Chernobyl.
Character Assignation: 1 Scotland, 2 Nairobi, 3 Attila, 4 Climb, 5 Oslo, 6 Oil, 7 Cu, 8 S. Character: Diabolus.
Letter Tracker: Tennis, Hockey, Football, Cricket, Baseball, Swimming, Cycling, Judo, Archery, Wrestling, Boxing, Diving, Riding, Climbing, Skiing, Yachting, Jogging, Polo.

USE YOUR IMAGINATION

Can you fill each of these boxes with a totally different shape?

WORD LADDER

Change one letter at a time (but not the position of any letter) to make a new word – and move from the word at the top of the ladder to the word at the bottom using the exact number of rungs provided.

F O O L

W I S E

WEATHER for PESSIMISTS

Today the weather will be:

Unrelentingly dismal and darkly dim.

TOP FIVE

Best songs for my funeral:

1 _____
_____

2 _____
_____

3 _____
_____

4 _____
_____

5 _____
_____

SYMBOLISM

What whole number value between 1 and 9 should be allocated to each different symbol in order to reach the sum totals shown at the end of each row and column?

■	●	◆	▲	=21
	◆	▲	◆	=15
▲		◆	■	=19
■	■	■		=21
=23	=12	=22	=19	

THINK ABOUT IT!

Can you picture this animal?

An eleraffe

EXCUSES FOR

Being late again:

_____
_____
_____
_____
_____

Answers to puzzles on the previous page

Get The Leader: George Bush
Arranging Things: Across (from the top): Accrue, Obtain, Change, Fiscal, Cheque, Counts. Down: Abacus.
A Matching Pair: B and E

Dominaddition:

3	2	6	1	5
0	4	5	2	4
6	6	3	1	4
4	5	0	2	0

FOR SALE

This is worth the asking price

of _____ because it

once belonged to _____

_____,

who used it for _____

_____

MISSING LINKS

Which word links the one on the left with the one on the right? We've done the first one, and when you've finished them all, the first letters of the link words will spell another word.

FENCE	**POST**	DATED
BAND		WORKER
FISHING		BALL
DUCK		HEARTED
RIGHT		POISE

SUM TOTAL

Place the digits 1-9, one per square, so that the sums are correct, according to the totals at the ends of the rows and columns. The calculations should be done in the order in which they appear, for example 6–2x5=20 should be read as 6–2(=4), then 4x5=20.

	x		–		=	33
x		–		+		
	+		x		=	21
–		+		+		
	–		+		=	11
=		=		=		
26		6		20		

DESIGN YOUR OWN

Bedroom

THOUGHT FOR THE DAY

"Work keeps us from three great evils: boredom, vice and need."

Voltaire

LEARNING LINES

We give you a line, you tell us who said it and the film:

"Fasten your seat belts. It's going to be a bumpy night."

WORDWHEEL

Using only the letters in the Wordwheel, you have ten minutes to find as many words as possible, none of which may be plurals, foreign words or proper nouns. Each word must be of three letters or more, all must contain the central letter and letters can only be used once in every word. There is at least one nine-letter word in the wheel.

Nine-letter word: _____

Wordwheel letters: E, R, I, V, G, N, P, E (central: A)

PRAYER FOR TODAY

Today I will pray for someone who badly needs help:

_____

DICE-SECTION

Printed onto every one of the six numbered dice below are six letters (one per side), which can be rearranged to form the answer to each clue; however, some sides are invisible to you. Use the clues and write every answer into the grid. When correctly filled, the letters in the shaded squares, reading in the order 1 to 6, will spell out a woman's name.

1						
2						
3						
4						
5						
6						

Clues:
1. Planet in our solar system
2. Very fearful
3. Forty-ninth state of the USA
4. Origin, of a river for example
5. Vendor
6. Beaded counting frame

Dice:
1. A, N, R
2. F, A, R
3. A, S, K
4. C, U, R
5. L, E, E
6. C, A, B

MONEY, MONEY, MONEY

The

LEK

is the currency of

_____

PRE-FAME NAME GAME

By what name do we know this famous person?

Allen Stewart Konigsberg

_____

TODAY'S GREATEST ACHIEVEMENT

Appearing sober and calm ☐

Undermining boss's scheme ☐

Saving universe (again) ☐

Answers to puzzles on the previous page

Learning Lines: Margo Channing (Bette Davis), *All About Eve* (1950).
Missing Links: Fence-Post-Dated, Band-Aid-Worker, Fishing-Net-Ball, Duck-Down-Hearted, Right-Angle-Poise.
The word is: PANDA.

Sum Total:

6	x	7	–	9
x		–		+
5	+	2	x	3
–		+		+
4	–	1	+	8

SPOT THE DIFFERENCE

Can you spot the eight differences between these two clowns?

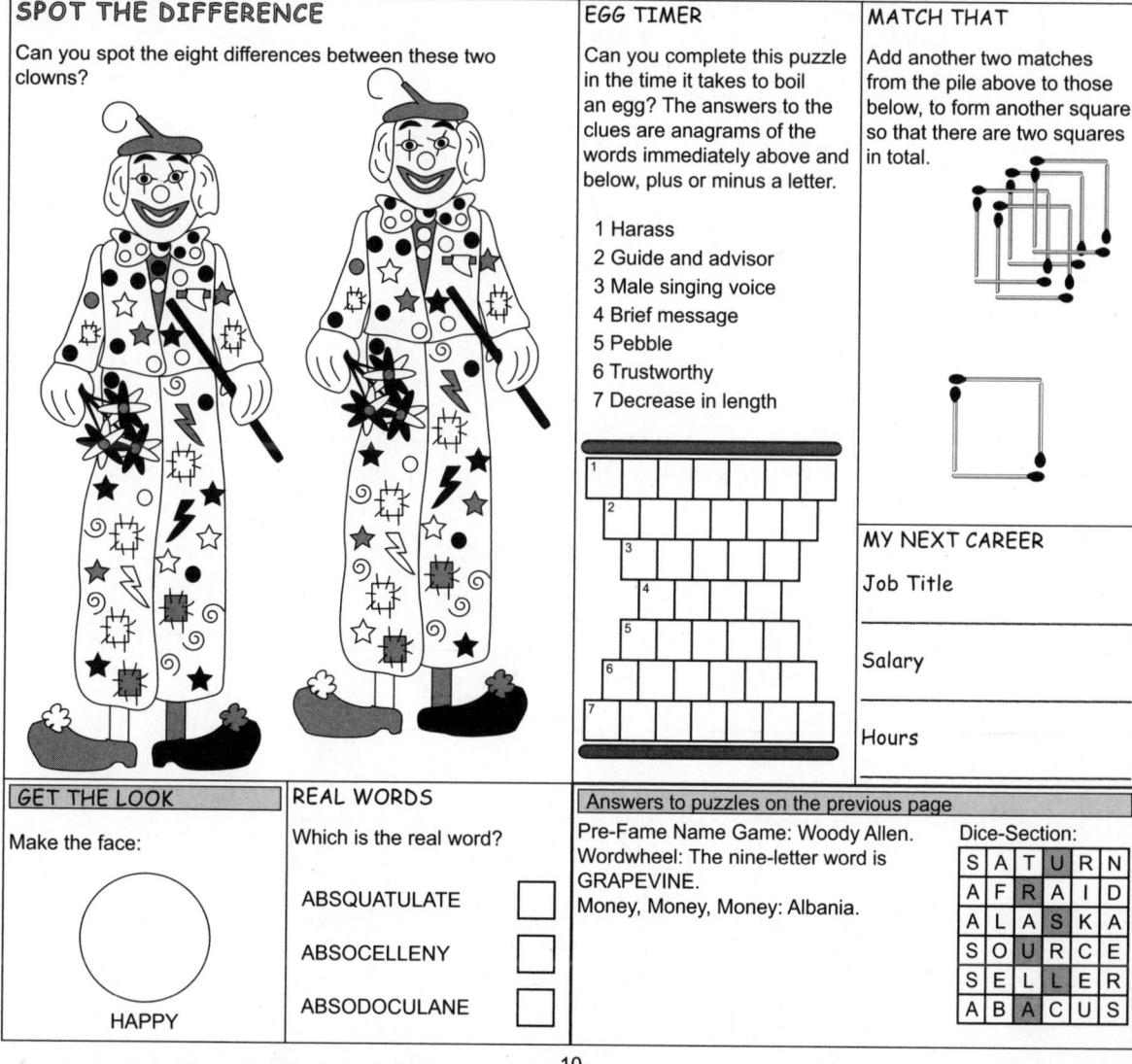

EGG TIMER

Can you complete this puzzle in the time it takes to boil an egg? The answers to the clues are anagrams of the words immediately above and below, plus or minus a letter.

1 Harass
2 Guide and advisor
3 Male singing voice
4 Brief message
5 Pebble
6 Trustworthy
7 Decrease in length

MATCH THAT

Add another two matches from the pile above to those below, to form another square, so that there are two squares in total.

MY NEXT CAREER

Job Title

_____

Salary

_____

Hours

GET THE LOOK

Make the face:

HAPPY

REAL WORDS

Which is the real word?

ABSQUATULATE ☐

ABSOCELLENY ☐

ABSODOCULANE ☐

Answers to puzzles on the previous page

Pre-Fame Name Game: Woody Allen.
Wordwheel: The nine-letter word is GRAPEVINE.
Money, Money, Money: Albania.

Dice-Section:

S	A	T	U	R	N
A	F	R	A	I	D
A	L	A	S	K	A
S	O	U	R	C	E
S	E	L	L	E	R
A	B	A	C	U	S

SWEET BAD MUSIC

So who on earth was responsible for this lyric?

Here's your favorite radio station, in your favorite radio city
The city by the bay, the city that rocks, the city that never sleeps)
Marconi plays the mamba, listen to the radio, don't you remember.

CAPITALS

The capital of

MONGOLIA

is:

_____

CLOCKWORDS

It's a race against the clock…
How many common words of three or more different letters can you make from those on the clockface (without using plurals, proper nouns or abbreviations) in ten minutes? All words must contain BOTH the letters indicated by the hands on the clock.

PROVERBS & SAYINGS

The letters on the tiles were once all in place, but dropped out, falling in a straight line into the lower grid. Some tiles dropped earlier than others, so those on the lowest row aren't all from the same row in the grid above. Can you put them back into position in order to reveal a well-known proverb or saying?

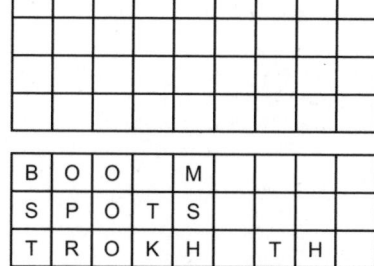

B	O	O		M					
S	P	O	T	S					
T	R	O	K	H			T	H	
C	O	O	I		L	A	N	Y	E

MISSING LETTERS

One letter of the alphabet is missing from each box. Find them all and place them in the order of the numbered boxes to reveal a six-letter word.

Word: _____

1	2	3
PUCZO	OVCGJ	VGPZA
QHVGL	BPKRS	JCHQL
DEWXK	LUYZE	OWTIK
YITAN	HMDIR	SFYRM
SBJFM	NWTXQ	DEXUN

4	5	6
AVZRN	KYZQB	YLPXW
LQCSI	CPLRJ	MZDGK
DMWHJ	SDXHM	FECJQ
PEYKT	TOGEW	NAHSR
GUXFO	NUAFV	IOUBV

WAYS TO PASS THE TIME

Drinking ☐

Sleeping ☐

Knitting ☐

PICK 'N' MIX

Choose three words to make your new fashion direction:

Co-ordinated   Electric
Classic   Gypsy
Deranged   Chic
Colour-blind   Nouvelle
Vogue   Chintz

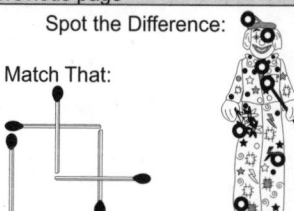
11

A IS TO B

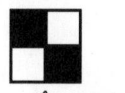

A is to B

as C  is to

D E

F G

TWO-WORD HOROSCOPES

Aries – You're serious?

Taurus – Oh, God.

Gemini – Don't panic.

Cancer – Horny, hopeless.

Leo – Mystery man.

Virgo – Oops. Again?

Libra – Wake up!

Scorpio – Colossal mess.

Sagittarius – Absurd attire.

Capricorn – Dream on.

Aquarius – Why not?

Pisces – Never mind.

DICEY ARITHMETIC

Using three of the arithmetical signs ÷, −, x and +, can you achieve the correct total?

    =

JIGSAW CROSSWORD

Fit the blocks into the empty grid to form a complete crossword which, when finished, will be symmetrical, similar to the example seen here:

```
K E D      E   T
  L        A   A
B L A      T L Y

T A L      H E S
  C          E
  R          B E

T R A    A Y      O R C      I        D E C
    R    N  ·     M  A       C        Y
A S T    D E N    I  L     N K S      E V I
```

WHO AM I?

I lace words

I am:
_____

TOP TEN

RED ☐

BLUE ☐

GREEN ☐

WHITE ☐

YELLOW ☐

ORANGE ☐

PURPLE ☐

BLACK ☐

PINK ☐

LEMON ☐

SAY IT, DO IT, BE IT

Your word for today is:

OVERWHELMING

Answers to puzzles on the previous page

Sweet Bad Music: Starship, *We Built This City*

Missing Letters: RABBIT.

Capitals: Ulaanbaatar.

Proverbs & Sayings: Too many cooks spoil the broth.

12

WHATEVER NEXT?

Which of the numbered alternatives comes next in this sequence:

J	A	S	O	N	?

1	2
R	D

3	4
C	J

BALANCING THE SCALES

Given that scales A and B balance perfectly, how many squares are needed to balance scale C?

TWO DOWN

Fit five of the seven listed words into the Across rows in the grid, so that the other two words read down the shaded columns numbered 2 and 3.

ADMIT   ELDER
GEESE   SENSE
SLOWS   SWISS
      WRIST

ON TARGET

The answers to the clues read from the outer circle to the centre, all ending with the same letter. When you've finished, the letters in the shaded ring will give a word.

1 Sailing vessel

2 Aircraft operator

3 Perfume

4 Envy, desire

5 Lamb's cry

6 Erupt

PLACE YOUR BETS

Contents of sock drawer:

41 rainbow variety ☐

6 grey and black ☐

1 unidentified odd stocking ☐

Lost cheque book and dust ☐

NAME THAT SONG

We give you the first line, you name the song: ♪

A few questions that I need to know, how you could ever hurt me so?

Song: _____

Answers to puzzles on the previous page

Who Am I? Oscar Wilde.
Dicey Arithmetic: The signs are minus, plus and times.
A Is To B: E – They are vertical mirror images.

Jigsaw Crossword:

O	R	C	H	E	S	T	R	A
M		A		E			R	
I		L		B	E	A	S	T
T	A	L	K	E	D		I	
C		R		L			C	
R		B	L	A	N	K	S	
D	E	C	A	Y		E		T
Y		N		N		A		A
E	V	I	D	E	N	T	L	Y

13

WORDSEARCH

Can you find all of the listed boys' names in the grid?
Words may run in either a forwards or backwards direction,
horizontally, vertically or diagonally, but always in a straight,
uninterrupted line.

AARON

ABNER

ABSALOM

ADAM

ALEXANDER

ALISTAIR

AMOS

AMYAS

ANGUS

ARCHIBALD

AUGUSTUS

```
A U G U S T U S W A L L Y
M A R M A D U K E L R A C
R I A T S I L A M A D A O
R N C H R I S T O P H E R
C E I A N G U S L F A F N
M H D M A X A A O E R R E
A R R N A B L Y H R C E L
R E T I A J I M T D H D I
T N L N S X N A R I I E U
R B R I E T E E A N B R S
E A A R O N I L B A A I O
B M O L A S B A A N L C M
S E B A S T I A N D D K A
```

BARNABAS	CHRISTIAN	FREDERICK
BARTHOLOMEW	CHRISTOPHER	MARMADUKE
BENJAMIN	CORNELIUS	MAX
BERTRAM	ELI	SEBASTIAN
CARL	FERDINAND	WALLY

PYRAMID PLUS

Every brick in this pyramid
contains a number which
is the sum of the two
numbers below it, so
that F=A+B, etc. No
two bricks contain
the same number,
or just a zero,
so work out
the missing
numbers!

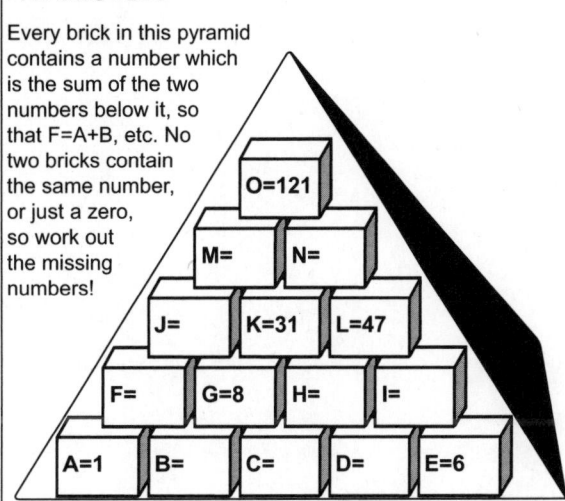

O=121

M=   N=

J=   K=31   L=47

F=   G=8   H=   I=

A=1   B=   C=   D=   E=6

POTATOE OR POTATO?

COOLLY

OR

COOLY

NAMED AND SHAMED

Least likely to succeed
_____

Suspected enemy agent
_____

Most insipid demeanour
_____

WEATHER for OPTIMISTS

Today the weather
will be:

Dull and damp with a
great opportunity to use
that new umbrella.

WHERE ON  ?

Where on earth is
Dildo?

Answer: _____

UNFINISHED PICTURE

Can you complete the left half of this picture?

MASS HYSTERIAS

Today we are all going to:

Carry umbrellas in case the sky falls down.

LETTER TRACKER

Begin in the central shaded square and follow a continuous path which will track from square to square, up, down and sideways, but never diagonally.

Your trail should cover every letter once only, in order to find:

Twenty-one colours.

T	P	E	A	G	R	E	E	N	P	U
E	O	H	C	T	E	L	O	I	P	R
L	R	A	N	G	E	G	O	V	L	E
R	A	C	L	E	I	I	I	R	P	A
U	E	S	L	Y	N	D	C	O	E	Y
L	B	W	O	N	T	E	B	T	R	B
R	I	M	S	O	U	I	G	E	G	L
C	D	E	V	U	R	Q	U	O	C	A
R	E	R	E	A	M	E	S	I	K	C
M	V	E	T	I	H	W	M	A	E	R
I	L	I	O	N	C	E	R	I	S	E

MONEY, MONEY, MONEY

The

KWANZA

is the currency of

_____

JOIN THE DOTS

BRIEF SURVIVAL GUIDE

ZOMBIE TAKEOVER:

1 Play dead

2 Cultivate a glassy stare

3 Machete madness

WHAT DOES IT MEAN?

What is the meaning of the word

BARATHRUM

Answer: _____

_____

Answers to puzzles on the previous page

Where On Earth? Newfoundland, Canada.
Potatoe or Potato? Coolly.
Pyramid Plus: A=1, B=3, C=5, D=18, E=6, F=4, G=8, H=23, I=24, J=12, K=31, L=47, M=43, N=78, O=121.

15

WORDFILLER

Can you place all the listed words into the grid below?

								E	

3 letters
ALI
ELI
TED

4 letters
AMOS
CARL
DALE
NEIL
NOEL
SEAN

5 letters
CLAUD

6 letters
CEDRIC
DANIEL
DENNIS

7 letters
CHARLES
CRISPIN
JOACHIM

9 letters
CHRISTIAN

COUPLINGS

Apart from two, every word listed below can be coupled with one of the others to make another word or phrase. Rearrange the letters of the two which can't be paired together, to form one word, the name of an outdoor activity.

1 PIPE	2 ROUTINE
3 GOLD	4 PINE
5 KENNEL	6 FRIDAY
7 WATER	8 GOOD
9 DOG	10 MEDAL
11 NEEDLE	12 MILK
13 CHURN	14 MEANING

Answer: _____

THE TANGLED TRAIL

Which of these anglers has landed the fish?

A   B   C

THE WHOLE PICTURE

Can you finish this picture?

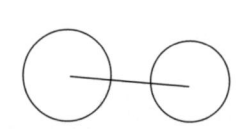

MIRROR WRITING

Write this word upside down:

_____

EXCUSES FOR

Leaving work early:

_____
_____
_____
_____
_____

SECRET MISSION

Your secret mission (should you choose to accept it) is:

To see how many household objects you can balance on the tip of your nose.

DO YOU KNOW...

...what happened on this date?

26 July 1908

LUCKY NUMBER

Discover your lucky number for today by following these instructions:

1. Think of a number between thirty-three and sixty-six;
2. Add together the last two digits of your year of birth;
3. Add the result of 1 above to the result of 2 above;
4. Reverse the digits in this number.

Now you have your lucky number
for today. Don't lose it – write it down: _____

COMPLETE THIS LIMERICK:

There was an old man from Devizes

Whose life was full of surprises

One day whilst in town

He met with a clown

_____

HEXAGONY

Can you place the hexagons in the grid, so that where any triangle touches another along a straight line, the contents of both are the same? One triangle is already filled.

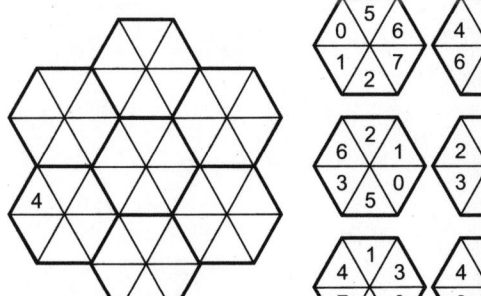

SHAPE RECOGNITION

Which are the only three pieces which will fit together perfectly, to form a complete circle?

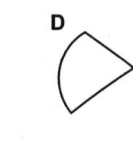

A

B

C

D

E

F

STARTING LINE

Which three letter word can be placed at the start, to form three seven-letter words?

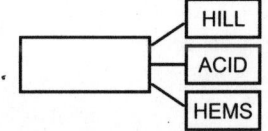

HILL
ACID
HEMS

PRE-FAME NAME GAME

By what name do we know this famous person?

Julia Elizabeth Wells

_____

WHATEVER YOU DO,
don't even THINK about...

The theme tune to any of these:
Dukes of Hazzard
Wheel of Fortune
Top Cat
Seinfeld
Carpet Commercial

GET THE LEADER

Can you unscramble the anagram to reveal the leader?

Bad also in name

Answer: _____

Answers to puzzles on the previous page

Do You Know... FBI founded in the USA (or Salvador Allende born).
Couplings: 3/10, 4/11, 7/1, 8/6, 9/5, 12/13.
The letters of 2 and 14 can be rearranged to form MOUNTAINEERING.
The Tangled Trail: Angler B.

Wordfiller:

STARTER LETTER

Write down one each of the listed items, all of which must begin with the starter letter:

G

Country	
Tree	
Boy's name	
Girl's name	
River	
City	
Animal	
Make of car	
Drink	

UNLIKELY CANDIDATE

POPE

_____

EYE-SPY

I spy with my little eye something beginning with:

_____

DOMINADDITION

Can you place the remaining dominoes in their correct positions, so that the total number of spots in each of the four rows and five columns equals the sum at the end of that row or column?

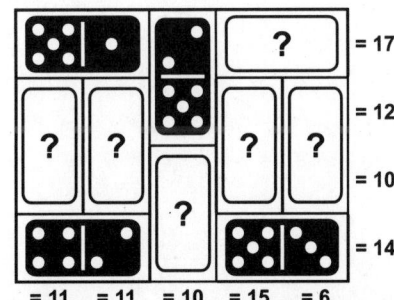

= 17
= 12
= 10
= 14

= 11   = 11   = 10   = 15   = 6

ARRANGING THINGS

If you fit six of these seven words into the grid below, the word left over will appear reading down the shaded squares.

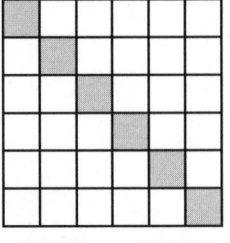

ANSWER   ATTACH
DENOTE   HYPHEN
LESSON   LETTER
POSTED

THIS WEEK'S PHOBIAS

Pogonophobia – Fear of beards
Anthrophobia – Fear of flowers
Panophobia – Fear of everything

WEATHER for PESSIMISTS

Today the weather will be:

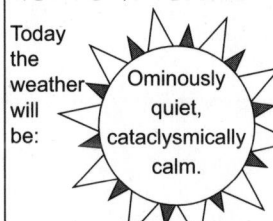

Ominously quiet, cataclysmically calm.

LEARNING LINES

We give you a line, you tell us who said it and the film:

"Look, you don't know me from Adam. But I was a better man with you as a woman than I ever was with a woman as a man. Know what I mean?"

Answers to puzzles on the previous page
Pre-Fame Name Game: Julie Andrews.
Get The Leader: Osama Bin Laden.
Starting Line: ANT.
Shape Recognition:

Hexagony:

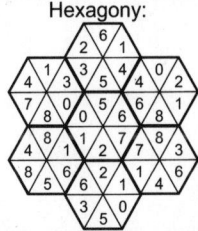

18

BOX CLEVER

When the above is folded to form a cube, which one of the following can be produced?

A B C D E

WORDWHEEL

Using only the letters in the Wordwheel, you have ten minutes to find as many words as possible, none of which may be plurals, foreign words or proper nouns. Each word must be of three letters or more, all must contain the central letter and letters can only be used once in every word. There is at least one nine-letter word in the wheel.

Nine-letter word: _____

SYMBOLISM

What whole number value between 1 and 9 should be allocated to each different symbol in order to reach the sum totals shown at the end of each row and column?

Best songs for my wedding:

1 _____
  _____
2 _____
  _____
3 _____
  _____
4 _____
  _____
5 _____
  _____

REAL WORDS

Which is the real word?

BODELLESCIOUS ☐

BROBDINGNAGIAN ☐

BOGNOMANIA ☐

DESIGN YOUR OWN

Office

Answers to puzzles on the previous page
Learning Lines: Michael Dorsey/Dorothy Michaels (Dustin Hoffman), *Tootsie* (1982)
Arranging Things: Across (from the top): Lesson, Denote, Attach, Posted, Hyphen, Answer. Down: Letter.

Dominaddition:

5	1	2	6	3
1	4	5	2	0
1	4	3	2	0
4	2	0	5	3

19

THIN DIVIDING LINES

By using two straight lines, can you divide this circle into four parts, each containing a star, a triangle and two squares?

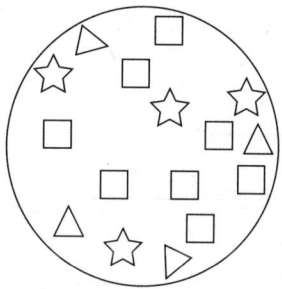

TOTAL CONCENTRATION

Can you fill in the missing numbers so that each row, each column and two longest diagonal lines meet the totals given?

							214

68	20	25	49		4		253
		51	37	48	27	14	226
4		33	26	27	35	47	175
57		41	38	61		61	365
60	17		64	23			273
47		1	20	7	16	14	107
40	27	52			33	68	272

280	155	230	243	243	225	295	291

WORD LADDER

Change one letter at a time (but not the position of any letter) to make a new word – and move from the word at the top of the ladder to the word at the bottom using the exact number of rungs provided.

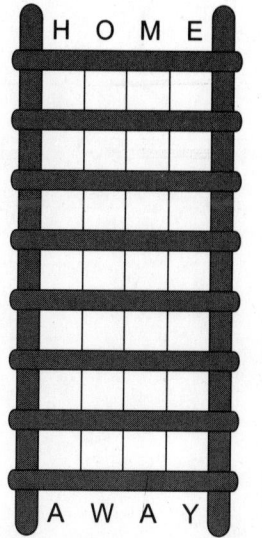

H O M E

A W A Y

CELEBRITY WRESTLING

CHARLTON HESTON

-v-

RUSSELL CROWE

TODAY'S GREATEST ACHIEVEMENT

Not panicking ☐

New sandwich filling ☐

Grand unified theory ☐

SWEET BAD MUSIC

So who on earth was responsible for this lyric?

You can tell your Ma,

I moved to Arkansas,

You can tell your dog

To bite my leg.

MATCH THAT

Remove one match to leave six!

Answers to puzzles on the previous page

Real Words: Brobdingnagian. Of or relating to a gigantic person or thing.
Wordwheel: The nine-letter word is CONFIGURE.
Box Clever: D.
Symbolism: Circle=3, Diamond=5, Square=1, Triangle=4.

SNAKES & LADDERS

This is a standard game, so when you land at the foot of a ladder, you climb it; and when you land on the head of a snake, you slide down its tail. You need to throw an exact number to land on 100 to win – counting backwards if you don't, eg if you land on 98 and throw a five, you will end up on 97. The dice is thrown for you and always lands in this recurring order: 6, 4, 3, 2, 1, 5, so you can start by immediately placing your counter on square 6. Good luck – hope you win!

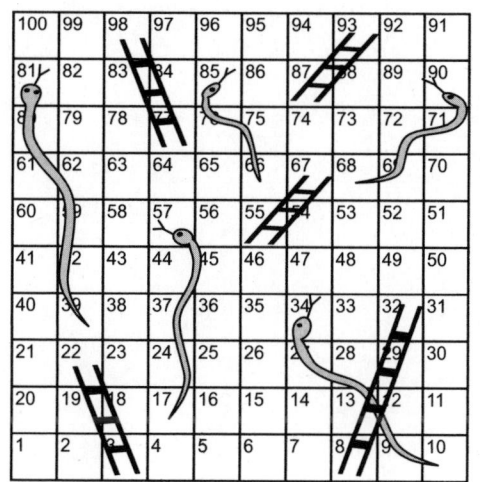

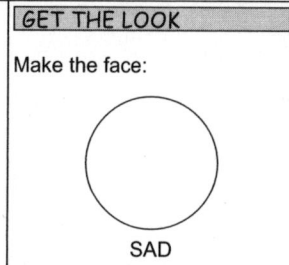
WAYS TO PASS THE TIME

Talking ☐

In silence ☐

Worrying ☐

WOMEN'S AGES

The letters A, B, D, E, I, G, L, N and R have been allocated different single digit numbers from 1-9 inclusive. Coincidentally, the women listed below are the same age as the total of the digits assigned to the letters in their names. How old is Barbara?

ANNA = 24   ANGELA = 28   DIANE = 30   ELAINE = 26

GLENDA = 30   LINDA = 29   NADINE = 35   BARBARA = _____

IN YOUR OWN LANGUAGE

Devise an Oriental-looking sign for your partner.

PICK 'N' MIX

Choose three words to describe tonight's video blockbuster:

Violent   Sensual
Comedy   Foreign
Drama   Epic
Worthy   Pointless
Spectacular   Gothic

WHERE ON EARTH ?

Where on earth is Brown Willy?

Answer: _____

Answers to puzzles on the previous page

Sweet Bad Music: Billy Ray Cyrus, *Achy Breaky Heart*.
Word Ladder: One solution is HOME, come, core, wore, wire, wiry, airy, awry, AWAY.
Total Concentration:
From left to right, top to bottom the missing numbers are: 34, 53, 4, 45, 41, 66, 27, 44, 38, 2, 9 and 43.

Thin Dividing Lines:

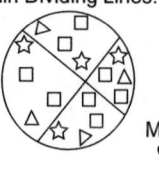

Match That:

21

NAME THAT SONG

We give you the first line, you name the song: 🎵

There she stood in the street, smiling from her head to her feet.

Song: _____

THOUGHT FOR THE DAY

Failure is just the first step on the road to success … or wherever.

CLOCKWORDS

It's a race against the clock… How many common words of three or more different letters can you make from those on the clockface (without using plurals, proper nouns or abbreviations) in ten minutes? All words must contain BOTH the letters indicated by the hands on the clock.

PATCHWORK

Fit the numbers 1, 2, 3, 4, 5 and 6 into the grid below, so that every horizontal row, every vertical column and the two long diagonal lines of six smaller squares contain six different numbers. Some are already in place.

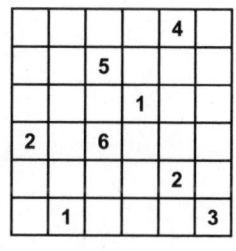

TOP TEN

DAISIES ☐

TULIPS ☐

ROSES ☐

POPPIES ☐

DAFFODILS ☐

BUTTERCUPS ☐

HYACINTHS ☐

SUNFLOWERS ☐

PANSIES ☐

BLUEBELLS ☐

CODEWORD

This is a crossword puzzle in code. Every number represents a different letter of the alphabet and this number remains the same throughout the puzzle. Use the check-box to keep a track on your progress.

1	2	3	4	5	6	7	8	9	10	11	12	13

14	15	16	17	18	19	20	21	22	23	24	25	26

CAPITALS

The capital of

NORTH KOREA

is:

_____

DICEY ARITHMETIC

Using three of the arithmetical signs ÷, −, x and +, can you achieve the correct total?

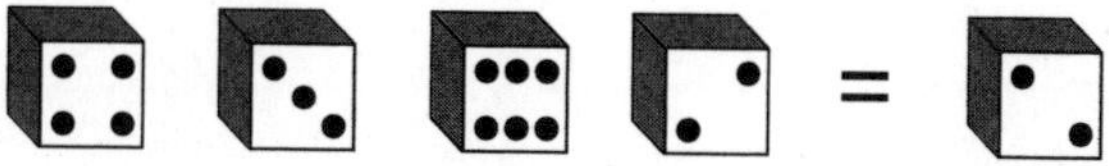

[dice] 4 [dice] 3 [dice] 6 [dice] 1 = [dice] 2

TWO DOWN

Fit five of the seven listed words into the Across rows in the grid, so that the other two words read down the shaded columns numbered 2 and 3.

ASIDE   HOOKS
NAKED   OTHER
PRINT   ROOTS
     WOMAN

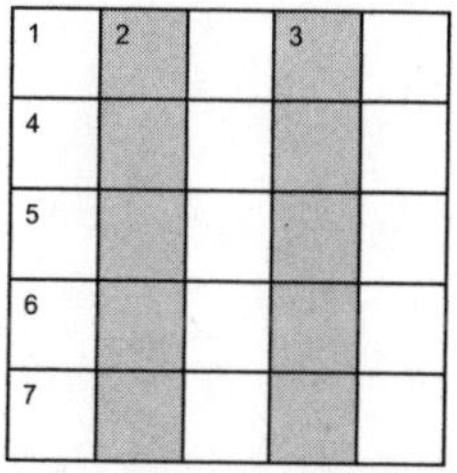

1	2		3	
4				
5				
6				
7				

MISSING LETTERS

One letter of the alphabet is missing from each box. Find them all and place them in the order of the numbered boxes to reveal a six-letter word.

Word: _____

1	2	3
DRYLU	TJVAE	ACGJV
VKQEF	KUFPI	BPKRS
MJGAP	BSLGX	HMDLF
CWHSO	HZOCQ	UZEIR
XIZTN	NYDMW	NWTXQ

4	5	6
JTXAP	HMTYA	OJAIV
YQBLF	GLSUB	PBWTF
ZGRMC	PCFIO	CXQKM
DWUSH	ZQDVJ	GYRDL
INVEO	KRWXN	EZSHU

JIGSAW CROSSWORD

Fit the blocks into the empty grid to form a complete crossword which, when finished, will be symmetrical, similar to the example seen here:

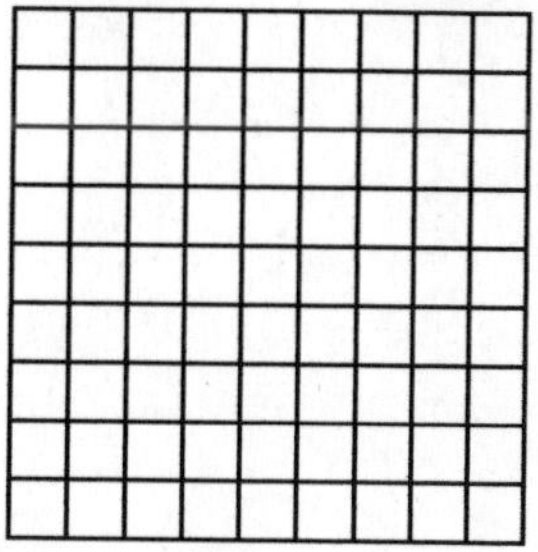

[example grid]

[block grids]

```
E G O    R   O
M I C    G A P
E N T    E   U

N   A    O P E
E L Y    R A R
S   S    E Y E

E   L    E   O    D D S    T T E    T Y R
A T O    S E W    I        A        O
S   S    T   H    E E K    O R S    R U N
```

[empty crossword grid]

WEATHER for OPTIMISTS

Today the weather will be:

Severe thunderstorms where the sky will turn a delicious shade of blue.

PLACE YOUR BETS

_____'s outfit today will be:

Smart, sober, sensible [ ]

Crude, crazy, crass [ ]

Wacky, weird, why? [ ]

WHAT DOES IT MEAN?

What is the meaning of the word

TRENCHERMAN

Answer: _____

_____

Answers to puzzles on the previous page

Name That Song:
All Right Now, Free.

Patchwork:

1	5	3	6	4	2
4	6	5	2	3	1
3	2	4	1	5	6
2	3	6	5	1	4
6	4	1	3	2	5
5	1	2	4	6	3

Codeword:

```
R E B U F F   P   D
A   I   R   C O L O N
S H R I E K E D   Z
H   T   Q   N   S E W
E X H A U S T I O N
R   D   E   R   M   A
  J A U N T I N E S S
B O Y   T   F   W   I
  I   S L O U C H E D
E N V O Y   G   A   E
  T   N   D E P T H S
```

23

MEALTIME MEMORY

It often surprises people how little they remember of day-to-day life. Can you remember your main meal of the day from Monday of last week through to the following Sunday?

Monday		Friday	
Tuesday		Saturday	
Wednesday		Sunday	
Thursday			

JUST A WORD

Can you find 'LAMB' hidden in the grid, wordsearch-style?

```
D L G I J M V E D T M A L
U L A W F G H J U B W D A
C E B M B D E W M I G L M
M E I O A M M D R W A I O
C B I L E L A I V U S M T
J U K M L E A L I E S T R
```

MY FAVOURITE THINGS

These are a few of my favourite things:

My favourite colour is:

_____

My favourite number is:

_____

My favourite snack is:

_____

My favourite day of the week is:

_____

A IS TO B

A is to B

as is to

D E

F G

CHARACTER ASSIGNATION

Fill in the answers to the clues, across the grid. Then read down the diagonal line of eight squares, to reveal: A character from Lewis Carroll's *Alice's Adventures in Wonderland*.

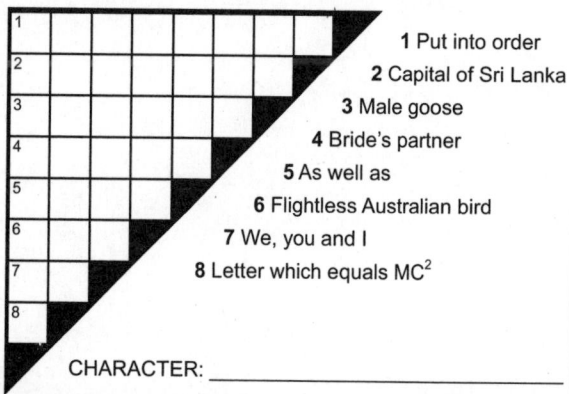

1 Put into order
2 Capital of Sri Lanka
3 Male goose
4 Bride's partner
5 As well as
6 Flightless Australian bird
7 We, you and I
8 Letter which equals MC^2

CHARACTER: _____

SECRET MISSION

Your secret mission (should you choose to accept it) is:

To look incredulous and/or shocked by anything anyone says to you today.

PRE-FAME NAME GAME

By what name do we know this famous person?

Frederick Austerlitz

_____

FROM HOUSE TO HOUSE

Make your own way around the houses.

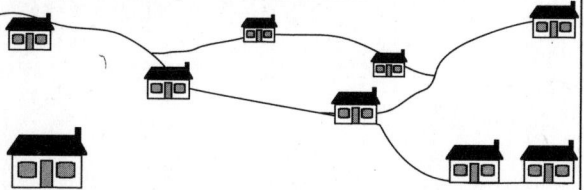

BALANCING THE SCALES

Given that scales A and B balance perfectly, how many squares are needed to balance scale C?

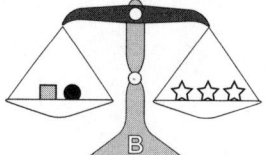

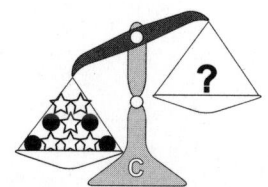

DICE-SECTION

Printed onto every one of the six numbered dice below are six letters (one per side), which can be rearranged to form the answer to each clue; however, some sides are invisible to you. Use the clues and write every answer into the grid. When correctly filled, the letters in the shaded squares, reading in the order 1 to 6, will spell out a man's name.

Season of the year

Beetle thought sacred by ancient Egyptians

Fuel for a car

Movement

Playing a rôle

___ the Sailor, hero of the *Arabian Nights*

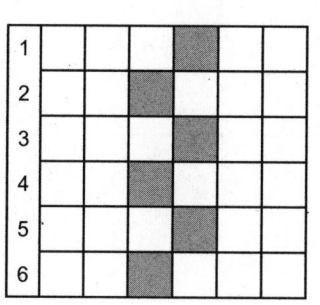

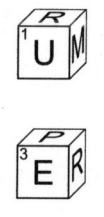

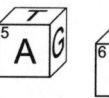

NAMED AND SHAMED

Needs personality infusion

_____

Most cloying couple

_____

Too innocent to be true

_____

EXCUSES FOR

Two weeks at the beach:

_____

_____

_____

_____

DO YOU KNOW...

...what happened on this date?

10 November 1775

Answers to puzzles on the previous page

Pre-Fame Name Game:
Fred Astaire.
Character Assignation:
1 Arranged, 2 Colombo,
3 Gander, 4 Groom, 5 Also,
6 Emu, 7 Us, 8 E.
Character: Dormouse.
A Is To B: G – They are horizontal reflections, with an increase of one spot in each triangle.

Just A Word:

D	L	G	I	J	M	V	E	D	T	M	A	L
U	L	A	W	F	G	H	J	U	B	W	D	A
C	E	B	M	**B**	D	E	W	M	I	G	L	M
M	E	I	O	**A**	M	M	D	R	W	A	I	O
C	B	I	L	E	L	**A**	I	V	U	S	M	T
J	U	K	M	L	E	A	**L**	I	E	S	T	R

THE TANGLED TRAIL

Which child is holding the string attached to the present?

A   B   C

LETTER TRACKER

Begin in the central shaded square and follow a continuous path which will track from square to square, up, down and sideways, but never diagonally.

Your trail should cover every letter once only, in order to find:

Eighteen presidents of the United States of America.

O	M	H	N	E	S	I	E	N	L	I
R	L	O	W	E	C	L	I	O	N	N
E	L	I	F	R	N	O	N	T	O	C
G	A	R	I	N	G	T	R	I	S	O
E	I	F	H	S	A	A	R	M	N	L
L	D	J	O	H	W	H	N	A	D	I
C	A	R	O	N	O	N	A	N	O	S
K	J	D	F	S	S	R	G	M	R	O
S	O	N	N	O	L	E	A	U	N	E
S	U	B	M	A	I	N	O	X	I	N
H	T	R	U	N	W	H	A	Y	E	S

EGG TIMER

Can you complete this puzzle in the time it takes to boil an egg? The answers to the clues are anagrams of the words immediately above and below, plus or minus a letter.

1 Secluded
2 Shrub used for hedging
3 Serpent
4 Mature, ready to eat
5 First in rank
6 Allow
7 High priest

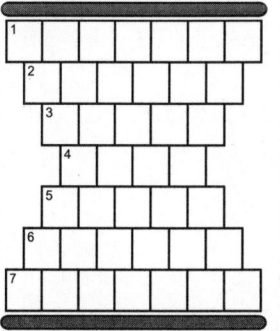

BRIEF SURVIVAL GUIDE

VAMPIRE INTRUSION:

1 Garlic rub

2 Keep stake handy

3 Don't answer that door!

GET THE LEADER

Can you unscramble the anagram to reveal the leader?

Unarmed and despises this

Answer: _____

Answers to puzzles on the previous page

Do You Know… Birth of the US Marine Corps.
Balancing The Scales: Four.

Dice-Section:

S	U	M	M	E	R
S	C	A	R	A	B
P	E	T	R	O	L
M	O	T	I	O	N
A	C	T	I	N	G
S	I	N	B	A	D

PROVERBS & SAYINGS

The letters on the tiles were once all in place, but dropped out, falling in a straight line into the lower grid. Some tiles dropped earlier than others, so those on the lowest row aren't all from the same row in the grid above. Can you put them back into position in order to reveal a well-known proverb or saying?

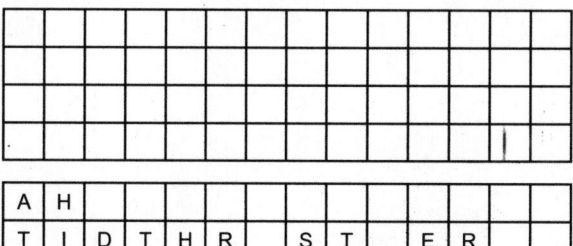

A	H										
T	I	D	T	H	R		S	T		E	R
S	N	W	E	Y	S		G	R	H	I	N
O	L	E	A	G	E	A	O	S	E	E	S	E	R

USE YOUR IMAGINATION

Can you fill each of these boxes with a different girl's name?

COUPLINGS

Apart from two, every word listed below can be coupled with one of the others to make another word or phrase. Rearrange the letters of the two which can't be paired together, to form one word, a professional occupation.

1 FORE	2 MASTER
3 MAGIC	4 BALL
5 SHINE	6 ROOMS
7 HEAD	8 PAY
9 CIRCLE	10 SUN
11 SLIP	12 GROUND
13 SNOW	14 SATCHEL

Answer: _____

WHATEVER YOU DO, don't even THINK about...

Any of the following:

Crack in the bathroom ceiling

Your working day

Damp patch in the bedroom

TOP FIVE

Best songs for a rainy day:

1 _____
_____

2 _____
_____

3 _____
_____

4 _____
_____

5 _____
_____

INSULT OF THE DAY

"I think this wine has been drunk before."

Anon

MIRROR WRITING

Write this word upside down:

ABROAD

_____

DESIGN YOUR OWN

Living room

WORDSEARCH

Can you find all of the listed Christmassy words in the grid? Words may run in either a forwards or backwards direction, horizontally, vertically or diagonally, but always in a straight, uninterrupted line.

ANGEL

BOWS

BOXING DAY

CAPON

CHIMNEY

CHRIST CHILD

CHRISTMAS EVE

CRACKER

```
F Q E O T E L T S I M C A
R E T T I L G T N F H H P
D Z H S M D H P O R R R Y
A N G E L G R C I A B I R
S B I V I E R S T N O S A
W O N L S A T S A K X T M
A W T E C C G H R I I M N
D S N K H N S O O N N A I
D T E I I O G P C C G S G
L R L D M P N P E E D E R
I D I E N A I I D N A V I
N U S L E C K N K S Y E V
G I E S Y A R G F E A S T
```

DECORATIONS	GUIDING STAR	SHOPPING
ELVES	KINGS	SILENT NIGHT
FEAST	LIGHTS	SLED
FRANKINCENSE	MISTLETOE	SWADDLING
GLITTER	PRESENT	VIRGIN MARY

WEATHER for PESSIMISTS

Today the weather will be:

Hot, too hot. Too damned hot.

WHERE ON E A ?

Where on earth is Onacock?

Answer: _____

Answers to puzzles on the previous page
Couplings: 1/12, 3/9, 7/2, 8/11, 10/5, 13/4. The letters of 6 and 14 can be rearranged to form SCHOOLMASTER.
Proverbs & Sayings: The grass is always greener on the other side.

28

THE WHOLE PICTURE

Can you finish this picture?

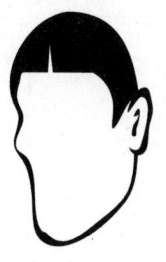

DOMINOLOGICAL

What is the value of the question mark?

= 7

= 9

= 6

= ?

WORDWHEEL

Using only the letters in the Wordwheel, you have ten minutes to find as many words as possible, none of which may be plurals, foreign words or proper nouns. Each word must be of three letters or more, all must contain the central letter and letters can only be used once in every word. There is at least one nine-letter word in the wheel.

Nine-letter word: _____

Wordwheel letters: A, B, S, T, K, N, E, A around central L

SWEET BAD MUSIC

So who on earth was responsible for this lyric?

Love is like a bomb, baby,
   c'mon get it on,
Livin' like a lover with a radar
   phone,
Lookin' like a tramp, like a
   video vamp,
Demolition woman, can I be
   your man?

STARTER LETTER

Write down one each of the listed items, all of which must begin with the starter letter:

R

Country	
Tree	
Boy's name	
Girl's name	
River	
City	
Animal	
Make of car	
Drink	

A HELPING HAND

Give Incey Wincey Spider a web.

GET THE LOOK

Make the face:

WORRIED

UNLIKELY CANDIDATE

WORLD LEADER

_____

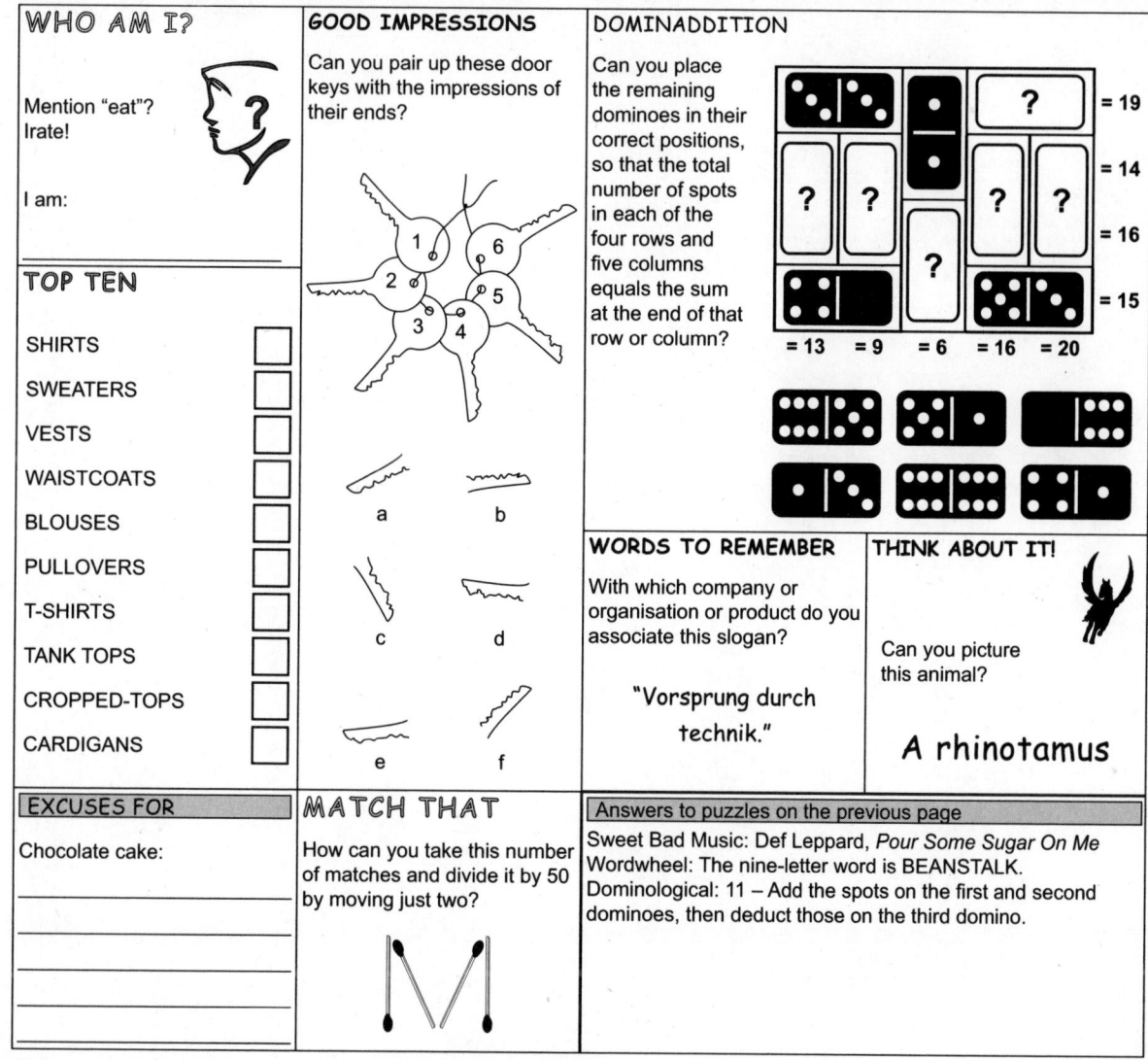

WHO AM I?

Mention "eat"?
Irate!

I am:
_____

TOP TEN

SHIRTS ☐
SWEATERS ☐
VESTS ☐
WAISTCOATS ☐
BLOUSES ☐
PULLOVERS ☐
T-SHIRTS ☐
TANK TOPS ☐
CROPPED-TOPS ☐
CARDIGANS ☐

GOOD IMPRESSIONS

Can you pair up these door keys with the impressions of their ends?

a   b

c   d

e   f

DOMINADDITION

Can you place the remaining dominoes in their correct positions, so that the total number of spots in each of the four rows and five columns equals the sum at the end of that row or column?

= 19
= 14
= 16
= 15

= 13   = 9   = 6   = 16   = 20

WORDS TO REMEMBER

With which company or organisation or product do you associate this slogan?

"Vorsprung durch technik."

THINK ABOUT IT!

Can you picture this animal?

A rhinotamus

MATCH THAT

How can you take this number of matches and divide it by 50 by moving just two?

Answers to puzzles on the previous page

Sweet Bad Music: Def Leppard, *Pour Some Sugar On Me*
Wordwheel: The nine-letter word is BEANSTALK.
Dominological: 11 – Add the spots on the first and second dominoes, then deduct those on the third domino.

SIMPLE AS A,B,C

Each row and column in this grid should contain two each of A, B and C. The clues relate to the squares only in that row across or column down. We only give as many clues as we think you need, so can you place the letters correctly?

Across:
1 The As are somewhere between the Cs.
5 The As are somewhere between the Bs.
6 The Bs are somewhere between the Cs.

Down:
1 The Cs are somewhere between the Bs.
2 Each A is directly next to and below a C.
3 The Bs are both higher than the As.
6 The As are both higher than the Bs.

	1	2	3	4	5	6
1						
2	A					
3				B		
4		B				
5				C		
6						

HEXAGONY

Can you place the hexagons in the grid, so that where any triangle touches another along a straight line, the contents of both are the same? One triangle is already filled.

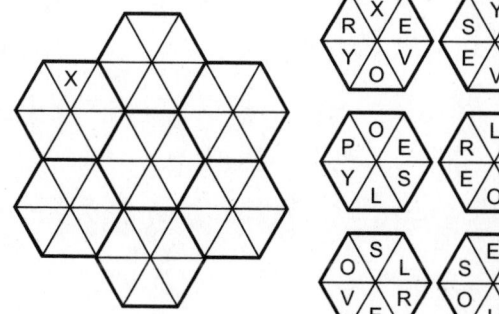

FOR SALE

This is worth the asking price

of _____ because it

once belonged to _____

_____ ,

who used it for _____

_____

Answers to puzzles on the previous page

Who Am I? Marie Antoinette
Dominaddition:

3	3	1	6	6
1	6	1	1	5
5	0	1	4	6
4	0	3	5	3

Words To Remember: Audi.

Match That: Use Roman numerals – M=1,000 and XX=20; 1,000 divided by 50 = 20.

Good Impressions: 1f, 2b, 3c, 4e, 5d, 6a.

What whole number value between 1 and 9 should be allocated to each different symbol in order to reach the sum totals shown at the end of each row and column?

◇	▢	△	▢	=29
◇	△		◇	=19
○	○	○		=9
	▢	△	△	=22

=15 =26 =17 =21

BERMUDA TRIANGLE

Travel through the 'Bermuda Triangle' by visiting one room at a time and collecting a letter from each. You can enter the outside passageway as often as you like, but can only visit each room once. When you've completed your tour, rearrange the fifteen letters to spell out a word.

```
        /\
       /T \
      /L  I\
     /T U M\
    /N E N A\
   /A P E E T\
```

WORD LADDER

Change one letter at a time (but not the position of any letter) to make a new word – and move from the word at the top of the ladder to the word at the bottom using the exact number of rungs provided.

T R U E

L O V E

Can you place all the listed words into the grid below?

3 letters	5 letters
ALE	MAGIC
EVE	PEACE
INN	
IVY	6 letters
	JINGLE
4 letters	
HOPE	8 letters
HYMN	NATIVITY
LIST	
OXEN	9 letters
PINE	MINCEMEAT
WISH	MISTLETOE

NAMED AND SHAMED

Worst dressed

_____

Bad hair day

_____

Bad fat day

_____

WAYS TO PASS THE TIME

Singing ▢

Dancing ▢

Shouting ▢

WHERE ON E A R I ⊥ ?

Where on earth is Titty Hill?

Answer: _____

NAME THAT SONG

We give you the first line, you name the song: ♪

I was blind, now I can see, you made a believer out of me.

Song: _____

DECORATE THE TREE

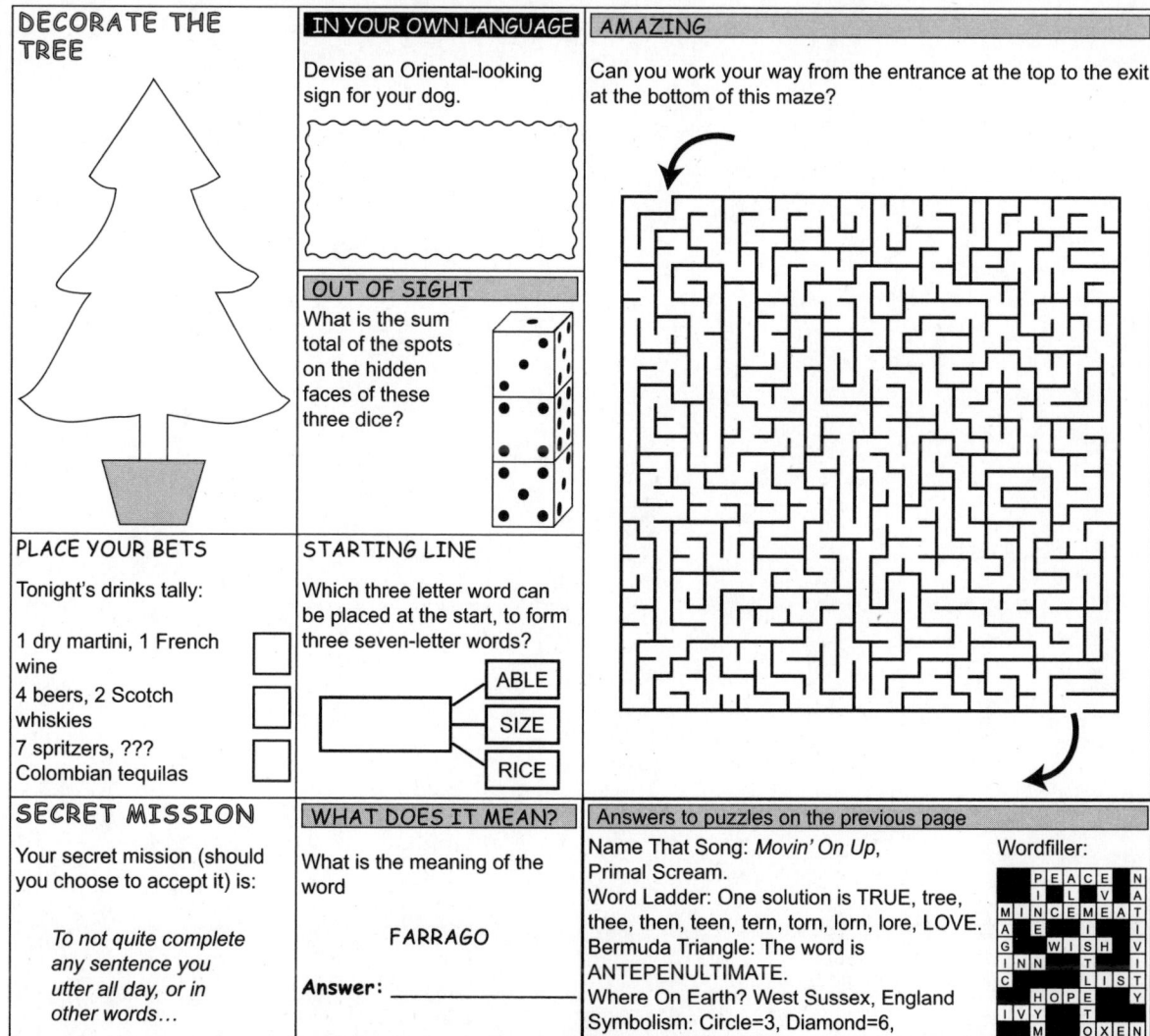

IN YOUR OWN LANGUAGE

Devise an Oriental-looking sign for your dog.

OUT OF SIGHT

What is the sum total of the spots on the hidden faces of these three dice?

AMAZING

Can you work your way from the entrance at the top to the exit at the bottom of this maze?

PLACE YOUR BETS

Tonight's drinks tally:

1 dry martini, 1 French wine ☐

4 beers, 2 Scotch whiskies ☐

7 spritzers, ??? Colombian tequilas ☐

STARTING LINE

Which three letter word can be placed at the start, to form three seven-letter words?

[____] ABLE
[____] SIZE
[____] RICE

SECRET MISSION

Your secret mission (should you choose to accept it) is:

To not quite complete any sentence you utter all day, or in other words…

WHAT DOES IT MEAN?

What is the meaning of the word

FARRAGO

Answer: _____

_____

Answers to puzzles on the previous page

Name That Song: *Movin' On Up*, Primal Scream.
Word Ladder: One solution is TRUE, tree, thee, then, teen, tern, torn, lorn, lore, LOVE.
Bermuda Triangle: The word is ANTEPENULTIMATE.
Where On Earth? West Sussex, England
Symbolism: Circle=3, Diamond=6, Square=8, Triangle=7.

Wordfiller:

TWO DOWN

Fit five of the seven listed words into the Across rows in the grid, so that the other two words read down the shaded columns numbered 2 and 3.

DOUBT   ITEMS
LAMBS   MOTOR
SMILE   TODAY
TRUST

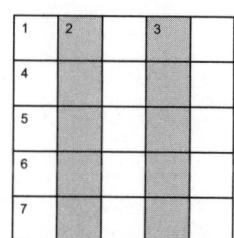

MISSING LINKS

Which word links the one on the left with the one on the right? We've done the first one, and when you've finished them all, the first letters of the link words will spell the name of a planet.

DELIVERY	**VAN**	GUARD
SELVAGE		FORWARDS
FORT		OWL
PLUG		DUCKLING
BRIGHT		PLUG

WHATEVER NEXT?

Which of the numbered alternatives comes next in this sequence:

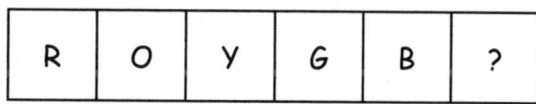

R	O	Y	G	B	?

1 I	2 C
3 V	4 T

DICEY ARITHMETIC

Using three of the arithmetical signs ÷, −, x and +, can you achieve the correct total?

     =

COMPLETE THIS LIMERICK:

There once was a lady from France

Who led men a terrible dance

Whilst courting, she said:

"I will not go to bed

_____."

LEARNING LINES

We give you a line, you tell us who said it and the film:

"Of all the gin joints in all the towns in all the world, she walks into mine."

MASS HYSTERIAS

Today we are all going to:

Paint stigmata on our palms.

Answers to puzzles on the previous page

What Does It Mean? A confused mass of objects or people or any disordered mixture.
Starting Line: CAP.
Out of Sight: 36.

Amazing:

34

ELIMINATION

Every oval shape contains a different letter from A to K inclusive.
Use the clues to determine their locations. Reference in the clues to
'due' means in any location along the same horizontal or vertical line.

1 E is due south of B and due west of J.
2 K is due north of D and due east of A.
3 G is due north of I.
4 C is due south of H and due east of F.
5 F is due north of E and due west of D.

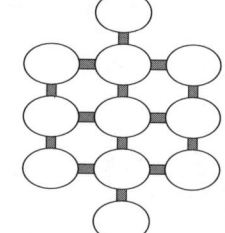

A MATCHING PAIR

Mr Lyte would like a matching
pair of lamps for his lounge.
Which two should he buy?

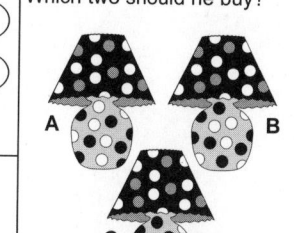

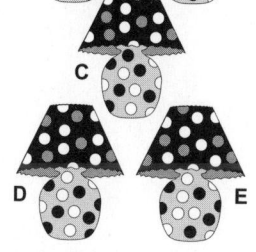

A   B   C   D   E

JIGSAW CROSSWORD

Fit the blocks into the empty grid to form a
complete crossword which, when finished, will be
symmetrical, similar to the example seen here:

```
V I D        S
    L    M A T
T R Y        S
```

```
P U N    N
R        E R I
I P T        M
```

```
T I L    N G    W      T   A    C H I
N        R      A L S  O   G    R   L
  G E    O O P     A   O M E    A   L
```

MISSING LETTERS

One letter of the alphabet is
missing from each box. Find
them all and place them in the
order of the numbered boxes
to reveal a six-letter word.

Word: _____

1	2	3
U Z E I R	P C F B O	R K W A J
N W T X Q	H M T Y A	O X Z B G
F C G J V	G L S U E	F P V C H
O P K Y S	Z Q D V J	N L D I U
H M D L A	K R W X N	M Y Q E T

4	5	6
D M W H J	J A V H N	J Q W G A
E P Y K B	B U F X O	B P V F H
G U X F O	K Z C P G	N R Y C K
Z V A S N	L Q W D I	L U X S D
L Q C R I	T E S Y M	T Z M E I

MY NEXT HOME

Place

_____

Type

_____

Price

_____

GET THE LEADER

Can you unscramble the
anagram to reveal the leader?

I squeeze the noble hand etc

Answer: _____

DO YOU KNOW...

...what
happened
on this
date?

29
December
1170

LETTER TRACKER

Begin in the central shaded square and follow a continuous path which will track from square to square, up, down and sideways, but never diagonally.

Your trail should cover every letter once only, in order to find:

Seventeen countries.

A	L	C	S	W	L	U	T	R	S	A
N	T	O	S	A	A	G	P	O	P	I
D	D	E	E	L	D	O	N	I	A	R
A	M	N	Y	E	A	R	A	U	S	T
R	K	A	R	C	U	O	L	L	A	N
O	N	G	N	U	H	H	Z	T	I	D
R	E	D	E	N	N	Y	E	R	W	S
W	W	A	R	F	A	N	A	L	E	M
A	S	N	C	E	M	D	L	U	X	B
Y	D	N	A	B	R	E	G	M	G	O
F	I	N	L	E	L	G	I	U	R	U

JOIN THE DOTS

PRE-FAME NAME GAME

By what name do we know this famous person?

Betty Joan Perske

NUMB-SKULL

Fit the listed numbers into the grid, crossword-fashion.

2 digits
12
23
25
34
41
45
64
76
77

3 digits
125
167
234
245
444
465

635
764
777

4 digits
2378
5463
7645

5 digits
85647

6 digits
656523
860767

8 digits
45356487

THOUGHT FOR THE DAY

The grass is always greener after ten days of relentless driving rain.

WEATHER for OPTIMISTS

Today the weather will be:

Warm and sunny enough to head for the beach.

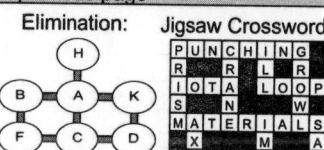

Answers to puzzles on the previous page

Do You Know...
Archbishop Thomas à Becket was murdered in Canterbury Cathedral.
Get The Leader: Queen Elizabeth the Second.
A Matching Pair: A and D.
Missing Letters: BISTRO.

Elimination:

Jigsaw Crossword:

36

ON TARGET

The answers to the clues read from the outer circle to the centre, all ending with the same letter. When you've finished, the letters in the shaded ring will give a word.

1 Bowl

2 Slice of cured pork

3 Country, capital Madrid

4 Warning signal

5 Popular American nut

6 Female ruler

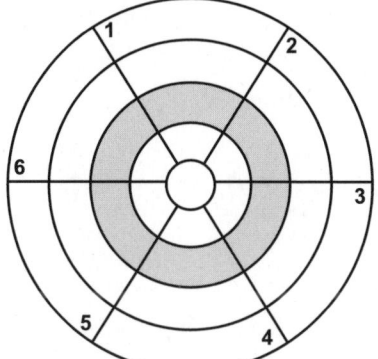

DESIGN YOUR OWN

Restaurant

TWO-WORD HOROSCOPES

Aries – No trousers?

Taurus – You loser!

Gemini – Full house!

Cancer – What now?

Leo – Stay schtum.

Virgo – Here's Johnny!

Libra – Surf's up.

Scorpio – You scoundrel.

Sagittarius – Beware moonlight...

Capricorn – Payback time.

Aquarius – So unfair!

Pisces – As usual.

POTATOE OR POTATO?

SUPERSEDE

OR

SUPERCEDE

SAY IT, DO IT, BE IT

Your word for today is:

QUARRELSOME

WHERE ON  ?

Where on earth is Fukum?

Answer: _____

BRIEF SURVIVAL GUIDE

CHAINSAW MASSACRE:

1 Discard decoy limbs

2 Sheetmetal underclothing

3 Don't stop running

Answers to puzzles on the previous page

Pre-Fame Name Game: Lauren Bacall.
Letter Tracker: Hungary, Ecuador, Austria, Spain, Portugal, Wales, Scotland, Denmark, Norway, Finland, Sweden, France, Belgium, Germany, Holland, Switzerland, Luxembourg.

Numb-Skull:

ARRANGING THINGS

If you fit six of these seven words into the grid below, the word left over will appear reading down the shaded squares.

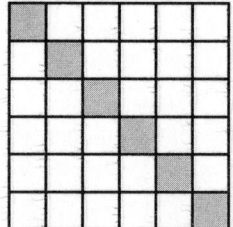

COURSE   GANGES
LIQUID   RAGING
RIVERS   THAMES
TIGRIS

SWEET BAD MUSIC

So who on earth was responsible for this lyric?

On the edge of oblivion

All the world is Babylon

And all the love and everyone

A ship of fools sailing on.

SHADOWLAND

Test your skills of observation. Only one of the five shadows is that of the stork. Which one?

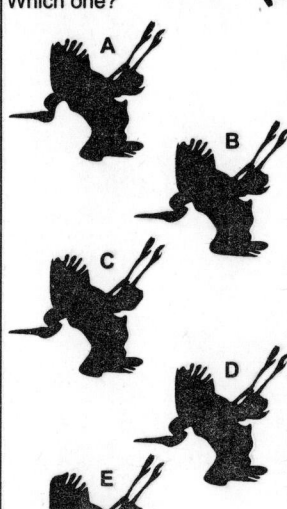

A

B

C

D

E

LUCKY NUMBER

Discover your lucky number for today by following these instructions:
1 Think of a number between ten and forty-two;
2 Think of the digit(s) of the month you were born;
3 Add the result of 1 above to the result of 2 above;
4 Reverse the digits in this number.

Now you have your lucky number for today. Don't lose it – write it down: _____

CHARACTER ASSIGNATION

Fill in the answers to the clues, across the grid. Then read down the diagonal line of eight squares, to reveal: A character from William Shakespeare's *Much Ado About Nothing*.

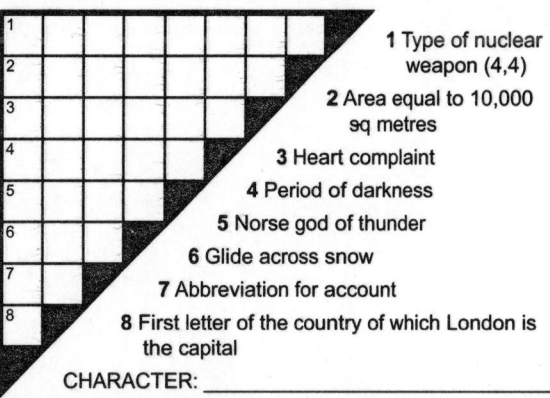

1 Type of nuclear weapon (4,4)

2 Area equal to 10,000 sq metres

3 Heart complaint

4 Period of darkness

5 Norse god of thunder

6 Glide across snow

7 Abbreviation for account

8 First letter of the country of which London is the capital

CHARACTER: _____

EXCUSES FOR

Whisky:

_____
_____
_____
_____
_____

COUPLINGS

Apart from two, every word listed below can be coupled with one of the others to make another word or phrase. Rearrange the letters of the two which can't be paired together, to form one word, the name of an Asian republic.

1 FAST	2 STRAW
3 REGION	4 HOUSE
5 COURT	6 PUPPY
7 MANOR	8 CENTRE
9 STORM	10 FINAL
11 LOVE	12 TROOPER
13 SAP	14 FOOD

Answer: _____

MIRROR WRITING

Write this word upside down:

_____

PAIR SHAPES

In the box below there are shapes in three different colours, black, white and grey. Any shape may have been rotated, but can you see which is the only shape to appear exactly twice in exactly the same colour?

WORDWHEEL

Using only the letters in the Wordwheel, you have ten minutes to find as many words as possible, none of which may be plurals, foreign words or proper nouns. Each word must be of three letters or more, all must contain the central letter and letters can only be used once in every word. There is at least one nine-letter word in the wheel.

Nine-letter word: _____

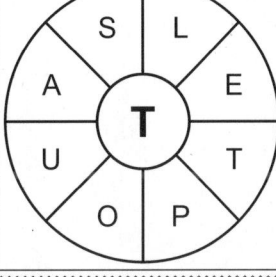

DESIGN YOUR OWN

Bar

THIS WEEK'S PHOBIAS

Aulophobia – Fear of flutes
Papyrophobia – Fear of paper
Basophobia – Fear of walking

REAL WORDS

Which is the real word?

DEITANTIOUS ☐

DENTANY ☐

DEIPNOSOPHIST ☐

Answers to puzzles on the previous page

Sweet Bad Music: Wang Chung, *Everybody Have Fun Tonight*
Arranging Things: Across (from the top): Thames, Rivers, Raging, Course, Liquid, Ganges. Down: Tigris.
Shadowland: D.
Character Assignation: 1 Atom bomb, 2 Hectare, 3 Angina, 4 Night, 5 Thor, 6 Ski, 7 AC, 8 E. Character: Beatrice.

A IS TO B

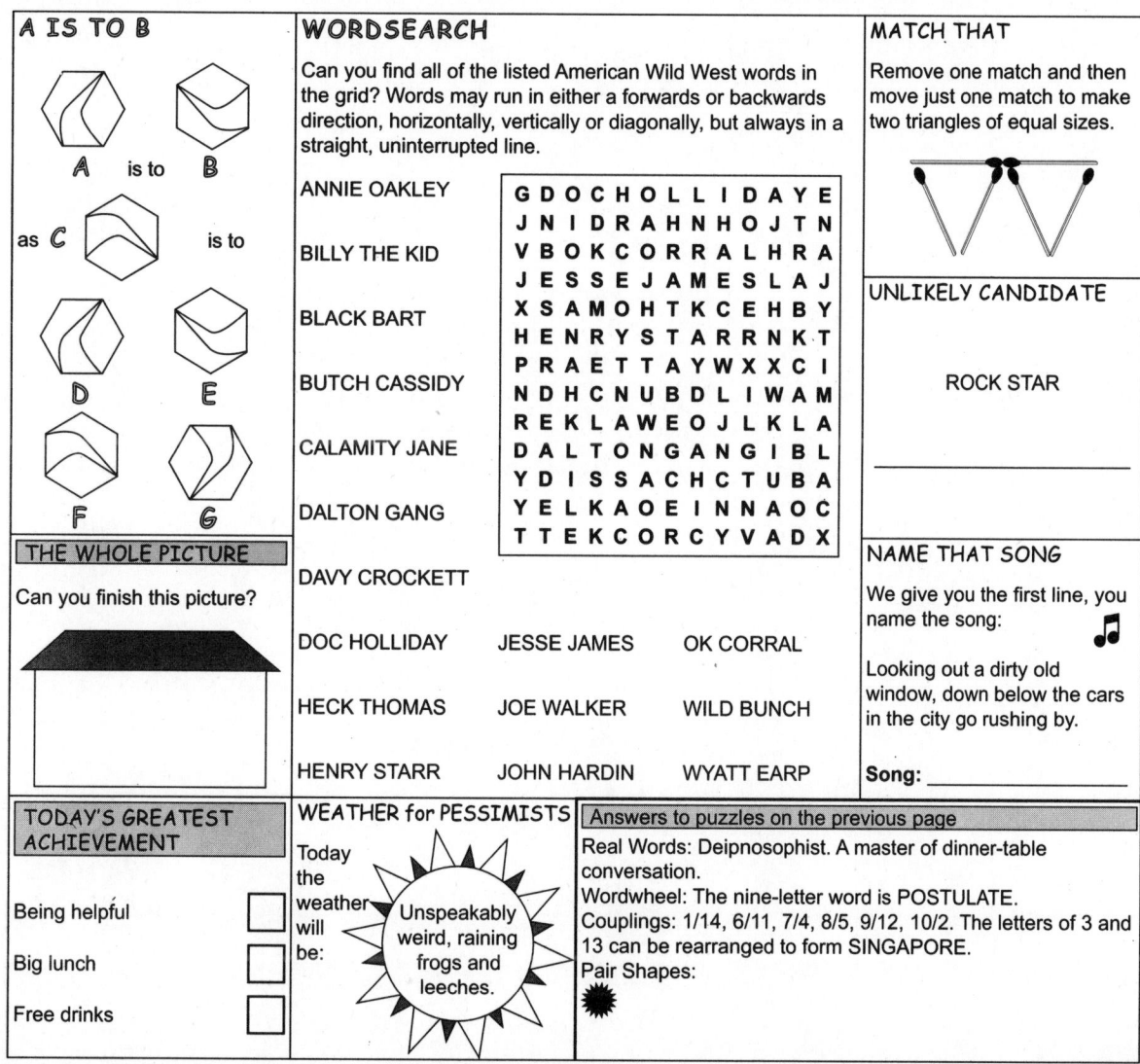

A is to B

as C is to

D E

F G

THE WHOLE PICTURE

Can you finish this picture?

WORDSEARCH

Can you find all of the listed American Wild West words in the grid? Words may run in either a forwards or backwards direction, horizontally, vertically or diagonally, but always in a straight, uninterrupted line.

ANNIE OAKLEY

BILLY THE KID

BLACK BART

BUTCH CASSIDY

CALAMITY JANE

DALTON GANG

```
G D O C H O L L I D A Y E
J N I D R A H N H O J T N
V B O K C O R R A L H R A
J E S S E J A M E S L A J
X S A M O H T K C E H B Y
H E N R Y S T A R R N K T
P R A E T T A Y W X X C I
N D H C N U B D L I W A M
R E K L A W E O J L K L A
D A L T O N G A N G I B L
Y D I S S A C H C T U B A
Y E L K A O E I N N A O C
T T E K C O R C Y V A D X
```

DAVY CROCKETT

DOC HOLLIDAY   JESSE JAMES   OK CORRAL

HECK THOMAS   JOE WALKER   WILD BUNCH

HENRY STARR   JOHN HARDIN   WYATT EARP

MATCH THAT

Remove one match and then move just one match to make two triangles of equal sizes.

UNLIKELY CANDIDATE

ROCK STAR

_____

NAME THAT SONG

We give you the first line, you name the song: ♪

Looking out a dirty old window, down below the cars in the city go rushing by.

Song: _____

TODAY'S GREATEST ACHIEVEMENT

Being helpful ☐

Big lunch ☐

Free drinks ☐

WEATHER for PESSIMISTS

Today the weather will be: Unspeakably weird, raining frogs and leeches.

Answers to puzzles on the previous page

Real Words: Deipnosophist. A master of dinner-table conversation.
Wordwheel: The nine-letter word is POSTULATE.
Couplings: 1/14, 6/11, 7/4, 8/5, 9/12, 10/2. The letters of 3 and 13 can be rearranged to form SINGAPORE.
Pair Shapes:
✸

40

THE TANGLED TRAIL

Which of these women is walking the dog?

A

B

C

CODEWORD

This is a crossword puzzle in code. Every number represents a different letter of the alphabet and this number remains the same throughout the puzzle. Use the check-box to keep a track on your progress.

22	8	16	16		5	1	19	5	13	9
8		8		15		2		19		5
21		23		11	2	26	7	18	13	9
22	18	23	23	15		26		3		9
	4			26	25	24	21	2		19
12	2	2			5			20	25	2
5		13	8	6	9	2			2	
26		26		14		15	26	2	13	15
10	8	18	3	2	26	20		4		4
8		4		19		12		25		26
2	17	25	15	19	2		4	5	6	2

(grid contains letters H, O, G filled in)

1	2	3	4	5	6	7	8	9	10	11	12	13

14	15	16	17	18	19	20	21	22	23	24	25	26

SUM TOTAL

Place the digits 1-9, one per square, so that the sums are correct, according to the totals at the ends of the rows and columns. The calculations should be done in the order in which they appear, for example 6–2x5=20 should be read as 6–2(=4), then 4x5=20.

SECRET MISSION

Your secret mission (should you choose to accept it) is:

To allow the aliens to use your mind as a surveillance device for the day.

Answers to puzzles on the previous page

Name That Song: *Kids In America*, Kim Wilde.
A Is To B: D – Rotate the whole pattern by ninety degrees in an anti-clockwise direction.

Match That:

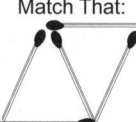

41

ANTONYM WALL

Pair up these set of letters correctly to spell out two words of the same length but with opposite meanings.

| ENT | MAN | POR |
| ARY | TEM | PER |

_____ & _____

SPOT THE BALL

Place a cross where you imagine the centre of the ball to be.

TOP TEN

WHISKY ☐
GIN ☐
LAGER ☐
VODKA ☐
BEER ☐
WINE ☐
SHERRY ☐
CHAMPAGNE ☐
TEQUILA ☐
VERMOUTH ☐

DOMINADDITION

Can you place the remaining dominoes in their correct positions, so that the total number of spots in each of the four rows and five columns equals the sum at the end of that row or column?

= 7
= 13
= 19
= 17

= 17   = 16   = 10   = 11   = 2

PATCHWORK

Fit the numbers 1, 2, 3, 4, 5 and 6 into the grid below, so that every horizontal row, every vertical column and the two long diagonal lines of six smaller squares contain six different numbers. Some are already in place.

	5			4	
5					
		2	3		
				3	1
2			6		
					6

LEARNING LINES

We give you a line, you tell us who said it and the film:

"No matter how many times you save the world, it always manages to get back in jeopardy again. Sometimes I just want it to stay saved, you know?"

WHAT DOES IT MEAN?

What is the meaning of the word

ANTINOMIAN

Answer: _____

_____

Answers to puzzles on the previous page

Pre-Fame Name Game: Bob Dylan.
The Tangled Trail: Woman A.

Sum Total:

7	+	8	x	4
−		x		+
1	x	6	−	3
+		+		+
9	−	2	x	5

Codeword:

WHATEVER NEXT?

Which of the numbered alternatives comes next in this sequence:

KH	QC	JD	TS	NH	EC
SD	SS	FH	FC	TD	?

1 KD	2 SC
3 SH	4 TS

DICE-SECTION

Printed onto every one of the six numbered dice below are six letters (one per side), which can be rearranged to form the answer to each clue; however, some sides are invisible to you. Use the clues and write every answer into the grid. When correctly filled, the letters in the shaded squares, reading in the order 1 to 6, will spell out a vegetable.

Ring, O-shape

Colourful citrus fruit

Patron saint of England

Stout cord used to tie parcels

Get rid of, take away

Choice

Dice:
1: L / I / E
2: O / A / R
3: E / G / G
4: T / I / N
5: R / O / E
6: T / O / P

GET THE LEADER

Can you unscramble the anagram to reveal the leader?

Fellow not to stay,
Rice replaces

Answer: _____

WHERE ON E A I O R ?

Where on earth is Intercourse?

Answer: _____

Answers to puzzles on the previous page

What Does It Mean?
One who rejects a socially established morality.

Learning Lines:
Mr Incredible, *The Incredibles* (2004).

Antonym Wall:
Permanent and Temporary.

Dominaddition:

1	2	2	1	1
6	5	2	0	0
6	5	3	5	0
4	4	3	5	1

Patchwork:

3	5	6	1	4	2
5	1	3	2	6	4
4	6	2	3	1	5
6	2	5	4	3	1
2	4	1	6	5	3
1	3	4	5	2	6

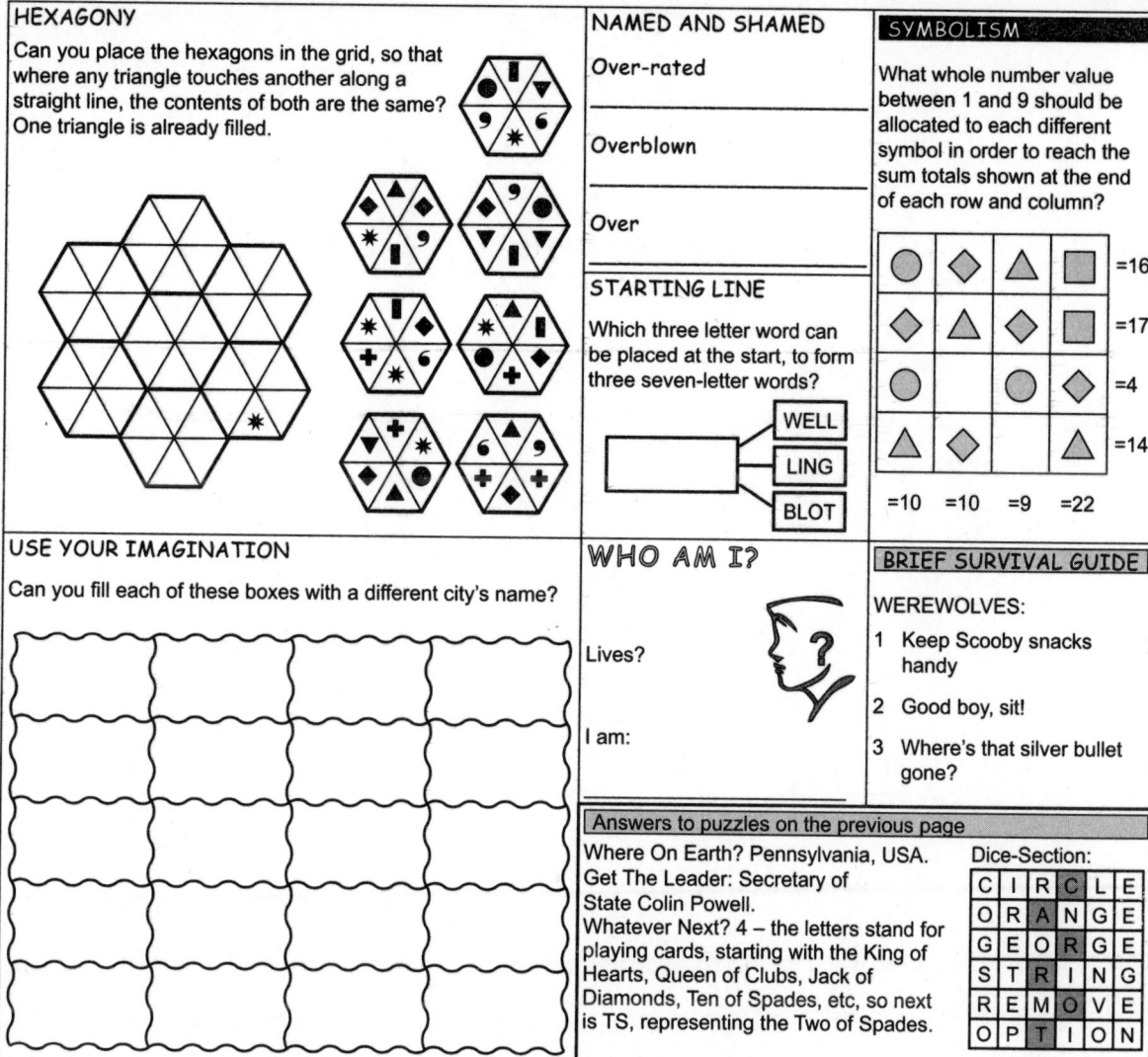

HEXAGONY

Can you place the hexagons in the grid, so that where any triangle touches another along a straight line, the contents of both are the same? One triangle is already filled.

NAMED AND SHAMED

Over-rated

_____

Overblown

_____

Over

STARTING LINE

Which three letter word can be placed at the start, to form three seven-letter words?

WELL
LING
BLOT

SYMBOLISM

What whole number value between 1 and 9 should be allocated to each different symbol in order to reach the sum totals shown at the end of each row and column?

○	◇	△	▢	=16
◇	△	◇	▢	=17
○		○	◇	=4
△	◇		△	=14

=10 =10 =9 =22

USE YOUR IMAGINATION

Can you fill each of these boxes with a different city's name?

WHO AM I?

Lives?

I am:

BRIEF SURVIVAL GUIDE

WEREWOLVES:

1 Keep Scooby snacks handy

2 Good boy, sit!

3 Where's that silver bullet gone?

Answers to puzzles on the previous page

Where On Earth? Pennsylvania, USA.
Get The Leader: Secretary of State Colin Powell.
Whatever Next? 4 – the letters stand for playing cards, starting with the King of Hearts, Queen of Clubs, Jack of Diamonds, Ten of Spades, etc, so next is TS, representing the Two of Spades.

Dice-Section:

C	I	R	C	L	E
O	R	A	N	G	E
G	E	O	R	G	E
S	T	R	I	N	G
R	E	M	O	V	E
O	P	T	I	O	N

44

PROVERBS & SAYINGS

The letters on the tiles were once all in place, but dropped out, falling in a straight line into the lower grid. Some tiles dropped earlier than others, so those on the lowest row aren't all from the same row in the grid above. Can you put them back into position in order to reveal a well-known proverb or saying?

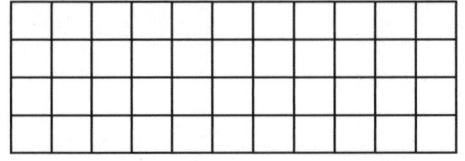

T			M					
H	H	R	S	O	O		L	
A	O	E	I	F	T	U	N	H
D	O	G	N	E	T	I	T	O	O	K

MISSING LETTERS

One letter of the alphabet is missing from each box. Find them all and place them in the order of the numbered boxes to reveal a six-letter word.

Word: _____

1	2	3
QALGV	CXQKM	NUXJE
HRWBK	OJAIV	FMZQC
CPFMS	GYRDL	VDTKI
DTXJN	NZSHU	WGYSP
YEOIU	PBWTF	ORHLB

4	5	6
QYVMF	RYBLU	NHMYA
DRNGS	VKQEF	GLSUB
HOWKT	MJGAP	PCFIO
XIUPC	CDWHS	ZQDVJ
EJZAB	XIZTN	EKRWX

TWO DOWN

Fit five of the seven listed words into the Across rows in the grid, so that the other two words read down the shaded columns numbered 2 and 3.

AIMED   FACES
FLASK   PUFFS
SNEAK   STICK
UNTIL

1	2		3	
4				
5				
6				
7				

TOP FIVE

Best songs for cooking a meal:

1 _____
_____

2 _____
_____

3 _____
_____

4 _____
_____

5 _____
_____

DICEY ARITHMETIC

Using three of the arithmetical signs ÷, −, x and +, can you achieve the correct total?

WEATHER for OPTIMISTS

Today the weather will be:

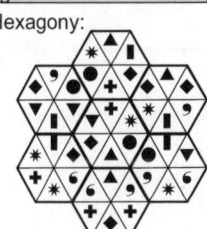

Extreme gale force winds with possible risk of property damage. Think about the insurance money and redecorate!

NAME THAT SONG

We give you the first line, you name the song:

You've done it all, you've broken every code

Song: _____

Answers to puzzles on the previous page

Who Am I? Elvis.
Starting Line: INK.
Symbolism: Circle=1, Diamond=2, Square=7, Triangle=6.

Hexagony:

45

SNAKES & LADDERS

This is a standard game, so when you land at the foot of a ladder, you climb it; and when you land on the head of a snake, you slide down its tail. You need to throw an exact number to land on 100 to win – counting backwards if you don't, eg if you land on 98 and throw a five, you will end up on 97. The dice is thrown for you and always lands in this recurring order: 5, 2, 4, 6, 3, 1, so you can start by immediately placing your counter on square 5. Good luck – hope you win!

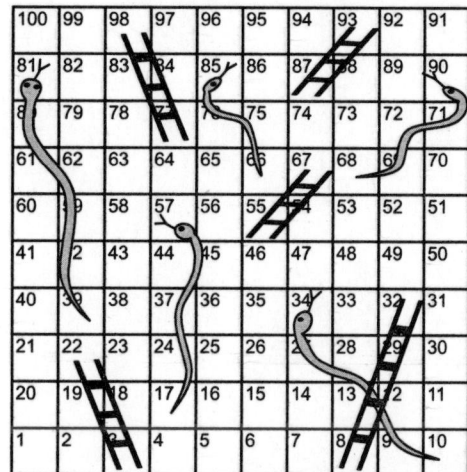

GET THE LOOK

Make the face:

LOST

MASS HYSTERIAS

Today we are all going to:

Keep an eye out for the giant cat-like beast that is roaming the area.

TOOLS OF THE TRADE

Here's a puzzle to test your skills! Fit the shapes into the grid so that the completed puzzle shows six six-letter tools. Three letters are already in place, to get you off to a good start…

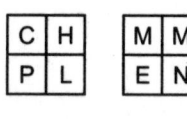

EXCUSES FOR

Staying in bed:

_____
_____
_____
_____

DO YOU KNOW…

…what happened on this date?

17 March 1776

Answers to puzzles on the previous page

Name That Song: *Make Me Smile (Come Up And See Me)*, Steve Harley and Cockney Rebel.
Two Down: Across: 1 Puffs, 4 Sneak, 5 Stick, 6 Aimed, 7 Flask. Down: 2 Until, 3 Faces.
Dicey Arithmetic: The signs are plus, times and divide.
Missing Letters: ZEALOT.
Proverbs & Sayings: Do not look a gift horse in the mouth.

CLOCKWORDS

It's a race against the clock…
How many common words of three or more different letters can you make from those on the clockface (without using plurals, proper nouns or abbreviations) in ten minutes? All words must contain BOTH the letters indicated by the hands on the clock.

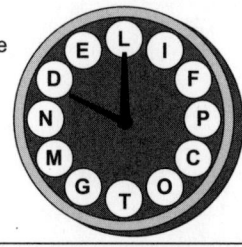

LETTER TRACKER

Begin in the central shaded square and follow a continuous path which will track from square to square, up, down and sideways, but never diagonally.

Your trail should cover every letter once only, in order to find:

Eighteen animals.

U	Q	S	E	S	R	W	L	C	A	J
I	R	R	E	H	O	O	A	K	A	H
M	L	E	N	E	V	L	G	I	T	E
O	R	A	I	R	C	N	E	T	H	E
N	Y	B	M	I	H	O	R	E	C	O
K	E	B	P	A	G	I	L	F	R	O
L	I	I	T	N	I	R	A	F	A	G
L	R	O	G	Z	P	A	N	K	A	N
A	L	L	E	E	E	A	D	T	N	A
G	E	E	R	E	E	E	L	E	P	H
A	Z	I	N	D	R	M	O	U	S	E

EGG TIMER

Can you complete this puzzle in the time it takes to boil an egg? The answers to the clues are anagrams of the words immediately above and below, plus or minus a letter.

1 Made very cross
2 Male goose
3 Impressive in scale
4 Pull along
5 Rank or degree
6 In tatters
7 Showed off

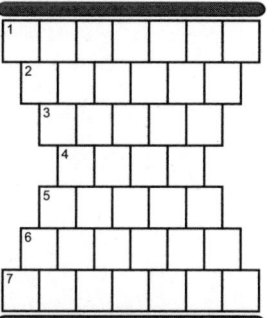

SWEET BAD MUSIC

So who on earth was responsible for this lyric?

To the extreme I rock a mic like a vandal,
Light up a stage and wax a chump like a candle,
Dance go rush to the speaker that booms,
I'm killing your brain like a poisonous mushroom.

Answers to puzzles on the previous page

Do You Know… The British evacuated Boston.

Tools Of The Trade:

C	H	I	S	E	L
P	L	I	E	R	S
J	I	G	S	A	W
S	A	N	D	E	R
H	A	M	M	E	R
W	R	E	N	C	H

47

48

WORDFILLER

Can you place all the listed words into the grid below?

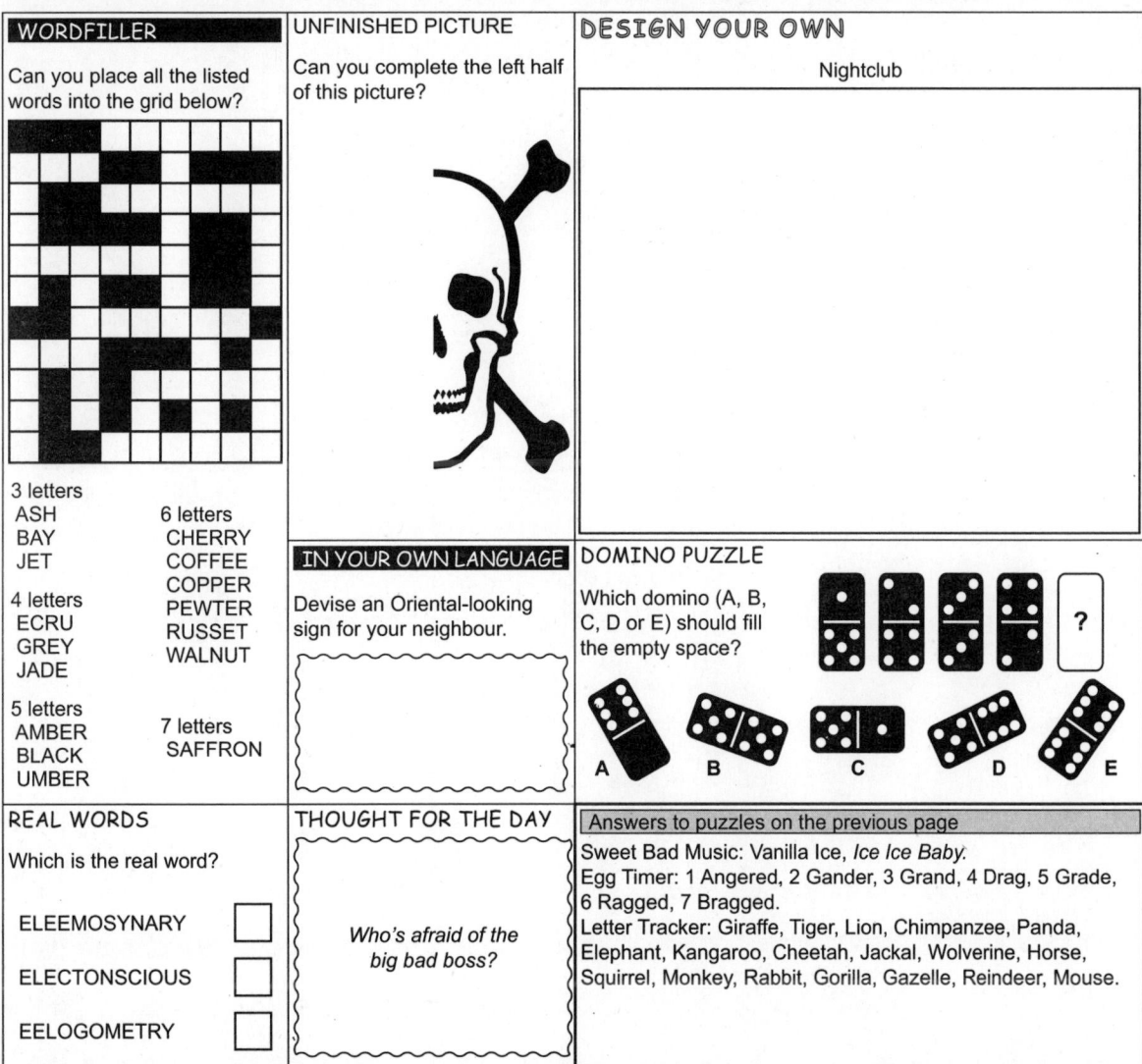

3 letters
ASH
BAY
JET

4 letters
ECRU
GREY
JADE

5 letters
AMBER
BLACK
UMBER

6 letters
CHERRY
COFFEE
COPPER
PEWTER
RUSSET
WALNUT

7 letters
SAFFRON

UNFINISHED PICTURE

Can you complete the left half of this picture?

DESIGN YOUR OWN

Nightclub

IN YOUR OWN LANGUAGE

Devise an Oriental-looking sign for your neighbour.

DOMINO PUZZLE

Which domino (A, B, C, D or E) should fill the empty space?

?

A   B   C   D   E

REAL WORDS

Which is the real word?

ELEEMOSYNARY ☐

ELECTONSCIOUS ☐

EELOGOMETRY ☐

THOUGHT FOR THE DAY

Who's afraid of the big bad boss?

Answers to puzzles on the previous page

Sweet Bad Music: Vanilla Ice, *Ice Ice Baby*.
Egg Timer: 1 Angered, 2 Gander, 3 Grand, 4 Drag, 5 Grade, 6 Ragged, 7 Bragged.
Letter Tracker: Giraffe, Tiger, Lion, Chimpanzee, Panda, Elephant, Kangaroo, Cheetah, Jackal, Wolverine, Horse, Squirrel, Monkey, Rabbit, Gorilla, Gazelle, Reindeer, Mouse.

WORDWHEEL

Using only the letters in the Wordwheel, you have ten minutes to find as many words as possible, none of which may be plurals, foreign words or proper nouns. Each word must be of three letters or more, all must contain the central letter and letters can only be used once in every word. There is at least one nine-letter word in the wheel.

Nine-letter word: _____

Wheel letters: N, S, I, E, T, T, R, G (centre) N

THE JEWEL IN THE CROWN

Who stole the jewels?
Put them back!

SHAPE RECOGNITION

Which are the only three pieces which will fit together to form a perfect square?

A   B   C   D   E   F

The

TAKA

is the currency of

_____

TOP TEN

SALMON ☐

TROUT ☐

SHARK ☐

OCTOPUS ☐

COD ☐

PLAICE ☐

SQUID ☐

HALIBUT ☐

SWORDFISH ☐

STURGEON ☐

WEATHER for PESSIMISTS

Today the weather will be:

Hideously humid and dispiritingly sunny.

UNLIKELY CANDIDATE

GLAMOUR MODEL

_____

WORDS TO REMEMBER

With which company or organisation or product do you associate this slogan?

"Drivers wanted."

PRE-FAME NAME GAME

By what name do we know this famous person?

Malcolm Little

_____

Answers to puzzles on the previous page

Real Words: Eleemosynary.
Of or pertaining to alms or almsgiving; charitable.
Domino Puzzle: C – The number of spots on the top of each domino rises by one each time and that on the bottom falls by one each time.

Wordfiller:

49

TODAY'S GREATEST ACHIEVEMENT

Listening to colleague/partner ☐

New chocolate biscuits ☐

Extra half an hour in bed ☐

MIRROR WRITING

Write this word upside down:

CAPITAL

_____

THE WHOLE PICTURE

Can you finish this picture?

OUT OF SIGHT

What is the sum total of the spots on the hidden faces of these three dice?

BERMUDA TRIANGLE

Travel through the 'Bermuda Triangle' by visiting one room at a time and collecting a letter from each. You can enter the outside passageway as often as you like, but can only visit each room once. When you've completed your tour, rearrange the fifteen letters to spell out a word.

CHARACTER ASSIGNATION

Fill in the answers to the clues, across the grid. Then read down the diagonal line of eight squares, to reveal:
A character from George Orwell's *Animal Farm*.

1 Unwilling to take risks, prudent

2 Charlie ___, silent movie comedian

3 Japanese gown

4 Chuck, toss

5 Pierce with a knife

6 Popular hot drink

7 Spanish word meaning 'the'

8 Twelfth letter of the alphabet

CHARACTER: _____

MATCH THAT

Move one match to change the perspective of this house:

GET THE LEADER

Can you unscramble the anagram to reveal the leader?

Abbot of prayers in church?

Answer: _____

WHERE ON EARTH?

Where on earth is the Pis Pis River?

Answer: _____

BALANCING THE SCALES

Given that scales A and B balance perfectly, how many squares are needed to balance scale C?

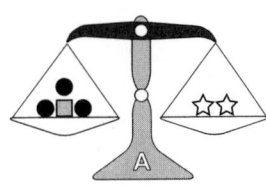

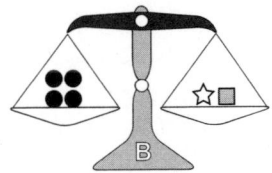

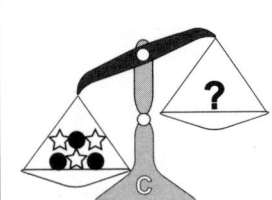

FOR SALE

This is worth the asking price

of _____ because it

once belonged to _____

_____,

who used it for _____

_____

WORD LADDER

Change one letter at a time (but not the position of any letter) to make a new word – and move from the word at the top of the ladder to the word at the bottom using the exact number of rungs provided.

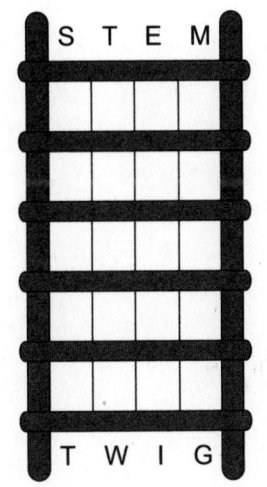

PICK 'N' MIX

Choose three words to describe the new art style:

Regurgitated   Cosmic
Brutalism   Abstract
Cathartic   Über-
Classicism   New
Figurative   Puritan

THIN DIVIDING LINES

Can you divide this grid into five sections of different shapes, each containing five different symbols?

Δ	φ	Σ	Π	Ш
Σ	Δ	Δ	φ	Δ
Π	Σ	φ	Σ	Ш
φ	Ш	Π	Δ	Π
Ш	Π	Σ	Ш	φ

SECRET MISSION

Your secret mission (should you choose to accept it) is:

To speak only in rhyming couplets all day.

WHAT DOES IT MEAN?

What is the meaning of the word

DELENDA

Answer: _____

_____

Answers to puzzles on the previous page

Where On Earth? Nicaragua.
Get The Leader: Archbishop of Canterbury.
Bermuda Triangle: The word is CANNIBALISATION.
Out Of Sight: 39.
Character Assignation: 1 Cautious, 2 Chaplin, 3 Kimono, 4 Throw, 5 Stab, 6 Tea, 7 El, 8 L. Character: Snowball.

Match That:

51

BROKEN-HEARTED

Don't be half-hearted in your attempts to get these couples back together again! Match both sides of each heart, to reveal their names.

___ & ___   ___ & ___   ___ & ___

___ & ___   ___ & ___   ___ & ___

DUA FL — A

NDY NA — B

NE EUR — C

GUS NA — D

JAC GR — E

RA KEL — F

RY SAN — G

AN HAN — H

TER SU — I

OUL LY — J

SA RHO — K

OB ACE — L

THINK ABOUT IT!

Can you picture this animal?

An iguar

WEATHER for OPTIMISTS

Today the weather will be:

Hail and ice showers are predicted which will make a lovely musical clattering sound on your roof.

PAIR SHAPES

In the box below there are shapes in three different colours, black, white and grey. Any shape may have been rotated, but can you see which is the only shape to appear exactly twice in exactly the same colour?

MY NEXT HOLIDAY

Country

_____

Temperature

_____

Scenery

_____

NAMED AND SHAMED

Biggest bum

_____

Overdone fake tan

_____

Over-bleached blond/e

_____

NAME THAT SONG

We give you the first line, you name the song:

Holding you closer, it's time that I told you everything's going to be fine.

Song: _____

Answers to puzzles on the previous page

What Does It Mean? Things to be deleted or destroyed.
Word Ladder: One solution is STEM, seem, seam, swam, swim, swig, TWIG.
Balancing The Scales: 6.

Thin Dividing Lines:

Δ	φ	Σ	Π	Ш
Σ	Δ	Δ	φ	Δ
Π	Σ	φ	Σ	Ш
φ	Ш	Π	Δ	Π
Ш	Π	Σ	Ш	φ

ODD ONE OUT

Which one is different to the rest?

A

B

C

D

E

STARTER LETTER

Write down one each of the listed items, all of which must begin with the starter letter:

B

Country	
Tree	
Boy's name	
Girl's name	
River	
City	
Animal	
Make of car	
Drink	

SYMBOLISM

What whole number value between 1 and 9 should be allocated to each different symbol in order to reach the sum totals shown at the end of each row and column?

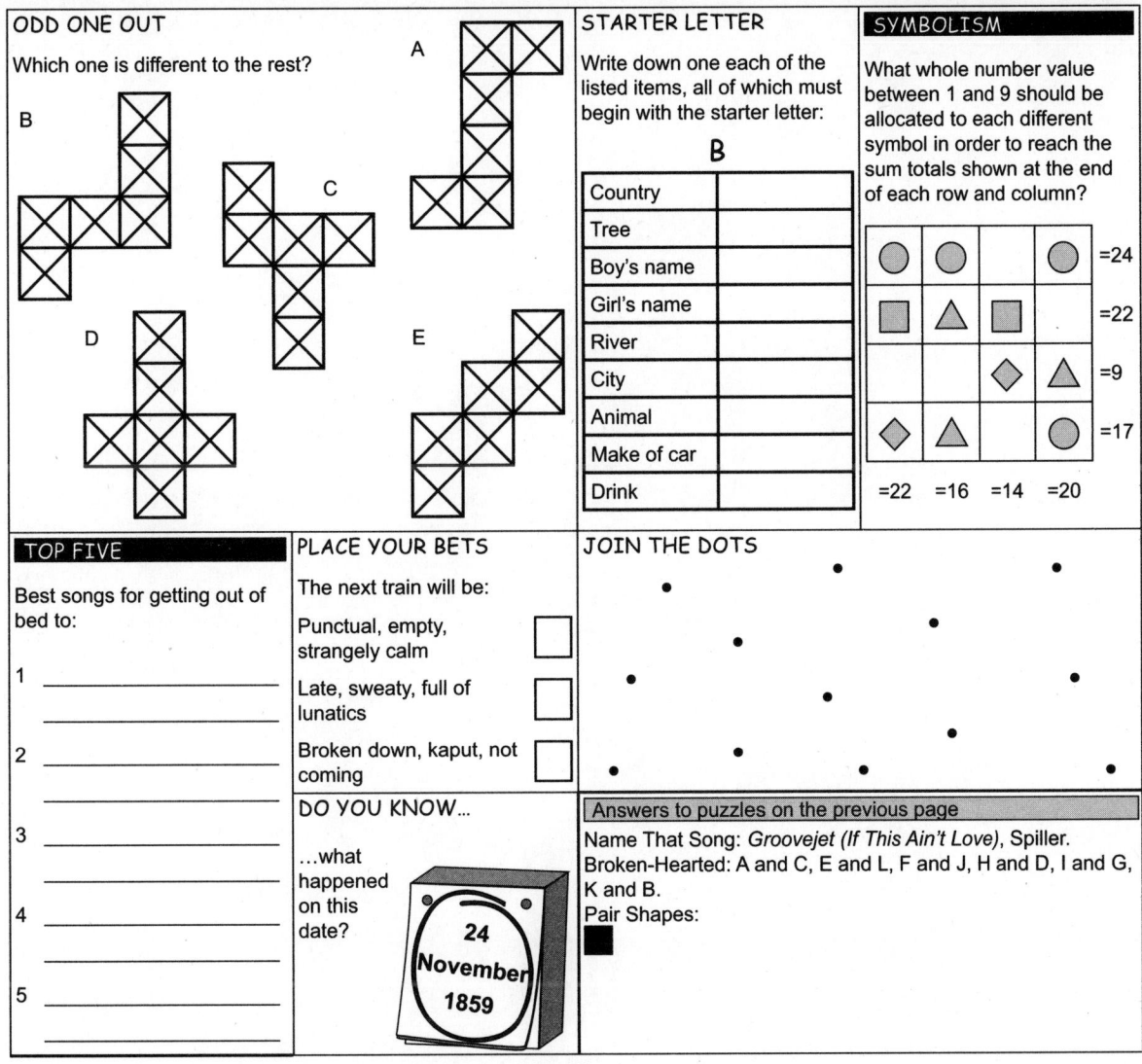

=24
=22
=9
=17

=22 =16 =14 =20

TOP FIVE

Best songs for getting out of bed to:

1 _____

2 _____

3 _____

4 _____

5 _____

PLACE YOUR BETS

The next train will be:

Punctual, empty, strangely calm ☐

Late, sweaty, full of lunatics ☐

Broken down, kaput, not coming ☐

DO YOU KNOW...

...what happened on this date?

24 November 1859

JOIN THE DOTS

Answers to puzzles on the previous page

Name That Song: *Groovejet (If This Ain't Love)*, Spiller.
Broken-Hearted: A and C, E and L, F and J, H and D, I and G, K and B.
Pair Shapes: ■

53

DOMINADDITION

Can you place the remaining dominoes in their correct positions, so that the total number of spots in each of the four rows and five columns equals the sum at the end of that row or column?

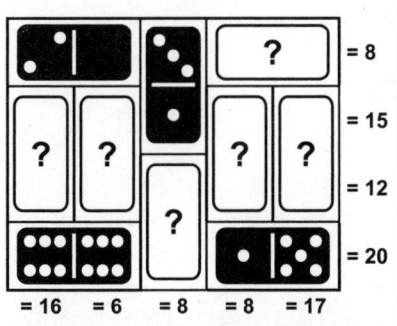

= 8
= 15
= 12
= 20

= 16   = 6   = 8   = 8   = 17

WORDSEARCH

Can you find all of the listed words relating to anatomy in the grid? Words may run in either a forwards or backwards direction, horizontally, vertically or diagonally, but always in a straight, uninterrupted line.

```
M W S K S S S C K T L M M
E A N I N E A P C C E X G
C E E I M V I U E T E E A
E H E R I R D R A C N N R
N V E T T E E C E O I O H
I O Y E L S A D B T B B P
T I E I K R D T I I R R A
S C B L P B S O G P U A I
E E F A K A O T O M E L D
T B L Z E N O N E L K L U
N O L R A E A F E V B O C
I X B E L B I D N A M C T
S I T T O L G I P E A U S
```

ANKLE

ARTERIES

BICEPS

BIG TOE

BILE DUCT

BLOODSTREAM

BREASTBONE

CAVITY

CHEEKBONE   EPIGLOTTIS

COLLARBONE   FEMUR   METACARPAL

DIAPHRAGM   INTESTINE   NECK

DUCTS   KNEE   VEINS

EPIDERMIS   MANDIBLE   VOICE BOX

GET THE LOOK

Make the face:

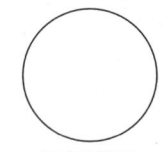

PLEASED

WAYS TO PASS THE TIME

Hopping ☐

Running ☐

Twirling ☐

BRIEF SURVIVAL GUIDE

PLANE CRASH:

1 Take a parachute

2 Remove your shoes

3 Wrap a blanket around your head

LEARNING LINES

We give you a line, you tell us who said it and the film:

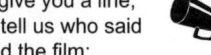

"Look at Roosevelt, look at Churchill, look at old fella what's his name in *The African Queen*."

MISSING LINKS

Which word links the one on the left with the one on the right? We've done the first one, and when you've finished them all, the first letters of the link words will spell the name of a country.

GRID	**IRON**	BAR
WATER		DANCE
ABSTRACT		GALLERY
WAY		DOWN
NEW		BOOK

COMPLETE THIS LIMERICK:

There was a young lady from Crewe

Who instead of lipstick used glue

She said with a smile:

"Kissing me takes a while

_____."

TWO DOWN

Fit five of the seven listed words into the Across rows in the grid, so that the other two words read down the shaded columns numbered 2 and 3.

AREAS   ERROR
GRIEF   HOURS
LEMON   OPERA
     TRAPS

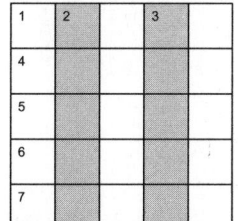

IN YOUR OWN LANGUAGE

Devise an Oriental-looking sign for your work colleague.

DOMINOLOGICAL

What is the value of the question mark?

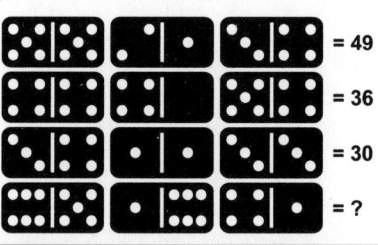

= 49

= 36

= 30

= ?

PRE-FAME NAME GAME

By what name do we know this famous person?

Israel Baline

_____

MASS HYSTERIAS

Today we are all going to:

Start hoarding metal objects, sugar and cotton reels.

Answers to puzzles on the previous page

Learning Lines: Schatze Page (Lauren Bacall), *How To Marry A Millionaire* (1953).

Dominaddition:

2	0	3	1	2
4	0	1	4	6
4	0	2	2	4
6	6	2	1	5

CAPITALS

The capital of

ICELAND

is:

_____

UNLIKELY CANDIDATE

OSCAR-WINNING ACTOR

_____

LETTER TRACKER

Begin in the central shaded square and follow a continuous path which will track from square to square, up, down and sideways, but never diagonally.

Your trail should cover every letter once only, in order to find:

Sixteen musical instruments.

P	R	A	H	E	N	L	S	A	X	O
E	U	P	P	H	O	E	I	E	N	P
N	O	H	O	L	K	E	P	F	O	H
I	U	M	T	Y	C	N	S	L	U	T
B	M	O	A	X	O	L	G	A	L	E
O	T	R	M	N	V	T	V	I	O	T
N	E	N	B	I	I	E	N	I	U	R
E	C	I	O	L	O	L	A	R	M	P
R	O	R	U	I	A	C	F	N	O	E
N	C	E	O	P	N	O	I	S	O	T
E	T	L	L	E	L	D	D	S	A	B

DICEY ARITHMETIC

Using three of the arithmetical signs ÷, −, x and +, can you achieve the correct total? Afterwards, see if you can spot an alternative way to do this.

     =

WHATEVER YOU DO, don't even THINK about...

Any of the following:

Hidden cameras watching you
That bad thing you did at kindergarten
The swarms of bees in the attic

SWEET BAD MUSIC

So who on earth was responsible for this lyric?

Did I ask too much,

More than a lot,

You gave me nothing,

Now it's all I got.

EXCUSES FOR

A fast-food fix:

_____
_____
_____
_____
_____

BOX CLEVER

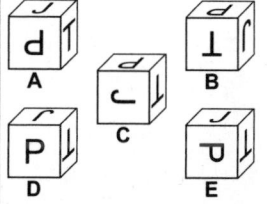

When the above is folded to form a cube, which one of the following can be produced?

A B C D E

JIGSAW CROSSWORD

Fit the blocks into the empty grid to form a complete crossword which, when finished, will be symmetrical, similar to the example seen here:

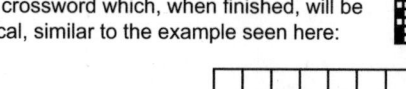

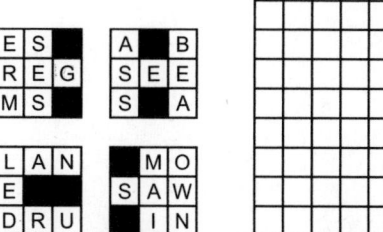

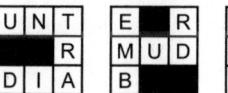  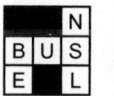 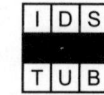

REAL WORDS

Which is the real word?

FUNOGOMETRY ☐

FUNOTOTALITY ☐

FUNAMBULIST ☐

TOP TEN

SANDALS ☐

LOAFERS ☐

BOOTS ☐

WELLIES ☐

FLIP-FLOPS ☐

TRAINERS ☐

PUMPS ☐

ROLLER-SKATES ☐

BASEBALL BOOTS ☐

BALLET SHOES ☐

CLOCKWORDS

It's a race against the clock…
How many common words of three or more different letters can you make from those on the clockface (without using plurals, proper nouns or abbreviations) in ten minutes? All words must contain BOTH the letters indicated by the hands on the clock.

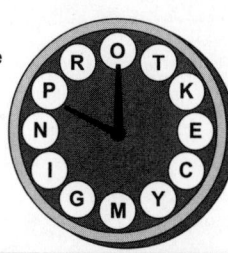

STARTING LINE

Which three letter word can be placed at the start, to form three seven-letter words?

ABLE
BOIL
KING

CELEBRITY WRESTLING

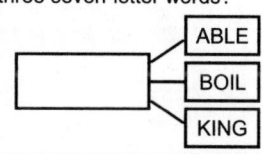

FRIEDRICH NIETZSCHE

-v-

JEAN-PAUL SARTRE

Answers to puzzles on the previous page

Sweet Bad Music: U2, *One.*
Dicey Arithmetic: The signs are divide, plus and minus – or plus, divide and times.
Letter Tracker: Violin, Xylophone, Harp, Euphonium, Tambourine, Cornet, Cello, Piano, Clarinet, Viola, Glockenspiel, Saxophone, Flute, Trumpet, Bassoon, Fiddle.
Capitals: Reykjavik.

LUCKY NUMBER

Discover your lucky number for today by following these instructions:
1. Think of a number between eight and eighty-four;
2. Think of the digits of your mother's age;
3. Add the result of 1 above to the result of 2 above;
4. Reverse the digits in this number.

Now you have your lucky number for today. Don't lose it – write it down: _____

DESIGN YOUR OWN

Classroom

LOOSE VOWELS

Someone has taken all the vowels out of what was once a completed crossword. Can you put them all back in again? You should use only those letters beneath the grid.

A A A A A A A

E E E E E E E E E E

I I

O O O O O O O O O O O O

U U

GET THE LEADERS

Can you unscramble the anagram to reveal the leaders (there are two this time!)?

Note darn huge gobby liars

Answer: _____

_____

NAME THAT SONG

We give you the first line, you name the song: ♪

There you go, flashing fever from your eyes.

Song: _____

Answers to puzzles on the previous page

Real Words: Funambulist.
A tight-rope walker or rope dancer.
Starting Line: PAR.
Box Clever: B.

Jigsaw Crossword:

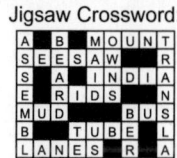

58

ARRANGING THINGS

If you fit six of these seven words into the grid below, the word left over will appear reading down the shaded squares.

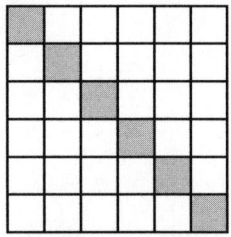

ATHENS   BOGOTA
KIGALI   ODESSA
SYDNEY   VERONA
VIENNA

WEATHER for PESSIMISTS

Today the weather will be: Worryingly mild and unsettlingly unsettled.

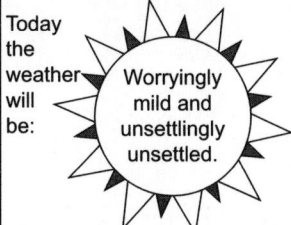

SECRET MISSION

Your secret mission (should you choose to accept it) is:

To infect your friends, colleagues and family with a sense of profound ennui and disdain for all of modern life.

COUPLINGS

Apart from two, every word listed below can be coupled with one of the others to make another word or phrase. Rearrange the letters of the two which can't be paired together, to form one word, the name of a river in the United States of America.

1 EASTER	2 LUCKY
3 WHEEL	4 FROG
5 SENSE	6 BICYCLE
7 TRAP	8 SALAD
9 BUNNY	10 TEEN
11 FRUIT	12 MOUSE
13 MARCH	14 CHARM

Answer: _____

WORDWHEEL

Using only the letters in the Wordwheel, you have ten minutes to find as many words as possible, none of which may be plurals, foreign words or proper nouns. Each word must be of three letters or more, all must contain the central letter and letters can only be used once in every word. There is at least one nine-letter word in the wheel.

Nine-letter word: _____

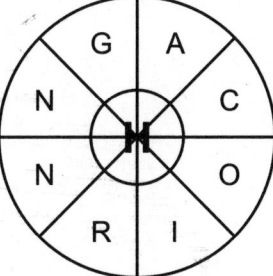

PATCHWORK

Fit the numbers 1, 2, 3, 4, 5 and 6 into the grid below, so that every horizontal row, every vertical column and the two long diagonal lines of six smaller squares contain six different numbers. Some are already in place.

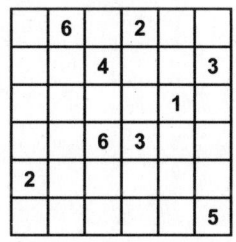

THE WHOLE PICTURE

Can you finish this picture?

WHERE ON EARTH?

Where on earth is Sexmoan?

Answer: _____

59

USE YOUR IMAGINATION

Can you fill each of these boxes with different animals' names?

MISSING LETTERS

One letter of the alphabet is missing from each box. Find them all and place them in the order of the numbered boxes to reveal a six-letter word.

Word: _____

1	2	3
LUHPA	APDZH	GPVJA
ZEQBT	TJXEN	ZNUBF
KCGYO	GUQKB	HYQLC
MDRIW	FIWMS	TIRWD
JVNXS	CVRYL	XKESM

4	5	6
YNTAK	DRYLU	KAGPZ
HVPBW	BVKQF	LBOSJ
JSLCG	MJGAP	WFVRC
DIMOF	CWHSO	HXMDY
RUEQX	XIZTN	UIQTE

MATCH THAT

Remove three matches to leave a square.

SOMETHING TO THINK ABOUT...

If it takes eight men three days to mow five meadows, how long will it take six men to mow three meadows, given that two of them spend most of their time bickering about the state of the nation?

WHATEVER NEXT?

Which of the numbered alternatives comes next in this sequence:

N	L	J	H	F	?

1	2
C	D

3	4
E	A

NAMED AND SHAMED

Nose job

_____

Boob job

_____

Facelift

_____

WHAT DOES IT MEAN?

What is the meaning of the word

GROWLERY

Answer: _____

_____

Answers to puzzles on the previous page

Where On Earth? Luzon, Philippines.
Arranging Things: Across (from the top):
Verona, Kigali, Odessa, Sydney, Athens,
Bogota. Down: Vienna.
Wordwheel: The nine-letter word is
ANCHORING.
Couplings: 1/9, 2/14, 4/13, 6/3, 11/8,
12/7. The letters of 5 and 10 can be
rearranged to form TENNESSEE.

Patchwork:

4	6	5	2	3	1
6	1	4	5	2	3
5	3	2	4	1	6
1	4	6	3	5	2
2	5	3	1	6	4
3	2	1	6	4	5

EYE-SPY

I spy with my little eye something beginning with:

K

MIRROR WRITING

Write this word upside down:

DORMER

TODAY'S GREATEST ACHIEVEMENT

Clean trousers ☐

Seat on the bus/train ☐

Opening all of the bills ☐

PROVERBS & SAYINGS

The letters on the tiles were once all in place, but dropped out, falling in a straight line into the lower grid. Some tiles dropped earlier than others, so those on the lowest row aren't all from the same row in the grid above. Can you put them back into position in order to reveal a well-known proverb or saying?

B	O		R		B			D	O
Y	O	M	O		E		Y	O	U	E	M
C	O	U	N	R	T	O	I	T	G	E	S
D	E	F	E	O	T	R	C	R	H	S	S

ON TARGET

The answers to the clues read from the outer circle to the centre, all ending with the same letter. When you've finished, the letters in the shaded ring will give a word.

1 Tall structure

2 Smudge, blur

3 Step

4 Maker of bread

5 Transparent

6 Cruise ship

PICK 'N' MIX

Choose three words to create the perfect meal:

Mushrooms   Salt
Potatoes   Carrots
Olive Oil   Beef
Chicken   Garlic
Bread   Butter

DO YOU KNOW...

...what happened on this date?

20 June 1863

Answers to puzzles on the previous page

What Does It Mean? A retreat for times of ill humour.
Missing Letters: FROZEN.
Whatever Next? 2 – each letter in the sequence occurs two places earlier in the alphabet than the previous letter.

Match That:
IX = 9 in Roman numerals (9 is 3 squared).

61

A IS TO B

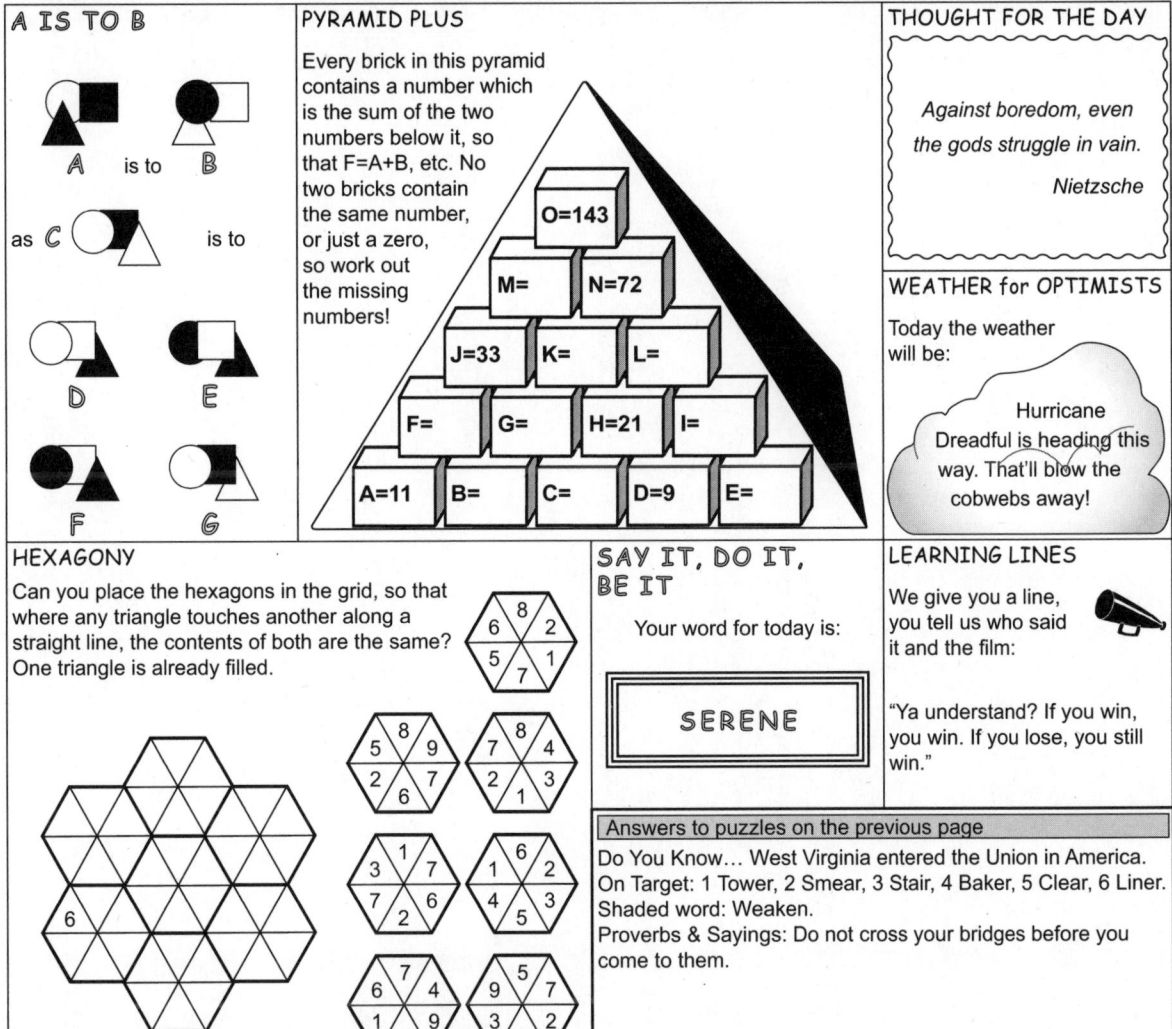

A is to B

as C is to

D E

F G

PYRAMID PLUS

Every brick in this pyramid contains a number which is the sum of the two numbers below it, so that F=A+B, etc. No two bricks contain the same number, or just a zero, so work out the missing numbers!

O=143

M=   N=72

J=33   K=   L=

F=   G=   H=21   I=

A=11   B=   C=   D=9   E=

WEATHER for OPTIMISTS

Today the weather will be:

Hurricane Dreadful is heading this way. That'll blow the cobwebs away!

HEXAGONY

Can you place the hexagons in the grid, so that where any triangle touches another along a straight line, the contents of both are the same? One triangle is already filled.

SAY IT, DO IT, BE IT

Your word for today is:

SERENE

LEARNING LINES

We give you a line, you tell us who said it and the film:

"Ya understand? If you win, you win. If you lose, you still win."

Answers to puzzles on the previous page

Do You Know… West Virginia entered the Union in America.
On Target: 1 Tower, 2 Smear, 3 Stair, 4 Baker, 5 Clear, 6 Liner.
Shaded word: Weaken.
Proverbs & Sayings: Do not cross your bridges before you come to them.

PRE-FAME NAME GAME

By what name do we know this famous person?

David Robert Hayward-Jones

_____

JUST A WORD

Can you find 'FROG' hidden in the grid, wordsearch-style?

```
F F H I G J E D F E A I O
D R O O I F R O E A C F D
E F I O U R S G H Y K L A
D E H I J O V O I E S A D
F D G A D G H J G L O G D
H B N I U G E C F H I E A
```

WORDSEARCH

Can you find all of the listed flowers in the grid below?
Words may run in either a forwards or backwards direction, horizontally, vertically or diagonally, but always in a straight, uninterrupted line.

```
Q R E H T A E H C T A F I
O E I L R C K S A E L O K
T W L F K A X G R L Y R O
F O O R L N E R N O S S S
U L I E O T I I A I S Y S
T F D E E H P W T V U T I
Y N A S T U R T I U M H E
D R L I L S U C O R C I W
N O G A R D P A N S E A L
A C A I T T E S N I O P E
C O L U M B I N E T D I D
Q K C O H Y L L O H O N E
N A R C I S S U S J V K P
```

ACANTHUS
ALYSSUM
CANDYTUFT
CARNATION
COLUMBINE
CORNFLOWER
CROCUS
EDELWEISS
FORSYTHIA   LUPIN
FREESIA   NARCISSUS   POINSETTIA
GLADIOLI   NASTURTIUM   SNAPDRAGON
HEATHER   PERIWINKLE   TAGETES
HOLLYHOCK   PINK   VIOLET

TOTAL CONCENTRATION

Can you fill in the missing numbers so that each row, each column and two longest diagonal lines meet the totals given?

107

56	41	24	7	49		36	260
10		23	41			59	170
36			41	11	19	26	188
26	20		15	15	55		172
10	17	22		51	28	14	190
	3	23	30	33		55	184
	50	46		8	10	28	187

| 160 | 182 | 182 | 225 | 180 | 197 | 225 | 186 |

PLACE YOUR BETS

Your new job will be:

Fulfilling, well-paid, glamorous ☐

Incomprehensible, odd, remote ☐

Dangerous, unstable, illegal ☐

BRIEF SURVIVAL GUIDE

GHOSTS:

1 Bang a large drum

2 Hide in the wardrobe

3 Turn the light on

CODEWORD

This is a crossword puzzle in code. Every number represents a different letter of the alphabet and this number remains the same throughout the puzzle. Use the check-box to keep a track on your progress.

22	8	16	16		5	1	19	5	13	9
8		8		15		2		19		5
21		23		11	2	26	7	18	13	9
22	18	23	23	15		26		3		9
	4			26	25	24	21	2		19
12	2	2			5 H			20	25	2
5		13	8	6	9 O	2			2	
26		26		14	G	15	26	2	13	15
10	8	18	3	2	26	20		4		4
8		4		19		12		25		26
2	17	25	15	19	2		4	5	6	2

1	2	3	4	5	6	7	8	9	10	11	12	13

14	15	16	17	18	19	20	21	22	23	24	25	26

A MATCHING PAIR

Tina would like two identical tops. Which should she buy?

A B C D E F

WHO AM I?

Mr Mojo risin'

I am:

TOP FIVE

Best songs for a spring morning:

1 _____
_____
2 _____
_____
3 _____
_____
4 _____
_____
5 _____

MONEY, MONEY, MONEY

The

NGULTRUM

is the currency of _____

POTATOE OR POTATO?

IRRESISTIBLE

OR

IRRESISTABLE

WAYS TO PASS THE TIME

Arguing ☐

Miming ☐

Tinkering ☐

STARTER LETTER

Write down one each of the listed items, all of which must begin with the starter letter:

E

Country	
Tree	
Boy's name	
Girl's name	
River	
City	
Animal	
Make of car	
Drink	

TWO DOWN

Fit five of the seven listed words into the Across rows in the grid, so that the other two words read down the shaded columns numbered 2 and 3.

ADULT   BROKE
CLOCK   COACH
COCOA   DUTCH
     ODOUR

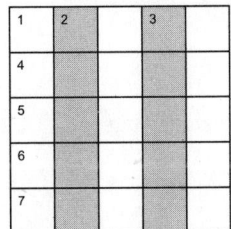

WORD LADDER

Change one letter at a time (but not the position of any letter) to make a new word – and move from the word at the top of the ladder to the word at the bottom using the exact number of rungs provided.

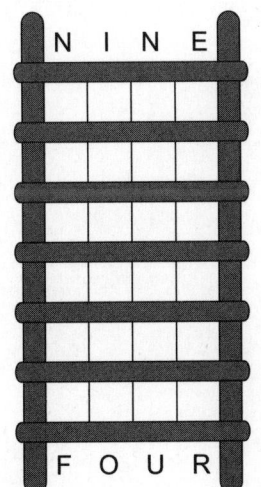

N I N E

F O U R

GET THE LOOK

Make the face:

DRUNK

WORDFILLER

Can you place all the listed words into the grid below?

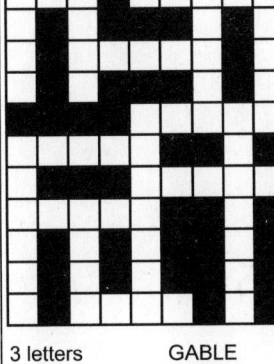

3 letters	GABLE
POT	IGLOO
	KIOSK
4 letters	LEVEL
DOME	RISER
PIER	
SHED	
TILE	6 letters
	GIRDER
5 letters	
BLOCK	7 letters
BRICK	BEDROOM
DRAIN	CHIMNEY

MASS HYSTERIAS

Today we are all going to:

Inspect every item of food for images of the saints.

SWEET BAD MUSIC

So who on earth was responsible for this lyric?

LA, Hollywood and the Sunset Strip is something everyone should see, Neon lights and the pretty, pretty girls all dressed so scantily.

Answers to puzzles on the previous page

Who Am I? Jim Morrison.
A Matching Pair: D and E.
Money, Money, Money: Bhutan.
Potatoe or Potato? Irresistible.

Codeword:

65

THE TANGLED TRAIL

Which of these women is walking the dog?

A

B

C

AMAZING

Can you work your way from the entrance at the top to the exit at the bottom of this maze?

SYMBOLISM

What whole number value between 1 and 9 should be allocated to each different symbol in order to reach the sum totals shown at the end of each row and column?

■		●	■	=23
▲	◆		▲	=8
▲	●		◆	=10
	◆	■	▲	=14

=15   =9   =14   =7

REAL WORDS

Which is the real word?

FRIGORIFIC ☐

FRIGORMORNIAN ☐

FRIGODASIAN ☐

EXCUSES FOR

Having pets:

_____

_____

_____

_____

Answers to puzzles on the previous page

Sweet Bad Music: Huey Lewis and the News, *The Heart Of Rock & Roll.*
Two Down: Across: 1 Coach, 4 Adult, 5 Cocoa, 6 Dutch, 7 Broke.
Down: 2 Odour, 3 Clock.
Word Ladder: One solution is NINE, fine, find, fond, food, fool, foul, FOUR.

Wordfiller:

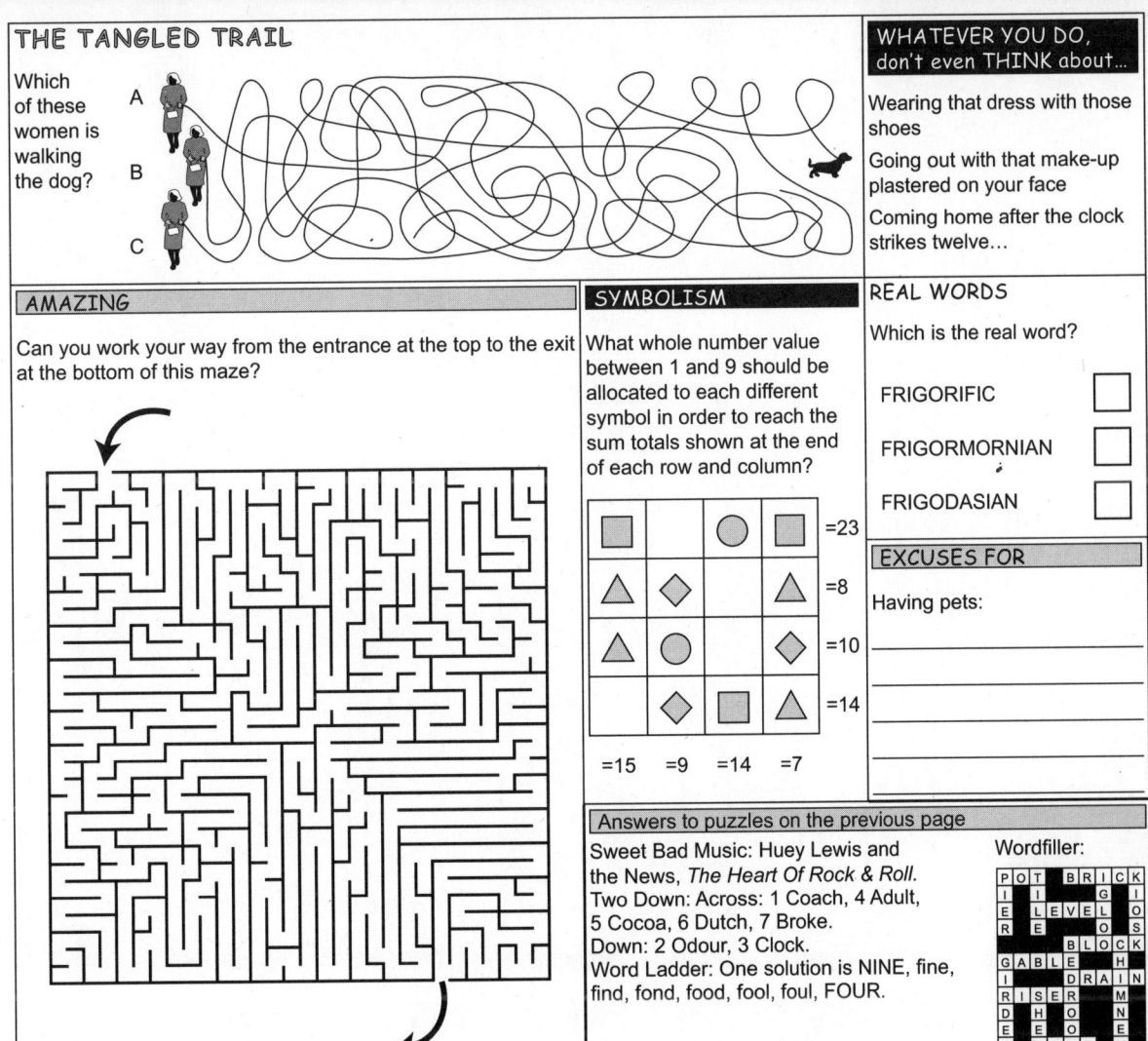

ON THE CARDS

These cards follow a particular pattern. Discover the trick and work out what value the joker should be.

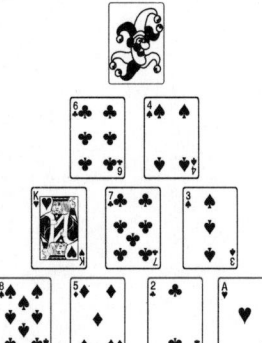

SNAKES & LADDERS

This is a standard game, so when you land at the foot of a ladder, you climb it; and when you land on the head of a snake, you slide down its tail. You need to throw an exact number to land on 100 to win – counting backwards if you don't, eg if you land on 98 and throw a five, you will end up on 97. The dice is thrown for you and always lands in this recurring order: 2, 3, 5, 1, 6, 4, so you can start by immediately placing your counter on square 2. Good luck – hope you win!

100	99	98	97	96	95	94	93	92	91
81	82	83	84	85	86	87	88	89	90
80	79	78	77	76	75	74	73	72	71
61	62	63	64	65	66	67	68	69	70
60	59	58	57	56	55	54	53	52	51
41	42	43	44	45	46	47	48	49	50
40	39	38	37	36	35	34	33	32	31
21	22	23	24	25	26	27	28	29	30
20	19	18	17	16	15	14	13	12	11
1	2	3	4	5	6	7	8	9	10

TOP TEN

CHOCOLATE ☐

VANILLA ☐

STRAWBERRY ☐

MINT ☐

PISTACHIO ☐

FUDGE ☐

RASPBERRY ☐

HAZELNUT ☐

CHOC CHIP ☐

TOFFEE ☐

UNLIKELY CANDIDATE

WINNER OF THE NOBEL PRIZE FOR PEACE

_____

NAME THAT SONG

We give you the first line, you name the song: 🎵

Libraries gave us power, then work came and made us free.

Song: _____

DICEY ARITHMETIC

Using three of the arithmetical signs ÷, −, x and +, can you achieve the correct total?

     =

Answers to puzzles on the previous page

Real Words: Frigorific. Causing cold; chilling.
Symbolism: Circle=5, Diamond=2, Square=9, Triangle=3.
The Tangled Trail: Woman A.

Amazing:

DOMINADDITION

Can you place the remaining dominoes in their correct positions, so that the total number of spots in each of the four rows and five columns equals the sum at the end of that row or column?

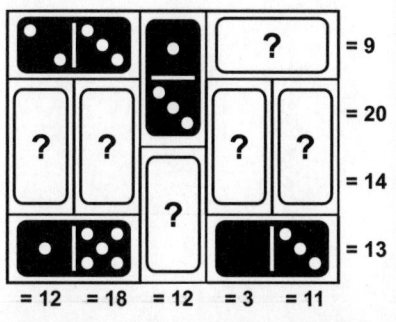

= 9
= 20
= 14
= 13

= 12   = 18   = 12   = 3   = 11

SHAPE RECOGNITION

Which are the only three pieces that will fit together to produce a five-pointed star?

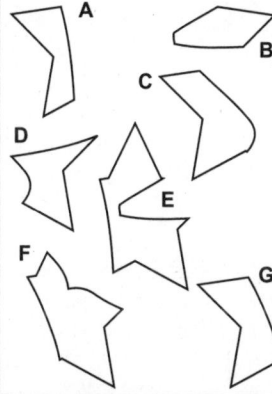

A

B

C

D

E

F

G

CLOCKWORDS

It's a race against the clock…
How many common words of three or more different letters can you make from those on the clockface (without using plurals, proper nouns or abbreviations) in ten minutes? All words must contain BOTH the letters indicated by the hands on the clock.

WHERE ON EARTH?

Where on earth is Ugly?

Answer: _____

GET THE LEADER

Can you unscramble the anagram to reveal the leader?

He felt place as Crown's heir

Answer: _____

Answers to puzzles on the previous page

Name That Song: *A Design For Life*, Manic Street Preachers.
Dicey Arithmetic: The signs are divide, times and minus.
On The Cards: The joker's value is 10. The pattern is one of alternate addition and subtraction for each row. The king has a value of 13 and each card in the same row as the king has a value which is the sum of the two cards directly below it, whilst each of those in the row above the king has a value which is the difference of the two cards directly below it. To continue the pattern, add the 6 to the 4, making the joker's value 10.

EGG TIMER

Can you complete this puzzle in the time it takes to boil an egg? The answers to the clues are anagrams of the words immediately above and below, plus or minus a letter.

1 Exceptional
2 Common flatfish
3 Location
4 Applaud
5 Grip firmly
6 Programming language
7 Royal residences

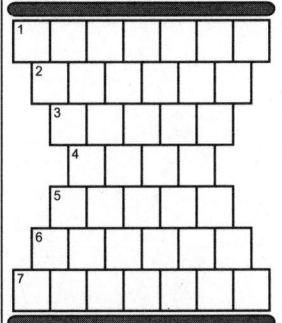

WORDWHEEL

Using only the letters in the Wordwheel, you have ten minutes to find as many words as possible, none of which may be plurals, foreign words or proper nouns. Each word must be of three letters or more, all must contain the central letter and letters can only be used once in every word. There is at least one nine-letter word in the wheel.

Nine-letter word: _____

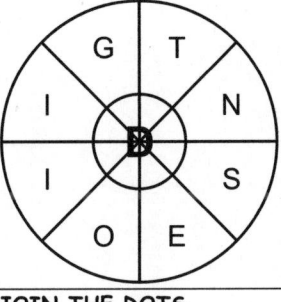

JOIN THE DOTS

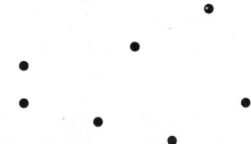

JIGSAW CROSSWORD

Fit the blocks into the empty grid to form a complete crossword which, when finished, will be symmetrical, similar to the example seen here:

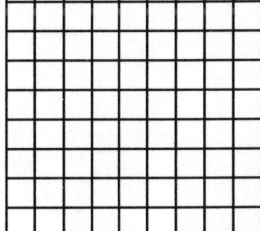

SECRET MISSION

Your secret mission (should you choose to accept it) is:

To purloin as many sugar sachets, plastic spoons and napkins as possible.

WHAT DOES IT MEAN?

What is the meaning of the word

BLOVIATE

Answer: _____

_____

Answers to puzzles on the previous page

Where On Earth? UK.
Get The Leader: Charles,
The Prince of Wales.
Dominaddition:

2	3	1	1	2
6	4	3	1	6
3	6	4	1	0
1	5	4	0	3

Shape Recognition:

69

Clear head ☐

Hangover cure ☐

First to the bar ☐

FOR SALE

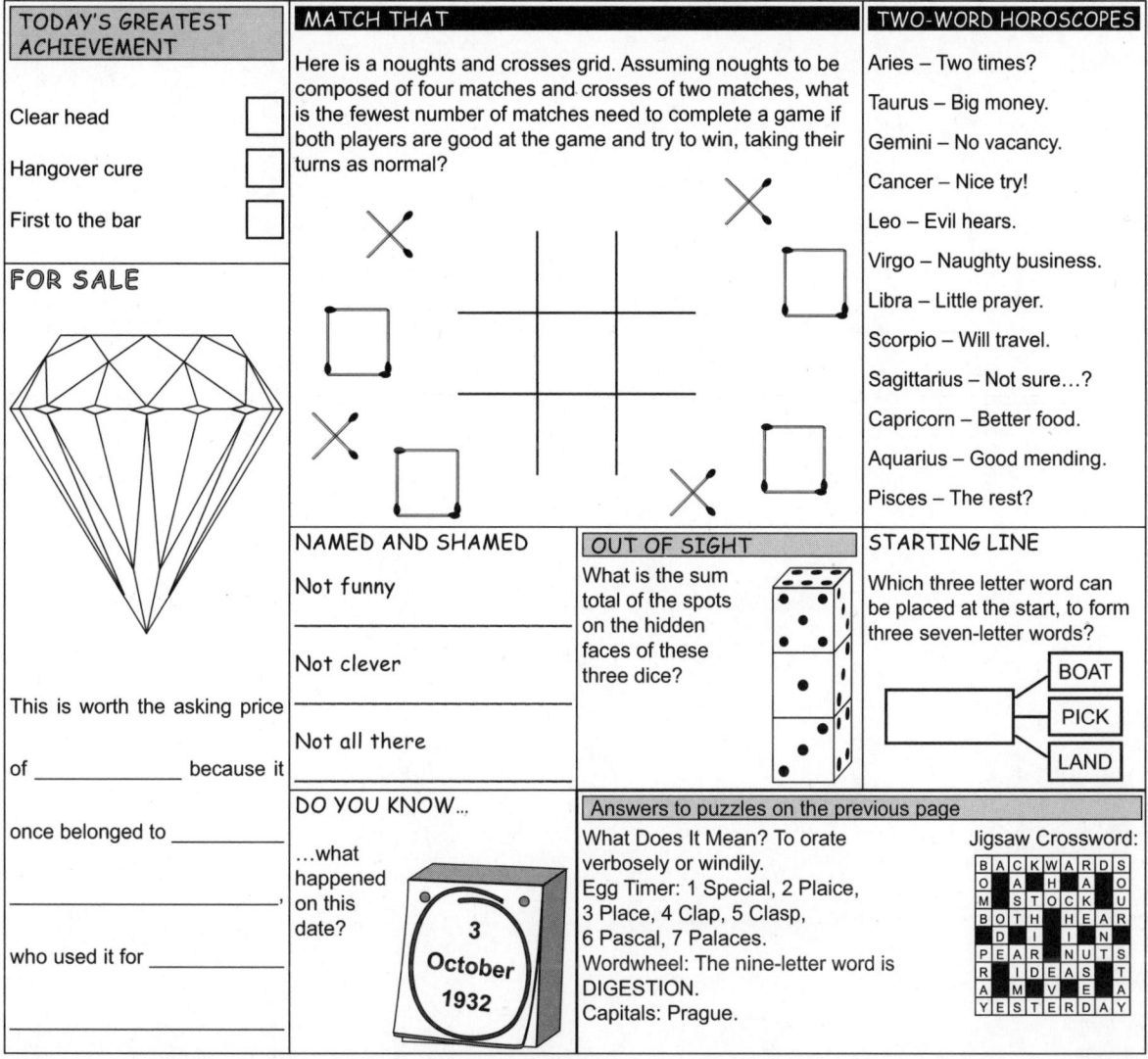

This is worth the asking price

of _____ because it

once belonged to _____

_____,

who used it for _____

_____

MATCH THAT

Here is a noughts and crosses grid. Assuming noughts to be composed of four matches and crosses of two matches, what is the fewest number of matches need to complete a game if both players are good at the game and try to win, taking their turns as normal?

NAMED AND SHAMED

Not funny

_____

Not clever

_____

Not all there

_____

DO YOU KNOW...

...what happened on this date?

3 October 1932

TWO-WORD HOROSCOPES

Aries – Two times?

Taurus – Big money.

Gemini – No vacancy.

Cancer – Nice try!

Leo – Evil hears.

Virgo – Naughty business.

Libra – Little prayer.

Scorpio – Will travel.

Sagittarius – Not sure…?

Capricorn – Better food.

Aquarius – Good mending.

Pisces – The rest?

OUT OF SIGHT

What is the sum total of the spots on the hidden faces of these three dice?

STARTING LINE

Which three letter word can be placed at the start, to form three seven-letter words?

BOAT
PICK
LAND

Answers to puzzles on the previous page

What Does It Mean? To orate verbosely or windily.
Egg Timer: 1 Special, 2 Plaice, 3 Place, 4 Clap, 5 Clasp, 6 Pascal, 7 Palaces.
Wordwheel: The nine-letter word is DIGESTION.
Capitals: Prague.

Jigsaw Crossword:

B	A	C	K	W	A	R	D	S
O		A		H		A		O
M		S	T	O	C	K		U
B	O	T	H		H	E	A	R
D			I		I		N	
P	E	A	R		N	U	T	S
R		I	D	E	A	S		T
A		M		V		E		A
Y	E	S	T	E	R	D	A	Y

MISSING LINKS

Which word links the one on the left with the one on the right? We've done the first one, and when you've finished them all, the first letters of the link words will spell a woman's name.

BACK	**FIRE**	PLACE
BULL		HOUR
FOR		LASTING
RAIN		BAND
HEAVENS		BOARD

WEATHER for PESSIMISTS

Today the weather will be:

Like hell freezing over.

WORDSEARCH

Can you find all of the listed words relating to Bonfire Night, 5 November in the grid? Words may run in either a forwards or backwards direction, horizontally, vertically or diagonally, but always in a straight, uninterrupted line.

ACCOMPLICES

BRILLIANCE

CASCADE

CATHOLIC

CELLARS

CHILDREN

CHINESE

EXCITING

FIFTH

FIRECRACKER

FLAMES

GOLDEN RAIN

JACKET POTATO

```
N I A R N E D L O G C J L
V E X C I T I N G K A B E
N W L R C D X F S C T S D
R E B D G O I E K A H T O
E S R K N F M E C J O A C
P T I D T A T P E G L N Y
A M L H L P C D L N I D T
P I L F O I A N L I C C E
H N I T V C H V A P C L F
C S A Z S X L C R M D E A
U T N A M A S K S U O A S
O E C H I N E S E J B R E
T R E K C A R C E R I F C
```

JUMPING JACK

MASKS

RÖMAN CANDLE

SAFETY CODE

STAND CLEAR

TOUCH PAPER

WESTMINSTER

ARRANGING THINGS

If you fit six of these seven words into the grid below, the word left over will appear reading down the shaded squares.

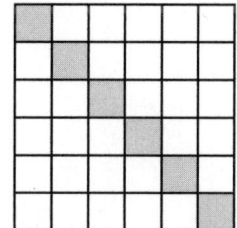

CANDLE   DONKEY
PARCEL   RIBBON
SEASON   TINSEL
TURKEY

PICK 'N' MIX

Choose three words to describe the current government:

Trustworthy	Brutal
Untrustworthy	Liars
Senseless	Lazy
Considerate	Useless
Cold-hearted	Sensible

NAME THAT SONG

We give you the first line, you name the song: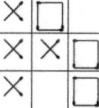

I saw the light on the night that I passed by her window.

Song: _____

Answers to puzzles on the previous page

Do You Know… Iraq was admitted to the League of Nations and won independence from British rule.

Starting Line: ICE.   Out of Sight: 38.

Match That (here is one solution): As crosses have fewest matches, they should go first (and hence last as well). This reduces the number of matches used. The total number of matches is thus 20.

WEATHER for OPTIMISTS

Today the weather will be:

Grey, cloudy skies but if you wear bright colours you will enjoy it.

PRE-FAME NAME GAME

By what name do we know this famous person?

Melvin Kaminsky

IN YOUR OWN LANGUAGE

Devise an Oriental-looking sign for your mother-in-law.

MIRROR WRITING

Write this word upside down:

EGOIST

COMPLETE THIS LIMERICK:

A man from the east coast of Spain

Was once very frightened of rain

But then he got jolly

When given a brolly

CHARACTER ASSIGNATION

Fill in the answers to the clues, across the grid. Then read down the diagonal line of eight squares, to reveal:
A character from George Du Maurier's *Trilby*.

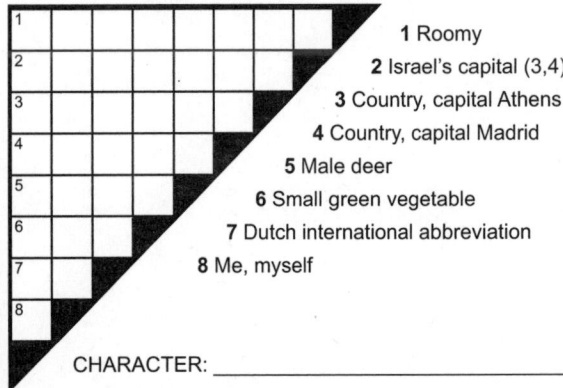

1 Roomy

2 Israel's capital (3,4)

3 Country, capital Athens

4 Country, capital Madrid

5 Male deer

6 Small green vegetable

7 Dutch international abbreviation

8 Me, myself

CHARACTER: _____

NUMB-SKULL

Fit the listed numbers into the grid, crossword-fashion.

2 digits
12
13
33
25
34
45
56

3 digits
183
222
229
466
492
495
541
668
732

4 digits
1273
3382
5456
9490

5 digits
43213
45569
53215
56221

6 digits
564211

7 digits
7864352

KEEP YOUR HAND IN

Make a glove puppet.

POTATOE OR POTATO?

TYRANNY

OR

TYRRANY

PLACE YOUR BETS

_____'s outfit today will be:

Polka-dot, peculiar ☐

Stripey, strident ☐

Drab, dreary ☐

LETTER TRACKER

Begin in the central shaded square and follow a continuous path which will track from square to square, up, down and sideways, but never diagonally.

Your trail should cover every letter once only, in order to find:

Seventeen flowers.

L	E	H	R	E	H	G	E	R	I	U
I	R	O	P	A	T	A	I	A	N	M
O	T	V	E	E	D	I	N	S	I	T
F	F	I	O	H	A	O	U	N	R	U
O	A	E	L	L	L	L	T	A	I	L
D	D	T	E	L	G	I	E	S	P	I
I	L	E	B	I	E	E	P	T	U	M
O	H	U	L	S	W	D	E	U	I	O
L	L	Y	B	S	L	E	S	R	T	R
C	O	H	S	Y	E	M	O	R	H	C
K	D	A	I	A	N	O	N	E	I	D

BRIEF SURVIVAL GUIDE

CAR CRASH:

1 Use the brakes

2 Use your seatbelt

3 Watch where you're going

REAL WORDS

Which is the real word?

GALLIGONSCIOUS ☐

GALLIGODECTIAN ☐

GALLIGASKINS ☐

THOUGHT FOR THE DAY

Law of conservation of confusion: the total amount of confusion in this world remains constant. It just gets shifted around.

INSULT OF THE DAY

"More of your conversation would infect my brain."

William Shakespeare, *Coriolanus*

Answers to puzzles on the previous page

Pre-Fame Name Game: Mel Brooks. Character Assignation: 1 Spacious, 2 Tel Aviv, 3 Greece, 4 Spain, 5 Stag, 6 Pea, 7 NL, 8 I. Character: Svengali.

Numb-Skull:

4	5		7	3	2		
9			8		5	4	1
5	4	5	6			6	
	9		4	5	5	6	9
1	2	7	3		3		4
			5		2	2	9
5	6	4	2	1	1		0
6		3			5	6	
2	2	2				6	
2		1	3		1	8	3
1		3	3	8	2		4

PROVERBS & SAYINGS

The letters on the tiles were once all in place, but dropped out, falling in a straight line into the lower grid. Some tiles dropped earlier than others, so those on the lowest row aren't all from the same row in the grid above. Can you put them back into position in order to reveal a well-known proverb or saying?

S	T	R		A		H							
T	H	O	O	S	G	Y		H	R				
T	A	N	'	U	A	H		A	O	S			
M	H	E	M	W	C	H	E	T	I	T	A	I	S

MISSING LETTERS

One letter of the alphabet is missing from each box. Find them all and place them in the order of the numbered boxes to reveal a six-letter word.

Word: _____

1	2	3
I O L A S	L Y V M F	T H L X E
G Z T P B	D R N G S	D Z P G O
F K H N C	H O W K T	K Y U M C
D U Y Q J	X I U P C	R F V I B
M X R V E	E J Z Q B	J Q A W N

4	5	6
Q G E Y W	S W J A N	F E C J Q
D R K F A	F R X O B	I O U B V
H L C M N	Z D K V G	Y L P X W
P S X B I	M H C L Q	N A H S R
O U J Z V	T I Y U P	M Z T G K

SUM TOTAL

Place the digits 1-9, one per square, so that the sums are correct, according to the totals at the ends of the rows and columns. The calculations should be done in the order in which they appear, for example 6–2x5=20 should be read as 6–2(=4), then 4x5=20.

	–		x		=	48
x		+		+		
	+		–		=	12
–		x		+		
	x		–		=	6
=		=		=		
40		50		15		

TOP FIVE

Best songs for driving in the car:

1 _____
_____

2 _____
_____

3 _____
_____

4 _____
_____

5 _____
_____

SWEET BAD MUSIC

So who on earth was responsible for this lyric?

You know where you are?
You're in the jungle baby!
You're gonna
diiiiiiiiiiiiiiiiiiiiiiiiiiiiiie!!!!!!

GET THE LOOK

Make the face:

ILL

MY NEXT PET

Animal
_____

Name
_____

Living space
_____

Answers to puzzles on the previous page

Real Words: Galligaskins. Wide, very loose breeches.
Letter Tracker: Gladioli, Edelweiss, Bluebell, Heather, Heliotrope, Violet, Daffodil, Hollyhock, Daisy, Anemone, Rose, Petunia, Geranium, Tulip, Iris, Nasturtium, Orchid.
Potatoe or Potato? Tyranny.

EYE-SPY

I spy with my little eye something beginning with:

_____

PAIR SHAPES

In the box below there are shapes in three different colours, black, white and grey. Any shape may have been rotated, but can you see which is the only shape to appear exactly twice in exactly the same colour?

THE WHOLE PICTURE

Can you finish this picture?

COUPLINGS

Apart from two, every word listed below can be coupled with one of the others to make another word or phrase. Rearrange the letters of the two which can't be paired together, to form one word, the name of a South American country.

1 RENT	2 HOT
3 HOLIDAY	4 HOUSE
5 WATER	6 FLOWER
7 BUTTER	8 POT
9 WARMING	10 AGAIN
11 WATER	12 PAT
13 BATH	14 BANK

Answer: _____

TWO DOWN

Fit five of the seven listed words into the Across rows in the grid, so that the other two words read down the shaded columns numbered 2 and 3.

ABOVE   BOWED
IDLED   ROYAL
SWELL   VALVE
     WEAVE

THIS WEEK'S PHOBIAS

Catoptrophobia – Fear of mirrors
Deciophobia – Fear of making decisions
Lachanophobia – Fear of vegetables

MASS HYSTERIAS

Today we are all going to:

Gibber like baboons.

WHAT DOES IT MEAN?

What is the meaning of the word

GALIMATIAS

Answer: _____

_____

Answers to puzzles on the previous page

Sweet Bad Music: Guns 'N' Roses, *Welcome To The Jungle.*
Missing Letters: WASTED.
Proverbs & Sayings: The way to a man's heart is through his stomach.

Sum Total:

7	–	1	x	8
x		+		+
6	+	9	–	3
–		x		+
2	x	5	–	4

75

WHATEVER NEXT?

Which of the lettered alternatives comes next in this sequence:

1=3	2=3	3=5	4=4	5=4	6=3
7=5	8=5	9=4	10=3	11=6	?

A	B
12=3	12=4

C	D
12=7	12=6

UNFINISHED PICTURE

Can you complete the left half of this picture?

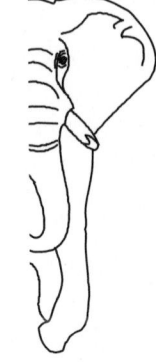

DICE-SECTION

Printed onto every one of the six numbered dice below are six letters (one per side), which can be rearranged to form the answer to each clue; however, some sides are invisible to you. Use the clues and write every answer into the grid. When correctly filled, the letters in the shaded squares, reading in the order 1 to 6, will spell out a woman's name.

Instrument used for fighting

Ocean floor

Beast

Sewing implement

One dozen

Person who rules or guides others

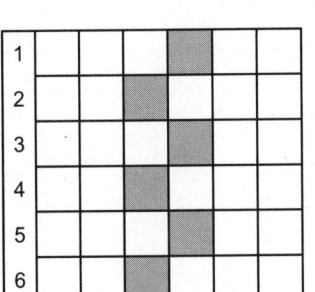

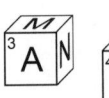

WAYS TO PASS THE TIME

Bossing ☐

Being busy ☐

Blathering ☐

DO YOU KNOW...

...what happened on this date?

31 October 1926

Answers to puzzles on the previous page

What Does It Mean? A confused mixture of unrelated things; nonsense.

Two Down: Across: 1 Above, 4 Royal, 5 Swell, 6 Weave, 7 Idled. Down: 2 Bowed, 3 Valve.

Couplings: 2/5, 4/9, 6/8, 7/12, 13/11, 14/3. The letters of 1 and 10 can be rearranged to form ARGENTINA.

Pair Shapes:
♠

LUCKY NUMBER

Discover your lucky number for today by following these instructions:

1. Think of a number between seventeen and fifty-one;
2. Think of the fourth and fifth digits of your telephone number;
3. Add the result of 1 above to the result of 2 above;
4. Reverse the digits in this number, then add four.

Now you have your lucky number for today. Don't lose it – write it down:

_____

SYMBOLISM

What whole number value between 1 and 9 should be allocated to each different symbol in order to reach the sum totals shown at the end of each row and column?

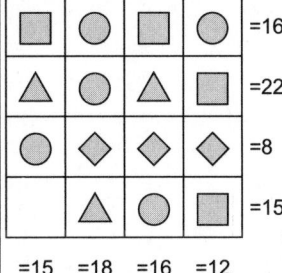

=16
=22
=8
=15

=15 =18 =16 =12

WORD LADDER

Change one letter at a time (but not the position of any letter) to make a new word – and move from the word at the top of the ladder to the word at the bottom using the exact number of rungs provided.

H O U R

W E E K

PRE-FAME NAME GAME

By what name do we know this famous person?

Nicholas Coppola

_____

THINK ABOUT IT!

Can you picture this animal?

A polar bat

ARRANGING THINGS

If you fit six of these seven words into the grid below, the word left over will appear reading down the shaded squares.

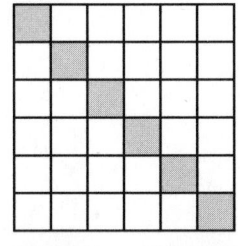

CARBON   CHROME
CICADA   CIRCLE
CLOCKS   COLLAR
         COSTLY

BERMUDA TRIANGLE

Travel through the 'Bermuda Triangle' by visiting one room at a time and collecting a letter from each. You can enter the outside passageway as often as you like, but can only visit each room once. When you've completed your tour, rearrange the fifteen letters to spell out a word.

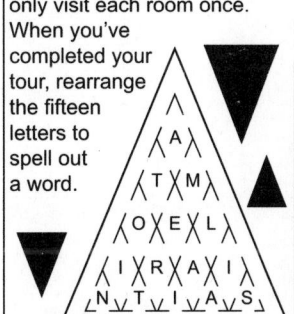

EXCUSES FOR

Driving too fast:

_____
_____
_____
_____

The

PULA

is the currency of

_____

Best seduction songs:

1 _____
   _____

2 _____
   _____

3 _____
   _____

4 _____
   _____

5 _____
   _____

DOMINADDITION

Can you place the remaining dominoes in their correct positions, so that the total number of spots in each of the four rows and five columns equals the sum at the end of that row or column?

= 12
= 9
= 17
= 23

= 16   = 8   = 7   = 12   = 18

DICEY ARITHMETIC

Using three of the arithmetical signs ÷, −, x and +, can you achieve the correct total?

SHADOWLAND

Test your skills of observation. Only one of the five shadows is that of the vintage car. Which one?

A
B
C
D
E

We give you the first line, you name the song: ♪

Have yourself a merry little Christmas.

Song: _____

THOUGHT FOR THE DAY

"I live in fear of not being misunderstood."

Oscar Wilde

Answers to puzzles on the previous page

Pre-Fame Name Game: Nicholas Cage.
Arranging Things: Across (from the top): Collar, Cicada, Carbon, Clocks, Costly, Chrome. Down: Circle.
Word Ladder: One solution is HOUR, sour, soar, sear, seer, seek, WEEK.
Bermuda Triangle: The word is MATERIALISATION.
Symbolism: Circle=5, Diamond=1, Square=3, Triangle=7.

PYRAMID PLUS

Every brick in this pyramid contains a number which is the sum of the two numbers below it, so that F=A+B, etc. No two bricks contain the same number, or just a zero, so work out the missing numbers!

O=

M=   N=58

J=   K=32   L=

F=   G=14   H=   I=

A=10   B=   C=   D=5   E=

WORDWHEEL

Using only the letters in the Wordwheel, you have ten minutes to find as many words as possible, none of which may be plurals, foreign words or proper nouns. Each word must be of three letters or more, all must contain the central letter and letters can only be used once in every word. There is at least one nine-letter word in the wheel.

Nine-letter word: _____

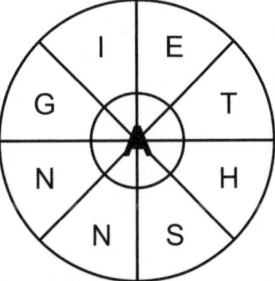

SECRET MISSION

Your secret mission (should you choose to accept it) is:

Just act natural for now – we will contact you again when the end is near.

BALANCING THE SCALES

Given that scales A and B balance perfectly, how many squares are needed to balance scale C?

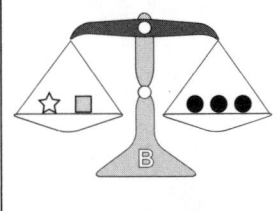

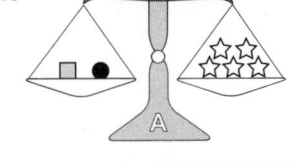

CAPITALS

The capital of

CHILE

is:

_____

WHERE ON  ?

Where on earth is Wankie? (It's now been renamed Hwange!)

Answer: _____

WEATHER for PESSIMISTS

Today the weather will be:

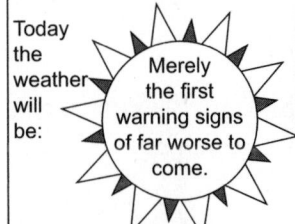

Merely the first warning signs of far worse to come.

Answers to puzzles on the previous page

Name That Song: *Merry Little Christmas*, Judy Garland.
Shadowland: A.
Dicey Arithmetic: The signs are plus, minus and times.
Money, Money, Money: Botswana.

Dominaddition:

4	1	1	2	4
2	3	0	1	3
5	3	0	3	6
5	1	6	6	5

USE YOUR IMAGINATION

Can you fill each of these boxes with a different country?

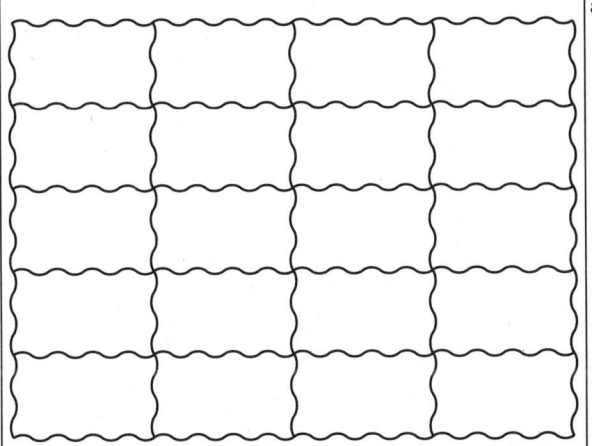

Remove six matches to leave a cube.

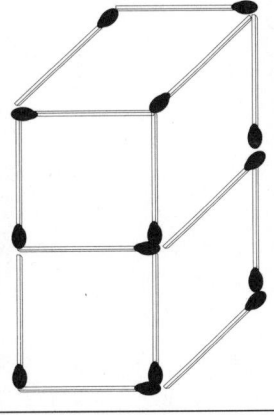

WEATHER for OPTIMISTS

Today the weather will be:

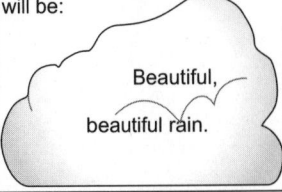

Beautiful, beautiful rain.

UNLIKELY CANDIDATE

MILITARY COMMANDER

_____

JIGSAW CROSSWORD

Fit the blocks into the empty grid to form a complete crossword which, when finished, will be symmetrical, similar to the example seen here:

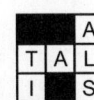

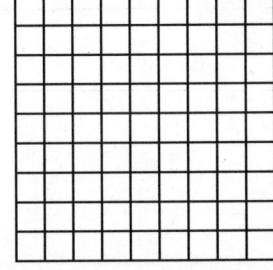

LEARNING LINES

We give you a line, you tell us who said it and the film:

"I am big. It's the pictures that got small."

BRIEF SURVIVAL GUIDE

MOTHER-IN-LAW VISIT:

1 Alcohol

2 The onset of a sudden and very contagious illness

3 Get lost on your way home

Where On Earth? Zimbabwe.
Wordwheel: The nine-letter word is HASTENING.
Capitals: Santiago.
Balancing The Scales: One.
Pyramid Plus: A=10, B=3, C=13, D=5, E=3, F=11, G=14, H=18, I=8, J=25, K=32, L=26, M=57, N=58, O=115.

REAL WORDS

Which is the real word?

GONGOOZLER ☐

GONGOZENIAR ☐

GONGENOCOCITY ☐

PICK 'N' MIX

Choose three words to describe the perfect holiday destination:

Sunny	Sea
Snowy	Riviera
Wilderness	Cottage
Mountains	Hotel
Activity	Beach

DOMINOLOGICAL

What is the value of the question mark?

= 2

= 3

= 4

= ?

EYE-SPY

I spy with my little eye something beginning with:

R

_____

STARTER LETTER

Write down one each of the listed items, all of which must begin with the starter letter:

P

Country	
Tree	
Boy's name	
Girl's name	
River	
City	
Animal	
Make of car	
Drink	

PATCHWORK

Fit the numbers 1, 2, 3, 4, 5 and 6 into the grid below, so that every horizontal row, every vertical column and the two long diagonal lines of six smaller squares contain six different numbers. Some are already in place.

3			1		
		3		4	
	5			3	
6					
		1	2		4
	4				

MY FAVOURITE THINGS

These are a few of my favourite things:

My favourite newspaper is:

_____

My favourite year was:

_____

My favourite item of clothing is:

_____

My favourite nursery rhyme is:

_____

MY NEXT CAR

Manufacturer

_____

Colour

_____

Size

_____

TODAY'S GREATEST ACHIEVEMENT

Hiding from the boss ☐

Finding new route home ☐

Finishing the ironing ☐

Answers to puzzles on the previous page

Learning Lines: Norma Desmond (Gloria Swanson), *Sunset Boulevard* (1950).

Match That:
27 is 3 cubed

Jigsaw Crossword:

81

WORDSEARCH

Can you find all of the listed cleaning words in the grid? Words may run in either a forwards or backwards direction, horizontally, vertically or diagonally, but always in a straight, uninterrupted line.

```
D W H I T E N E R R S P L
S I X A W S E E B E W L A
S H S R E T S U D H H U T
O S E I M A O F I T C N H
F I C I N S V T T A A G E
T L I E C F E N M E E E R
E O M R S S E O O L L R M
N P U E P G O C P H B N U
E B P I R R B S T S P H U
R I R E B G N I N A E L C
W I T B U C K E T W N F A
T E R E S N A E L C T T V
D S Q U E E G E E S N I R
```

BEESWAX

BLEACH

BROOM

BUCKET

CLEANING

CLEANSER

DETERGENT

DISINFECTANT

DUSTER

FOAM

LATHER

MOP

PLUNGER

POLISH

PUMICE

RINSE

SCRUB

SOFTENER

SQUEEGEE

VACUUM

WASH

LEATHER

WHITE SPIRIT

WHITENER

WIPES

THIN DIVIDING LINES

By using three straight lines, can you divide this cloud into four parts, each containing a star, a sun, a moon, a snowflake and a bolt of lightning?

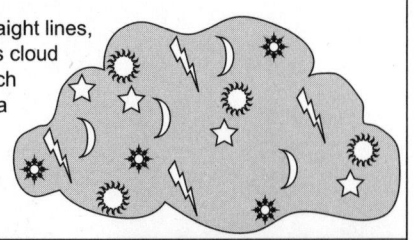

WORDS TO REMEMBER

With which company or organisation or product do you associate this slogan?

"Where do you want to go today?"

POTATOE OR POTATO?

HARRASS

OR

HARASS

STARTING LINE

Which three letter word can be placed at the start, to form three seven-letter words?

KIND

HOOD

DATE

NAMED AND SHAMED

Tyrant

_____

Traitor

_____

Tell-tale

WHO AM I?

Old West action

I am:

SWEET BAD MUSIC

So who on earth was responsible for this lyric?

And in the master's chambers
They gathered for the feast,
They stab it with their steely knives,
But they just can't kill the beast.

GET THE LOOK

Make the face:

MORTIFIED

MONEY PROBLEM

Tom and Jerry shared out a certain sum of money in the ratio 5:4 respectively; and Tom ended up with £275.00. How much was in the kitty before the share-out?

£_____

PLACE YOUR BETS

The last sandwich left will be:

Tasty chicken salad ☐

Dried-up sausage and onion ☐

An inedible, rubbery mystery ☐

GOOD IMPRESSIONS

Can you pair up these door keys with the impressions of their ends?

a   b

c   d

e   f

LETTER TRACKER

Begin in the central shaded square and follow a continuous path which will track from square to square, up, down and sideways, but never diagonally.

Your trail should cover every letter once only, in order to find:

Twenty rivers.

E	M	T	I	B	M	Y	A	U	M	I
S	A	H	Z	E	A	Z	R	R	U	R
S	H	A	G	A	N	G	E	S	O	S
N	A	L	O	N	I	G	E	M	I	S
N	O	U	D	I	N	E	R	A	N	U
M	N	T	A	H	R	A	H	D	O	B
E	K	S	R	N	O	M	U	N	G	E
N	O	I	O	C	Z	A	D	O	C	S
G	I	V	L	O	R	A	S	O	N	E
D	N	G	N	I	L	D	E	H	R	I
U	S	V	O	L	G	A	N	O	E	N

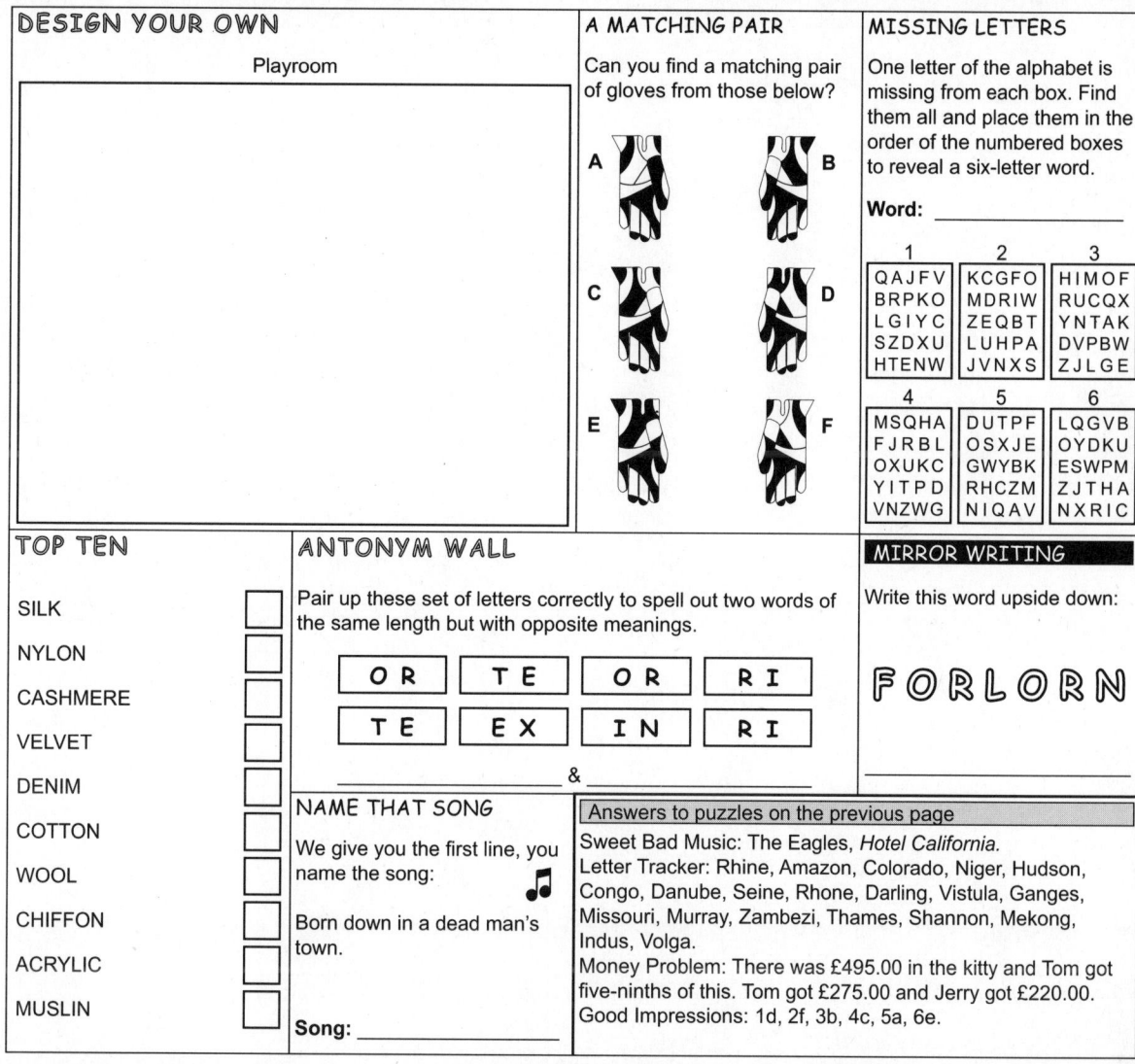

DESIGN YOUR OWN

Playroom

A MATCHING PAIR

Can you find a matching pair of gloves from those below?

A   B

C   D

E   F

MISSING LETTERS

One letter of the alphabet is missing from each box. Find them all and place them in the order of the numbered boxes to reveal a six-letter word.

Word: _____

1	2	3
QAJFV	KCGFO	HIMOF
BRPKO	MDRIW	RUCQX
LGIYC	ZEQBT	YNTAK
SZDXU	LUHPA	DVPBW
HTENW	JVNXS	ZJLGE

4	5	6
MSQHA	DUTPF	LQGVB
FJRBL	OSXJE	OYDKU
OXUKC	GWYBK	ESWPM
YITPD	RHCZM	ZJTHA
VNZWG	NIQAV	NXRIC

TOP TEN

SILK ☐

NYLON ☐

CASHMERE ☐

VELVET ☐

DENIM ☐

COTTON ☐

WOOL ☐

CHIFFON ☐

ACRYLIC ☐

MUSLIN ☐

ANTONYM WALL

Pair up these set of letters correctly to spell out two words of the same length but with opposite meanings.

OR	TE	OR	RI
TE	EX	IN	RI

_____ & _____

NAME THAT SONG

We give you the first line, you name the song: ♪

Born down in a dead man's town.

Song: _____

MIRROR WRITING

Write this word upside down:

FORLORN

_____

WORDFILLER

Can you place all the listed words into the grid below?

3 letter word	6 letter words
USA	TOBAGO
	ZAMBIA
4 letter words	
CUBA	
GUAM	**7 letter words**
LAOS	BAHRAIN
MALI	GEORGIA
TOGO	
5 letter words	**8 letter words**
EGYPT	BULGARIA
INDIA	THAILAND

CLOCKWORDS

It's a race against the clock…
How many common words of three or more different letters can you make from those on the clockface (without using plurals, proper nouns or abbreviations) in ten minutes? All words must contain BOTH the letters indicated by the hands on the clock.

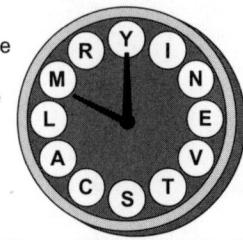

ON TARGET

The answers to the clues read from the outer circle to the centre, all ending with the same letter. When you've finished, the letters in the shaded ring will give a word.

1 Flower part
2 Take without asking permission
3 Last, concluding
4 Delicate, weak
5 Relating to the kidneys
6 Up to that time

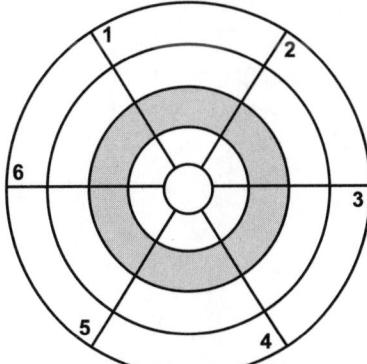

TWO DOWN

Fit five of the seven listed words into the Across rows in the grid, so that the other two words read down the shaded columns numbered 2 and 3.

CLEAR	CRISP
FEVER	NEEDS
SCENE	SLEEP
YARDS	

WHERE ON EARTH?

Where on earth is Chinaman's Knob?

Answer: _____

GET THE LEADER

Can you unscramble the anagram to reveal the leader?

Blind flirt, or complete sinner?

Answer: _____

Answers to puzzles on the previous page

Name That Song: *Born In The USA*, Bruce Springsteen.
A Matching Pair: B and C.
Antonym Wall: Exterior and Interior.
Missing Letters: MYSELF.

HEXAGONY

Can you place the hexagons in the grid, so that where any triangle touches another along a straight line, the contents of both are the same? One triangle is already filled.

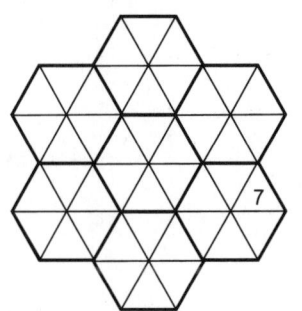

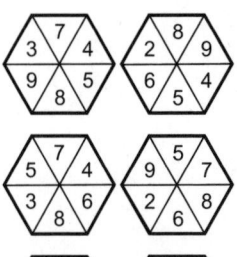

SUDOKU

Each heavily outlined box of nine smaller squares should contain the digits 1-9, as should every row of nine squares and every column of nine squares in the grid below. Only one number should be placed in every smaller square. Can you fill in the missing numbers?

	9	8						1
7		6		9			4	5
			1	6	2			
	4				5	7	3	9
		9	6		7	1		
8	7	2	9				5	
		4	7	3	6			
1	2			5		6		4
5				1	9	8		

WHATEVER NEXT?

Which of the numbered alternatives comes next in this sequence:

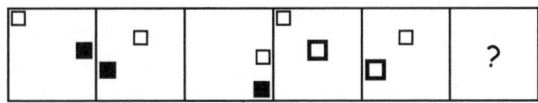

WAYS TO PASS THE TIME

Rollerskating ☐

Bicycling ☐

Scootering ☐

PRE-FAME NAME GAME

By what name do we know this famous person?

Maurice J Micklewhite

MASS HYSTERIAS

Today we are all going to:

Invest our life-savings in tulips.

Answers to puzzles on the previous page

Where On Earth? Australia.
Get The Leader: Former President Bill Clinton.
Two Down: Across: 1 Scene, 4 Sleep, 5 Fever, 6 Yards, 7 Crisp. Down: 2 Clear, 3 Needs.
On Target: 1 Petal, 2 Steal, 3 Final, 4 Frail, 5 Renal, 6 Until. Shaded word: Tenant.

Wordfiller:

THE TANGLED TRAIL

Which child is holding the string attached to the balloon?

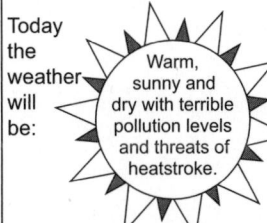

A   B   C

CODEWORD

This is a crossword puzzle in code. Every number represents a different letter of the alphabet and this number remains the same throughout the puzzle. Use the check-box to keep a track on your progress.

18	12	24	5		2	15	24	13	15	4
8		15		22		18		3		11
14		23		12	2	5	25	8	9	11
14	24	11	18	19		11		15		19
	15			11	10	9	12	26		24
15	20	11			11			19 K	11 E	21 Y
6		13	12	25	5	13			16	
1		18		11		1	12	7	11	9
15	16	12	18	15	9	12		12		25
13		25		18		11		25		8
5	11	5	18	1	21		13	19	17	4

1	2	3	4	5	6	7	8	9	10	11	12	13

14	15	16	17	18	19	20	21	22	23	24	25	26

JUST A WORD

Can you find 'MIX' hidden in the grid, wordsearch-style?

```
L K O I P S D G B X E T Q
E F T G H N B J U S X E A
D F H I X J E D F E A I O
D J I L X P S X B G E A U
D J N R Y T G H X X I M L
R P X I S A O E C B H N A
```

TWO-WORD HOROSCOPES

Aries – Now then.

Taurus – Get it.

Gemini – Gooseberry tart.

Cancer – Did you?

Leo – Goodness hides.

Virgo – Look sharp!

Libra – It's over.

Scorpio – Last time.

Sagittarius – Cool dude!

Capricorn – Darker pathways.

Aquarius – Oh, but…

Pisces – Try again.

WEATHER for PESSIMISTS

Today the weather will be:

Warm, sunny and dry with terrible pollution levels and threats of heatstroke.

WHAT DOES IT MEAN?

What is the meaning of the word

QUIDNUNC

Answer: _____

_____

Answers to puzzles on the previous page

Pre-Fame Name Game: Michael Caine.

Whatever Next? 4 – Each square is in either a left, centre or right position and each moves down.

Hexagony:

Sudoku:

2	9	8	5	7	4	3	6	1
7	1	6	3	9	8	2	4	5
4	3	5	1	6	2	8	9	7
6	4	1	2	8	5	7	3	9
3	5	9	6	4	7	1	2	8
8	7	2	9	1	3	4	5	6
9	8	4	7	3	6	5	1	2
1	2	3	8	5	9	6	7	4
5	6	7	4	2	1	9	8	3

FOR SALE

This is worth the asking price

of _____ because it

once belonged to _____

_____,

who used it for _____

_____

EXCUSES FOR

That new outfit:

_____

_____

_____

_____

_____

DOMINADDITION

Can you place the remaining dominoes in their correct positions, so that the total number of spots in each of the four rows and five columns equals the sum at the end of that row or column?

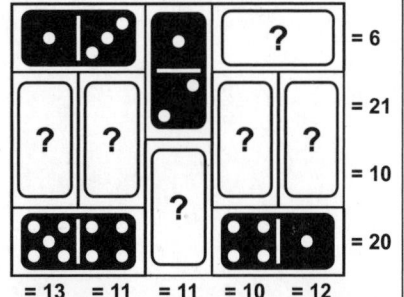

= 6
= 21
= 10
= 20

= 13 = 11 = 11 = 10 = 12

SYMBOLISM

What whole number value between 1 and 9 should be allocated to each different symbol in order to reach the sum totals shown at the end of each row and column?

△	△		○	=14
☐	△	△		=16
◇	☐	○	◇	=12
○	☐	☐	☐	=14

=15 =20 =12 =9

ARRANGING THINGS

If you fit six of these seven words into the grid below, the word left over will appear reading down the shaded squares.

BATTER   BRUNCH
BURGER   CANAPE
CUTLET   JUNKET
PASTRY

BRIEF SURVIVAL GUIDE

CHILDBIRTH:

1 Drugs

2 Drugs

3 Drugs

DO YOU KNOW...

...what happened on this date?

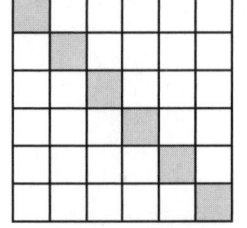

20 March 1995

Answers to puzzles on the previous page

What Does It Mean? A busybody; one who seeks to know all the latest news or gossip.

The Tangled Trail: Child C.

Just A Word:

```
L K O I P S D G B X E T Q
E F T G H N B J U S X E A
D F H I X J E D F E A I O
D J I L X P S X B G E A U
D J N R Y T G H X X I M L
R P X I S A O E C B H N A
```

Codeword:

```
C O L T   B A L S A M
U   A   J   C   Q     E
F   Z   O B T R U D E
F L E C K   E   A     K
    A     E N D O W   L
A X E     E     K E Y
G   S O R T S     V
H   C   E   H O P E D
A V O C A D O   O   R
S   R   C     E   R U
T E T C H Y   S K I M
```

WORDWHEEL

Using only the letters in the Wordwheel, you have ten minutes to find as many words as possible, none of which may be plurals, foreign words or proper nouns. Each word must be of three letters or more, all must contain the central letter and letters can only be used once in every word. There is at least one nine-letter word in the wheel.

Nine-letter word: _____

DICEY ARITHMETIC

Using three of the arithmetical signs ÷, −, x and +, can you achieve the correct total? Afterwards, see if you can spot an alternative way to do this.

    =

WORD LADDER

Change one letter at a time (but not the position of any letter) to make a new word – and move from the word at the top of the ladder to the word at the bottom using the exact number of rungs provided.

NAME THAT SONG

We give you the first line, you name the song: 🎵

I, I love the colorful clothes she wears.

Song: _____

Answers to puzzles on the previous page

Do You Know… There was a Sarin nerve gas attack on the Tokyo subway.
Arranging Things: Across (from the top): Brunch, Canape, Cutlet, Burger, Pastry, Junket. Down: Batter.
Symbolism: Circle=2, Diamond=3, Square=4, Triangle=6.

Dominaddition:

1	3	1	1	0
6	4	2	3	6
1	0	2	2	5
5	4	6	4	1

SAY IT, DO IT, BE IT

Your word for today is:

REGAL

MATCH THAT

What is the lowest prime number you can make by removing four of these matches?

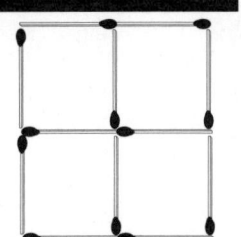

SNAKES & LADDERS

This is a standard game, so when you land at the foot of a ladder, you climb it; and when you land on the head of a snake, you slide down its tail. You need to throw an exact number to land on 100 to win – counting backwards if you don't, eg if you land on 98 and throw a five, you will end up on 97. The dice is thrown for you and always lands in this recurring order: 5, 1, 6, 2, 3, 4, so you can start by immediately placing your counter on square 5. Good luck – hope you win!

100	99	98	97	96	95	94	93	92	91
81	82	83	84	85	86	87	88	89	90
80	79	78	77	76	75	74	73	72	71
61	62	63	64	65	66	67	68	69	70
60	59	58	57	56	55	54	53	52	51
41	42	43	44	45	46	47	48	49	50
40	39	38	37	36	35	34	33	32	31
21	22	23	24	25	26	27	28	29	30
20	19	18	17	16	15	14	13	12	11
1	2	3	4	5	6	7	8	9	10

NAMED AND SHAMED

Sad

_____

Bad

_____

Mad

LEARNING LINES

We give you a line, you tell us who said it and the film:

"Old age. It's the only disease, Mr Thompson, that you don't look forward to being cured of."

JOIN THE DOTS

UNLIKELY CANDIDATE

GAME SHOW HOST

_____

COMPLETE THIS LIMERICK:

A woman who lived in a house

One day discovered a mouse

When with trembling knees

She gave it some cheese

_____

Devise an Oriental-looking sign for your brother.

Your bank balance

Your in-tray

Crushed toenails

CHARACTER ASSIGNATION

Fill in the answers to the clues, across the grid. Then read down the diagonal line of eight squares, to reveal:
A race from H G Wells's *The Time Machine*.

1 Fish-tank

2 Funnel-shaped wind

3 Fisherman

4 Christmas song

5 Ballpoint pen brand name

6 Nervous twitch

7 Alright!

8 Compass point abbreviation, opposite north

CHARACTER: _____

ANIMAL MAGIC

Here's a puzzle to test your skills! Fit the shapes into the grid so that the completed puzzle shows six six-letter animals. Three letters are already in place, to get you off to a good start...

```
I L    C K
E R    L R

J A    G E
W A    B A
```

```
J A    R B    A R    A L    G U
M O    D G    E Y    U S    N K
```

Grid: R, A, R

PICK 'N' MIX

Choose three words to create the perfect cocktail:

Vodka	Lemon
Lime	Orange
Water	Rum
Whisky	Gin
Tequila	Soda

REAL WORDS

Which is the real word?

HORNSWOBBIT ☐

HORNSWOGGLE ☐

HORNSWIGGLE ☐

PROVERBS & SAYINGS

The letters on the tiles were once all in place, but dropped out, falling in a straight line into the lower grid. Some tiles dropped earlier than others, so those on the lowest row aren't all from the same row in the grid above. Can you put them back into position in order to reveal a well-known proverb or saying?

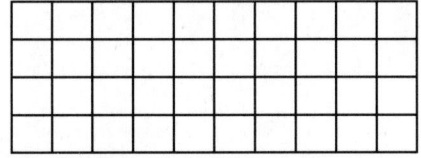

T	W								
A	H	A		D	E	C	P		
A	A	Y	Y	K	O	E	E	S	R
D	N	E	A	P	P	L	T	O	A

DESIGN YOUR OWN

Island

EGG TIMER

Can you complete this puzzle in the time it takes to boil an egg? The answers to the clues are anagrams of the words immediately above and below, plus or minus a letter.

1 Playhouse
2 Source of danger
3 Centre, core
4 Despise
5 Swindle
6 Small container for shampoo, etc
7 Schoolbag

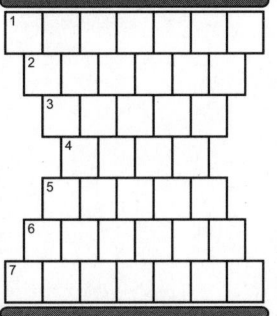

SWEET BAD MUSIC

So who on earth was responsible for this lyric?

If music be the food of love,
Then laughter is it's queen,
And likewise if behind is in front,
Then dirt in truth is clean.

WEATHER for OPTIMISTS

Today the weather will be:

Freezing temperatures causing dangerous driving conditions. Get a cab!

Begin in the central shaded square and follow a continuous path which will track from square to square, up, down and sideways, but never diagonally.

Your trail should cover every letter once only, in order to find:

Sixteen words relating to motoring.

H	C	T	U	L	C	S	R	A	E	G
C	N	T	R	O	R	B	R	A	K	E
O	O	F	A	T	A	R	E	L	T	S
M	I	F	O	L	A	C	C	E	H	L
B	T	I	R	T	E	T	L	I	G	I
U	S	C	R	A	**P**	U	O	B	E	C
T	S	E	U	N	U	N	D	A	N	C
T	U	X	S	C	O	P	E	R	E	E
Y	A	H	N	E	R	O	S	P	B	N
R	D	I	I	R	E	W	R	L	M	U
E	S	E	S	E	L	H	O	A	T	E

DOMINO PUZZLE

Which domino (A, B, C, D or E) should fill the empty space?

A B C D E

BOX CLEVER

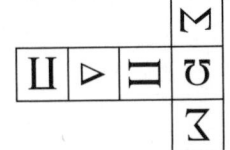

When the above is folded to form a cube, which one of the following can be produced?

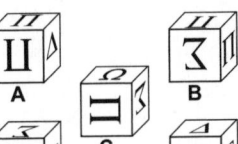

A B C D E

STARTING LINE

Which three letter word can be placed at the start, to form three seven-letter words?

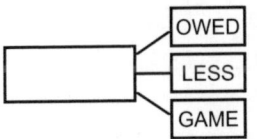

OWED
LESS
GAME

CELEBRITY WRESTLING

ICE T

-v-

FIFTY CENT

PLACE YOUR BETS

Your new outfit defines you as:

Cool, trendy and happening ☐

Calm, clean and meticulous ☐

Confused and out of touch ☐

WHAT DOES IT MEAN?

What is the meaning of the word

EPICARICACY

Answer: _____

_____

CAPITALS

The capital of

BURKINA FASO

is:

_____

THINK ABOUT IT!

Can you picture
this animal?

A zebodile

TOP TEN

APPLES ☐

ORANGES ☐

BANANAS ☐

PINEAPPLES ☐

PEARS ☐

STRAWBERRIES ☐

BLUEBERRIES ☐

RASPBERRIES ☐

PLUMS ☐

CHERRIES ☐

COUPLINGS

Apart from two, every word listed below can be coupled with one of the others to make another word or phrase. Rearrange the letters of the two which can't be paired together, to form one word, the name of a former president of the USA.

1 CLIP	2 TABLE
3 RAIN	4 HOUSE
5 CHRISTMAS	6 PAPER
7 BALD	8 COURT
9 WINE	10 CLOUD
11 MANNERS	12 HEROES
13 MERRY	14 EAGLE

Answer: _____

WHERE ON E A ?
I⊕R
1

Where on earth is
Elephant Butte?

Answer: _____

WORDSEARCH

Can you find all of the listed clothing items in the grid? Words may run in either a forwards or backwards direction, horizontally, vertically or diagonally, but always in a straight, uninterrupted line.

```
Y S S E R D T H G I N B L
W E T A H R E L W O B B M
A E S I F E D O R A C R M
I R L B U S A D R A B A T
S A L L R S Z D R I C S L
T G O O I I S D S K Z S P
C N S U J N I S I C T I I
O U M S E G G N E R A E N
A D I O A G T T I R Q R A
T I L N N O K H O K D E F
S R P J S W S A Q N I I O
E A G H A N O R A K S B R
V S S E R D R E V O U A E
```

ANORAK

BIKINI

BLOUSON

BOWLER HAT

BRASSIERE

CARDIGAN

DRESS SUIT

DRESSING GOWN

DUNGAREES

FEDORA

HEADSCARF

JEANS

MACKINTOSH

NIGHTDRESS

OVERDRESS

PINAFORE

PLIMSOLLS

SARI

SCARF

SHIRT

TABARD

VEST

WAISTCOAT

WELLINGTONS

Answers to puzzles on the previous page

What Does It Mean? Taking pleasure in others' misfortune.
Starting Line: END.
Domino Puzzle: A – The spots on the top alternate between two and four, whilst those on the bottom decrease in number by one each time.
Box Clever: E.
Letter Tracker: Petrol, Accelerator, Brake, Gears, Clutch, Combustion, Traffic, Exhaust, Tyres, Diesel, Horsepower, Insurance, Roundabout, Lights, Licence, Numberplate.

MISSING LINKS

Which word links the one on the left with the one on the right? We've done the first one, and when you've finished them all, the first letters of the link words will spell a man's name.

SUN	**DAY**	LIGHT
TAKE		LESS
GRAPE		YARD
STEAM		FILINGS
SPOTTED		TURPIN

PRE-FAME NAME GAME

By what name do we know this famous person?

Charles Lutwidge Dodgson

_____

SPOT THE BALL

Place a cross where you imagine the centre of the ball to be.

MISSING LETTERS

One letter of the alphabet is missing from each box. Find them all and place them in the order of the numbered boxes to reveal a six-letter word.

Word: _____

1	2	3
PUCZO	XOLFV	ITAPM
QHVGL	HPKRD	HBKSF
REWXK	CMGTW	ZCUQO
YITAN	JSYQA	GJXLD
SBJFM	INZBU	NWYRE

4	5	6
QKASP	NZSXA	NASMF
BTJWF	KEGJY	BTGZL
GLXNC	PBCMU	OXUCH
HRDVM	DHWRF	DPYIK
IZUYE	VOQLI	RVWQJ

TWO DOWN

Fit five of the seven listed words into the Across rows in the grid, so that the other two words read down the shaded columns numbered 2 and 3.

DARES   DELAY
MARRY   ODIUM
TRIBE   URBAN
USING

1	2		3	
4				
5				
6				
7				

SUM TOTAL

Place the digits 1-9, one per square, so that the sums are correct, according to the totals at the ends of the rows and columns. The calculations should be done in the order in which they appear, for example 6–2x5=20 should be read as 6–2(=4), then 4x5=20.

	−		x		=	21
−		−		+		
	+		x		=	24
x		+		+		
	−		x		=	6
=		=		=		
32		8		13		

MIRROR WRITING

Write this word upside down:

GARDENS

_____

GET THE LEADER

Can you unscramble the anagram to reveal the leader?

Now more grand jobs

Answer: _____

Answers to puzzles on the previous page

Where On Earth? New Mexico, USA.
Couplings: 2/11, 3/10, 6/1, 7/14, 8/4, 13/5. The letters of 9 and 12 can be rearranged to form EISENHOWER.
Capitals: Ouagadougou.

MY FAVOURITE THINGS

These are a few of my favourite things:

My favourite song is:

_____

My favourite band is:

_____

My favourite holiday destination is:

_____

My favourite friend is:

_____

PATCHWORK

Fit the numbers 1, 2, 3, 4, 5, 6 and 7 into the grid below, so that every horizontal row, every vertical column and the two long diagonal lines of six smaller squares contain six different numbers. Some are already in place.

	1			5	
3			4		2
	3			5	
4		7			
	6		5		7
	4			7	2
5		2		1	

SHAPE RECOGNITION

Which are the only four pieces which will fit together perfectly to produce an octagon like the one shown here?

A B C D E F G H I J K L

LUCKY NUMBER

Discover your lucky number for today by following these instructions:

1. Think of a number between twelve and thirty-seven;
2. Think of a number between forty and fifty-nine;
3. Add the result of 1 above to the result of 2 above;
4. Reverse the digits in this number, then add five.

Now you have your lucky number for today. Don't lose it – write it down: _____

POTATOE OR POTATO?

DESICCATE

OR

DESSICATE

WAYS TO PASS THE TIME

Reading ☐

Rocking ☐

Reprimanding ☐

BRIEF SURVIVAL GUIDE

SCHOOL:

1. Don't draw attention to yourself

2. Don't get caught

3. Don't go

NAME THAT SONG

We give you the first line, you name the song: ♪

Once I had a love and it was a gas

Song: _____

Answers to puzzles on the previous page

Pre-Fame Name Game: Lewis Carroll.
Get The Leader: James Gordon Brown.
Two Down: Across: 1 Odium, 4 Marry, 5 Tribe, 6 Delay, 7 Using. Down: 2 Dares, 3 Urban.
Missing Links: Sun-Day-Light, Take-Aim-Less, Grape-Vine-Yard, Steam-Iron-Filings, Spotted-Dick-Turpin.
The word is: DAVID.

Sum Total:

9	–	2	x	3
–		–		+
5	+	1	x	4
x		+		+
8	–	7	x	6

Missing Letters: DEVOTE.

A IS TO B

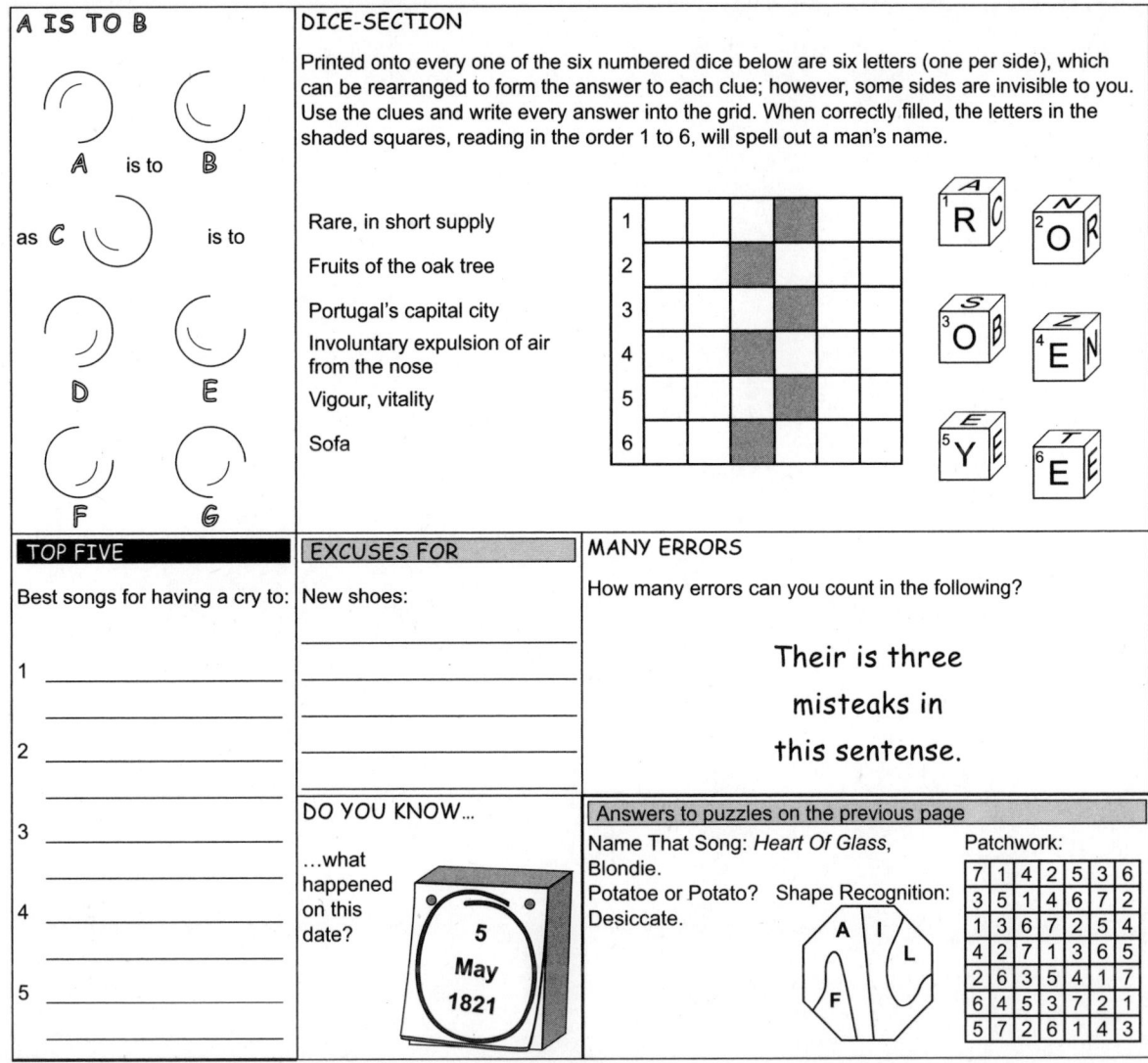

A is to B

as C is to

D   E

F   G

DICE-SECTION

Printed onto every one of the six numbered dice below are six letters (one per side), which can be rearranged to form the answer to each clue; however, some sides are invisible to you. Use the clues and write every answer into the grid. When correctly filled, the letters in the shaded squares, reading in the order 1 to 6, will spell out a man's name.

Rare, in short supply

Fruits of the oak tree

Portugal's capital city

Involuntary expulsion of air from the nose

Vigour, vitality

Sofa

Dice:
1: R C (A)
2: O R (N)
3: O B (S)
4: E N (Z)
5: Y E (E)
6: E E (T)

TOP FIVE

Best songs for having a cry to:

1 _____

2 _____

3 _____

4 _____

5 _____

EXCUSES FOR

New shoes:

_____
_____
_____
_____
_____

DO YOU KNOW...

...what happened on this date?

5 May 1821

MANY ERRORS

How many errors can you count in the following?

Their is three
misteaks in
this sentense.

PYRAMID PLUS

Every brick in this pyramid contains a number which is the sum of the two numbers below it, so that F=A+B, etc. No two bricks contain the same number, or just a zero, so work out the missing numbers!

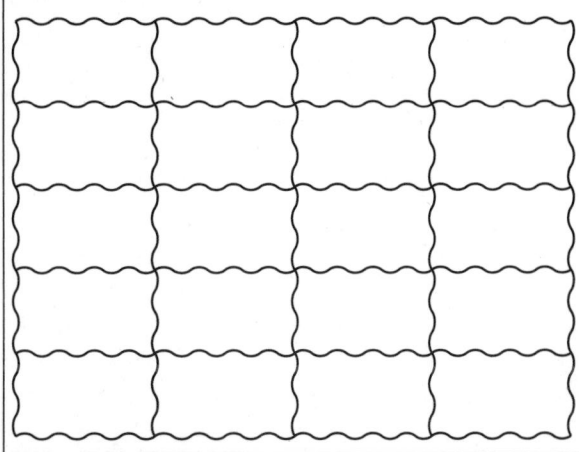

O=111

M=   N=

J=38   K=   L=

F=20   G=   H=9   I=

A=   B=   C=   D=6   E=

USE YOUR IMAGINATION

Can you fill each of these boxes with a different band's name?

EYE-SPY

I spy with my little eye something beginning with:

S

THE WHOLE PICTURE

Can you finish this picture?

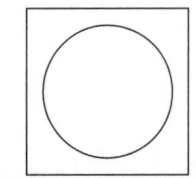

WEATHER for PESSIMISTS

Today the weather will be:

Just a minor portent of the misery that awaits us all.

WHATEVER YOU DO, don't even THINK about...

Your tax forms

Subcutaneous eruptions

Metal tooth fillings

LEARNING LINES

We give you a line, you tell us who said it and the film:

"You've seen a general inspecting troops before haven't you? Just walk slow, act dumb and look stupid! "

Answers to puzzles on the previous page

Do You Know… Napoleon Bonaparte died in exile on the island of St Helena.
A Is To B: G – The small arc moves 90 degrees anticlockwise and the large arc moves 180 degrees.
Many Errors: 5 – 'Their' should be 'there', 'is' should be 'are', 'misteaks' should be 'mistakes' and 'sentense' should be 'sentence'. That makes four, so the fifth is 'three' which should be 'four'.

Dice-Section:

S	C	A	R	C	E
A	C	O	R	N	S
L	I	S	B	O	N
S	N	E	E	Z	E
E	N	E	R	G	Y
S	E	T	T	E	E

GET THE LOOK

Make the face:

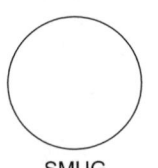

SMUG

OUT OF SIGHT

What is the sum total of the spots on the hidden faces of these three dice?

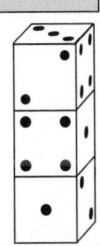

WORDWHEEL

Using only the letters in the Wordwheel, you have ten minutes to find as many words as possible, none of which may be plurals, foreign words or proper nouns. Each word must be of three letters or more, all must contain the central letter and letters can only be used once in every word. There is at least one nine-letter word in the wheel.

Nine-letter word: _____

I C A H R Y N M (centre K)

THOUGHT FOR THE DAY

"The human brain is a complex organ with the wonderful power of enabling man to find reasons for continuing to believe whatever it is that he wants to believe."

Voltaire

HEXAGONY

Can you place the hexagons in the grid, so that where any triangle touches another along a straight line, the contents of both are the same? One triangle is already filled.

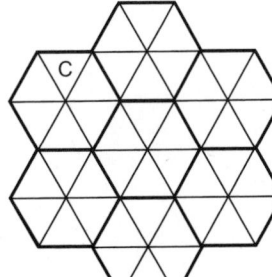

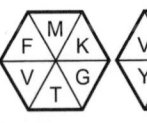

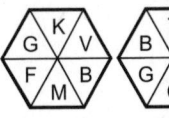

SYMBOLISM

What whole number value between 1 and 9 should be allocated to each different symbol in order to reach the sum totals shown at the end of each row and column?

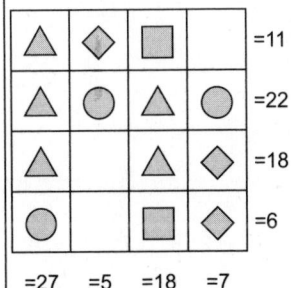

MASS HYSTERIAS

Today we are all going to:

Strap ourselves to the nearest tree in case of flooding.

SECRET MISSION

Your secret mission (should you choose to accept it) is:

To write "You'll be lucky if it gets there" on all mail boxes.

Answers to puzzles on the previous page

Learning Lines: Major John Reisman (Lee Marvin), *Dirty Dozen* (1967).
Pyramid Plus: A=5, B=15, C=3, D=6, E=4, F=20, G=18, H=9, I=10, J=38, K=27, L=19, M=65, N=46, O=111.

DICEY ARITHMETIC

Using three of the arithmetical signs ÷, −, x and +, can you achieve the correct total?

    =

UNLIKELY CANDIDATE

SUPERMODEL

_____

WEATHER for OPTIMISTS

Today the weather will be:

Heavy snow making any journeys difficult. You'll have a lovely day at home in front of the fire.

BERMUDA TRIANGLE

Travel through the 'Bermuda Triangle' by visiting one room at a time and collecting a letter from each. You can enter the outside passageway as often as you like, but can only visit each room once. When you've completed your tour, rearrange the fifteen letters to spell out a word.

BROLLY GOOD DESIGN

MATCH THAT

A trapezium is a four-sided shape with only one pair of parallel sides. By using only these nine matches, can you create THREE trapeziums and FIVE triangles?

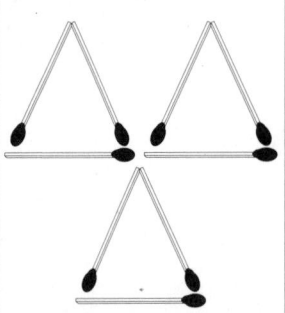

NAMED AND SHAMED

Compulsive shopper

_____

Meanest money-grabber

_____

Big spender

_____

WHAT DOES IT MEAN?

What is the meaning of the word

KENSPECKLE

Answer: _____

Answers to puzzles on the previous page

Wordwheel: The nine-letter word is MACHINERY.
Out Of Sight: 46.
Symbolism: Circle=3, Diamond=2, Square=1, Triangle=8.

Hexagony:

100

CLOCKWORDS

It's a race against the clock…
How many common words of three or more different letters can you make from those on the clockface (without using plurals, proper nouns or abbreviations) in ten minutes? All words must contain BOTH the letters indicated by the hands on the clock.

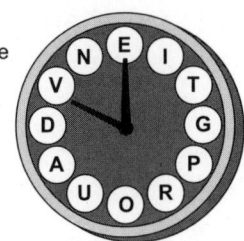

DOMINADDITION

Can you place the remaining dominoes in their correct positions, so that the total number of spots in each of the four rows and five columns equals the sum at the end of that row or column?

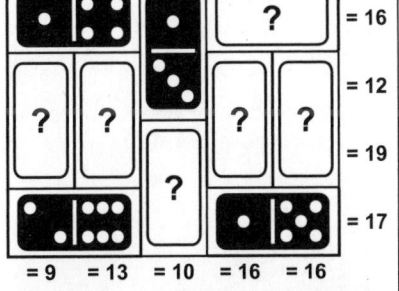

= 16
= 12
= 19
= 17

= 9   = 13   = 10   = 16   = 16

WORDFILLER

Can you place all the listed words into the grid below?

3 letters
RAM

4 letters
BEAR
FAWN
LAMB
LION
MOLE
PONY
SLUG
WASP

5 letters
GENET
LLAMA
OUNCE

6 letters
BANTAM

7 letters
BULLOCK
NARWHAL
RACCOON

9 letters
CHAMELEON

NAME THAT SONG

We give you the first line, you name the song:

♪

I, I will be king

Song: _____

SWEET BAD MUSIC

So who on earth was responsible for this lyric?

I've got two tickets to Iron
    Maiden, baby,
Come with me Friday, don't
    say maybe.

MONEY, MONEY, MONEY

The

RINGGIT

is the currency of

_____

PICK 'N' MIX

Choose three words to describe the perfect day:

Holiday   Solitude
Alcohol   Sun
Picnic   Easy
Busy   Lazy
Friends   Fun

Answers to puzzles on the previous page

What Does It Mean? Easily recognisable or distinguishable; conspicuous.
Dicey Arithmetic: The signs are minus, times and divide.
Bermuda Triangle: The word is CHARACTERISTICS.
Match That:
Trapeziums = sections 1, 2, 3 and 2, 3, 4 and 1, 3, 4.
Large triangle = sections 1, 2, 3, 4 together
Small triangles = sections 1, 2, 3, 4 separately.

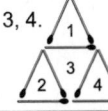

GET THE LEADER

Can you unscramble the anagram to reveal the leader?

No, open a trap on Elba!

Answer: _____

WHO AM I?

So? I'm cuter!

I am: _____

TODAY'S GREATEST ACHIEVEMENT

A slimmer waist

A wider chest

Longer hair

WORD LADDER

Change one letter at a time (but not the position of any letter) to make a new word – and move from the word at the top of the ladder to the word at the bottom using the exact number of rungs provided.

S T A R T

C E A S E

COMPLETE THIS LIMERICK:

There once was a Cockney called Brad

Whose own rhyming slang was quite bad

They said "apples and pears"

So he ate up the stairs

_____

ODD ONE OUT

Which one is different to the rest?

A

B

C

D

E

F

JIGSAW CROSSWORD

Fit the blocks into the empty grid to form a complete crossword which, when finished, will be symmetrical, similar to the example seen here:

A L L
E
D R

E M P
S I
T H E

T Y
E
A T R

A
E P T
A

S M
S U
W A S

S U N
U G
E S

I
I O N
S I

E I R
E X C
T

E S T
R R
A M A

MY NEXT SHOPPING TRIP

Where
_____

What
_____

Budget

IN YOUR OWN LANGUAGE

Devise an Oriental-looking sign for a next-door neighbour.

BROKEN-HEARTED

Don't be half-hearted in your attempts to get these couples back together again! Match both sides of each heart, to reveal their names.

___ & ___   ___ & ___   ___ & ___

___ & ___   ___ & ___   ___ & ___

JER LI   A

RY NDA   B

OYD IA   C

AN ONA   D

SI JEN   E

BRI IL   F

YNE MI   G

GIL TR   H

LL CEL   I

ES UDY   J

WA NAO   K

MON NY   L

DESIGN YOUR OWN

House

PLACE YOUR BETS

The roads this morning will be:

Empty, fast and easy ☐

Stagnant, hopeless and upsetting ☐

Full of colourful people and their lovely cars ☐

REAL WORDS

Which is the real word?

INFUNBUSTULOUS ☐

INFUNDINIUM ☐

INFUNDIBULUM ☐

Answers to puzzles on the previous page

Who Am I? Tom Cruise.
Get The Leader: Napoleon Bonaparte.
Word Ladder: One solution is START, stare, share, shore, chore, chose, chase, CEASE.
Odd One Out: A – All the others are images of a right hand.

Jigsaw Crossword:

	S	M	A	L	L	E	S	T
S	U		E		R		R	
W	A	S		D	R	A	M	A
E		I			A		I	
E	X	C	E	P	T	I	O	N
T		A			S		I	
E	M	P	T	Y		S	U	N
S		I		E		U		G
T	H	E	A	T	R	E	S	

103

PROVERBS & SAYINGS

The letters on the tiles were once all in place, but dropped out, falling in a straight line into the lower grid. Some tiles dropped earlier than others, so those on the lowest row aren't all from the same row in the grid above. Can you put them back into position in order to reveal a well-known proverb or saying?

H		F		S	D				
A	I	E		O	O		N		
A	R	R	T	M	L	O	E	Y	
P	A	S	O	E	O	N	A	N	D

LETTER TRACKER

Begin in the central shaded square and follow a continuous path which will track from square to square, up, down and sideways, but never diagonally.

Your trail should cover every letter once only, in order to find:

Twenty animals.

A	N	D	H	Y	E	N	B	I	L	H
L	E	U	P	Y	O	A	R	M	E	A
H	E	R	O	R	C	G	E	U	L	M
T	A	C	X	Y	A	M	G	R	R	S
N	M	E	L	L	L	A	O	A	E	T
A	S	U	O	H	C	I	L	T	B	E
P	E	O	G	E	H	M	E	S	A	A
T	O	M	D	G	I	P	A	W	E	V
R	I	R	O	D	N	A	L	O	L	E
O	S	E	H	E	C	I	B	F	A	R
T	A	L	L	I	H	X	E	F	U	B

TOP TEN

BEEF

PORK

VENISON

LAMB

DUCK

GOOSE

TURKEY

CHICKEN

RABBIT

PHEASANT

WAYS TO PASS THE TIME

Noting

Knotting

Kissing

TWO DOWN

Fit five of the seven listed words into the Across rows in the grid, so that the other two words read down the shaded columns numbered 2 and 3.

AGENT	ANGER
FOGGY	RADAR
RANGE	SWORD
WAGON	

(Grid with rows numbered 1–7; shaded columns numbered 2 and 3)

STARTING LINE

Which three letter word can be placed at the start, to form three seven-letter words?

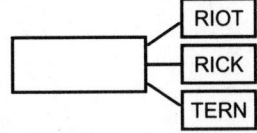

- RIOT
- RICK
- TERN

JOIN THE DOTS

(Grid of dots)

TOTAL CONCENTRATION

Can you fill in the missing numbers so that each row, each column and two longest diagonal lines meet the totals given?

							356
63	60	40	65		74		440
46	73	8		51	58	34	304
75		97	91			6	439
		43	94	29	13	35	330
70	15	77	55		9	31	320
27	11		80	56	89		309
46	76	79		14		1	279
423	319	353	449	295	375	207	480

MISSING LETTERS

One letter of the alphabet is missing from each box. Find them all and place them in the order of the numbered boxes to reveal a six-letter word.

Word: _____

1	2	3
PAUMG	KSWFO	QAZGV
BRVZJ	ZMRBJ	HRWBK
YILEF	ITXEG	CPFMS
SXHQD	NDULP	DTXJN
NTCKO	YHQVC	YEOIU

4	5	6
JTXAP	KQYWA	AIXKQ
YQBLF	BZPSF	LBYGS
ZGRMC	JMRTC	FMVCJ
DWUSH	ILUGN	NUDZP
INVEO	ODVXH	HEXTO

EXCUSES FOR

A night out:

_____
_____
_____
_____
_____

WHERE ON EARTH?

Where on earth is Lickey End?

Answer: _____

BALANCING THE SCALES

Given that scales A and B balance perfectly, how many squares are needed to balance scale C?

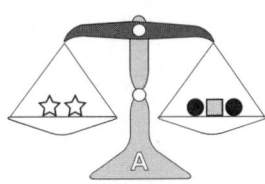

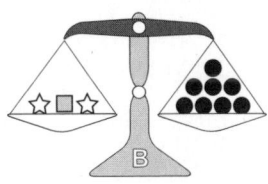

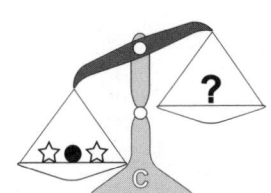

COUPLINGS

Apart from two, every word listed below can be coupled with one of the others to make another word or phrase. Rearrange the letters of the two which can't be paired together, to form one word, the name of a popular summer fruit.

1 RUBBER	2 ENGINE
3 PUDDING	4 STARRY
5 THANKS	6 WEDDING
7 PARTY	8 BASIN
9 FIRE	10 CHURCH
11 BREW	12 GIVING
13 DUCK	14 POPPER

Answer: _____

DOMINOLOGICAL

What is the value of the question mark?

= 9
= 15
= 15
= ?

STARTER LETTER

Write down one each of the listed items, all of which must begin with the starter letter:

A

Country	
Tree	
Boy's name	
Girl's name	
River	
City	
Animal	
Make of car	
Drink	

DO YOU KNOW...

...what happened on this date?

30 September 1399

MIRROR WRITING

Write this word upside down:

HOBBIES

_____

BRIEF SURVIVAL GUIDE

MARRIAGE:

1 Separate beds

2 Separate rooms

3 Separate houses

Answers to puzzles on the previous page

Where On Earth? West Midlands, England.
Starting Line: PAT.
Two Down: Across: 1 Sword, 4 Radar, 5 Agent, 6 Foggy, 7 Anger. Down: 2 Wagon, 3 Range.
Total Concentration: From left to right, top to bottom, the missing numbers are: 75, 63, 34, 64, 7, 99, 96, 20, 63, 9, 37, 30 and 33.
Missing Letters: WALKER.

FOR SALE

This is worth the asking price

of _____ because it

once belonged to _____

_____,

who used it for _____

_____

WORDSEARCH

Can you find all of the listed words related to farming in the grid? Words may run in either a forwards or backwards direction, horizontally, vertically or diagonally, but always in a straight, uninterrupted line.

ANIMALS

ARABLE

BARLEY

BINDER

BUTTER

CABBAGE

CLOVER

CORNFIELD

CULTIVATION

```
E S R O H S E G A B B A C
G R A N A R Y E Z I A M I
D D Y L R B A R L E Y A R
L C L O V E R M C D N R R
E I N S E C T I C I D E I
I K B E S K E N M C S D G
F C U L T I V A T I O N A
N A T B I Z L T L G K I T
R T T A N S C I P N Z B I
O S E R G G T O X U K O O
C Y R A L R W N Z F H C N
R A D L E I F T A E H W N
B H Y F D A I R Y M A I D
```

DAIRYMAID	GRANARY	INSECTICIDE
FERTILISER	HARVESTING	IRRIGATION
FUNGICIDE	HAYSTACK	MAIZE
GERMINATION	HORSE	WHEATFIELD

ARRANGING THINGS

If you fit six of these seven words into the grid below, the word left over will appear reading down the shaded squares.

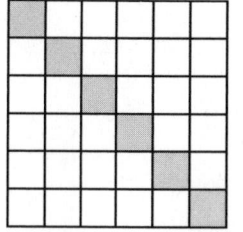

BARLEY	BRYONY
CELERY	LAUREL
LYCHEE	MEDLAR
MYRTLE	

GET THE LOOK

Make the face:

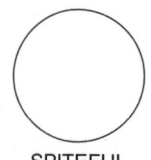

SPITEFUL

WEATHER for PESSIMISTS

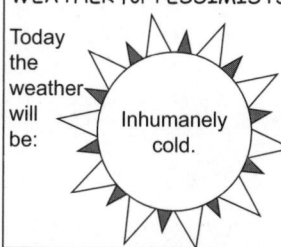

Today the weather will be: Inhumanely cold.

WHAT DOES IT MEAN?

What is the meaning of the word

IMBROGLIO

Answer: _____

_____

Answers to puzzles on the previous page

Do You Know… Henry IV was proclaimed King Henry IV of England after the abdication of King Richard II.
Dominological: 18 – Deduct the total number of spots on the second domino from the total of the spots on the first, then add the total number of spots on the third domino.
Couplings: 1/13, 3/8, 5/12, 7/14, 9/2, 10/6. The letters of 4 and 11 can be rearranged to form STRAWBERRY.
Balancing The Scales: 2.

107

WHATEVER YOU DO, don't even THINK about...

Mouldy fruit

Soggy newspaper

Paper cuts in your fingers

WHATEVER NEXT?

Which of the lettered alternatives comes next in this sequence:

| 8 | 12 | 20 | 32 | 52 | ? |

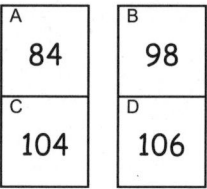

A	B
84	98

C	D
104	106

NUMB-SKULL

Fit the listed numbers into the grid, crossword-fashion.

2 digits
12
41
45

3 digits
167
169
334
444
461
486
487
492
494
500
636
764
864

4 digits
1252
3021
4364
4957
6221

5 digits
13123
34179
64043

6 digits
560201
656523

ON TARGET

The answers to the clues read from the outer circle to the centre, all ending with the same letter. When you've finished, the letters in the shaded ring will give a word.

1 Breakwater, pier

2 Examine closely

3 Currency

4 Very amusing

5 Foe

6 Stupid, ridiculous

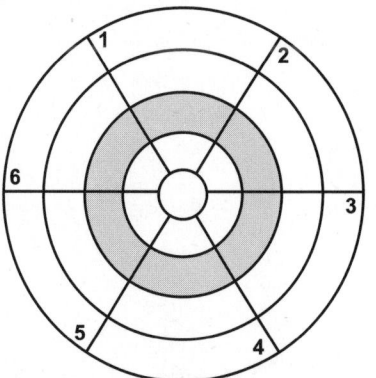

SECRET MISSION

Your secret mission (should you choose to accept it) is:

To plant a large shrub in your neighbours' garden while they are away.

LEARNING LINES

We give you a line, you tell us who said it and the film:

"We're alike, me and cat. A couple of poor nameless slobs."

CHARACTER ASSIGNATION

Fill in the answers to the clues, across the grid. Then read down the diagonal line of eight squares, to reveal:
A character from Charles Dickens' *Bleak House*.

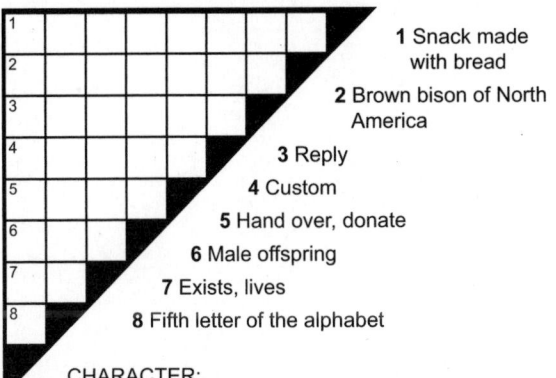

1 Snack made with bread

2 Brown bison of North America

3 Reply

4 Custom

5 Hand over, donate

6 Male offspring

7 Exists, lives

8 Fifth letter of the alphabet

CHARACTER: _____

EYE-SPY

I spy with my little eye something beginning with:

_____

WORDWHEEL

Using only the letters in the Wordwheel, you have ten minutes to find as many words as possible, none of which may be plurals, foreign words or proper nouns. Each word must be of three letters or more, all must contain the central letter and letters can only be used once in every word. There is at least one nine-letter word in the wheel.

Nine-letter word: _____

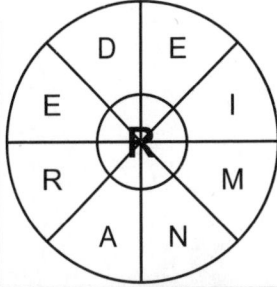

TOP FIVE

Best songs for cleaning your home to:

1 _____

_____

2 _____

_____

3 _____

_____

4 _____

_____

5 _____

_____

MASS HYSTERIAS

Today we are all going to:

Throw each other in the duck pond and see who floats.

UNLIKELY CANDIDATE

GROUND-BREAKING SCIENTIST

_____

NAME THAT SONG

We give you the first line, you name the song:

A heart that's full up like a landfill.

Song: _____

Answers to puzzles on the previous page

Learning Lines: Holly Golightly (Audrey Hepburn), *Breakfast At Tiffany's* (1961).
On Target: 1 Jetty, 2 Study, 3 Money, 4 Funny, 5 Enemy, 6 Silly.
Shaded word: Tunnel.
Whatever Next? A – 8+12=20, 20+12=32, 32+20=52 and next is 52+32=84.

Numb-Skull:

MATCH THAT

Remove six of these matches and leave three remaining.

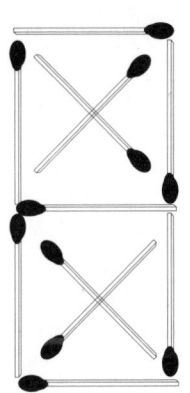

PYRAMID PLUS

Every brick in this pyramid contains a number which is the sum of the two numbers below it, so that F=A+B, etc. No two bricks contain the same number, or just a zero, so work out the missing numbers!

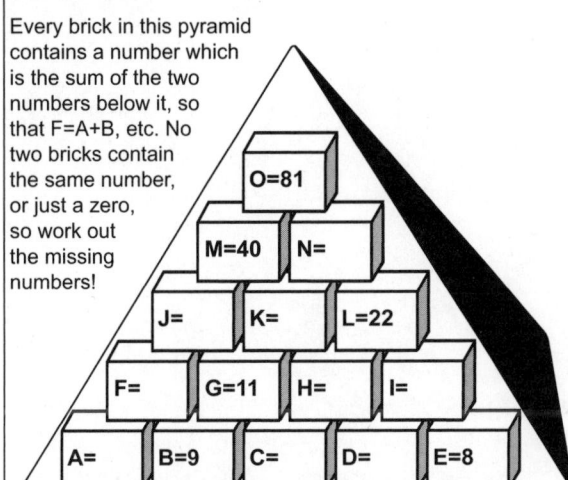

O=81

M=40 N=

J= K= L=22

F= G=11 H= I=

A= B=9 C= D= E=8

LUCKY NUMBER

Discover your lucky number for today by following these instructions:

1 Think of a number between five and fifty-five;
2 Think of the middle two digits of the year in which you were born;
3 Add the result of 1 above to the result of 2 above;
4 Reverse the digits in this number.

Now you have your lucky number for today. Don't lose it – write it down:

_____

WEATHER for OPTIMISTS

Today the weather will be:

Cold and damp with a great opportunity to wear your new coat.

NAMED AND SHAMED

Lecherous leech

_____

Neurotic catastrophe

_____

Senseless

_____

SWEET BAD MUSIC

So who on earth was responsible for this lyric?

She has robes and
She has monkeys,
Lazy diamond-studded
    flunkies.

THOUGHT FOR THE DAY

If you can't make yourself feel better, the least you can do is make someone else feel worse.

WORDS TO REMEMBER

With which company or organisation or product do you associate this slogan?

"Reach out and touch someone."

Answers to puzzles on the previous page

Name That Song: *No Surprises*, Radiohead.
Wordwheel: The nine-letter word is REMAINDER.
Character Assignation: 1 Sandwich, 2 Buffalo, 3 Answer, 4 Habit, 5 Give, 6 Son, 7 Is, 8 E. Character: Hortense.

DICEY ARITHMETIC

Using three of the arithmetical signs ÷, −, x and +, can you achieve the correct total?

    =

SNAKES & LADDERS

This is a standard game, so when you land at the foot of a ladder, you climb it; and when you land on the head of a snake, you slide down its tail. You need to throw an exact number to land on 100 to win – counting backwards if you don't, eg if you land on 98 and throw a five, you will end up on 97. The dice is thrown for you and always lands in this recurring order: 4, 5, 2, 3, 1, 6, so you can start by immediately placing your counter on square 4. Good luck – hope you win!

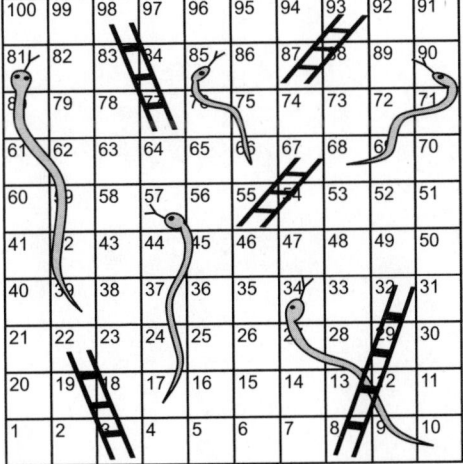

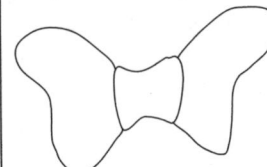
TWO-WORD HOROSCOPES

Aries – Lazy ways.

Taurus – What's cooking?

Gemini – Broader vistas.

Cancer – Little glories.

Leo – Big news.

Virgo – Terrible vision.

Libra – Grow some.

Scorpio – Pitiful offerings.

Sagittarius – No warning.

Capricorn – Top times.

Aquarius – No, no…

Pisces – Stay home.

PICK 'N' MIX

Choose three words to describe the best horror film:

Gory	Evil
Psychological	Death
Scream	Fear
Slasher	Brutal
Suspense	Laughter

GET THE LEADER

Can you unscramble the anagram to reveal the leader?

Fought on till weekend

Answer: _____

REAL WORDS

Which is the real word?

JOBBERNOWL ☐

JOBBERNICITY ☐

JOBBERNOCHY ☐

Answers to puzzles on the previous page

Sweet Bad Music: The Doors, *Love Street*.
Words To Remember: AT & T̄.
Pyramid Plus: A=1, B=9, C=2, D=6, E=8, F=10, G=11, H=8, I=14, J=21, K=19, L=22, M=40, N=41, O=81.

Match That:

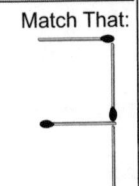

TOP TEN

INK ☐

OIL PAINT ☐

PENCIL ☐

CHARCOAL ☐

CRAYON ☐

WATERCOLOUR ☐

CHALK ☐

FELT-TIP PEN ☐

ACRYLIC PAINT ☐

SPRAY PAINT ☐

PAIR SHAPES

In the box below there are shapes in three different colours, black, white and grey. Any shape may have been rotated, but can you see which is the only shape to appear exactly twice in exactly the same colour?

SAY IT, DO IT, BE IT

Your word for today is:

COOL

WORDFILLER

Can you place all the listed words into the grid below?

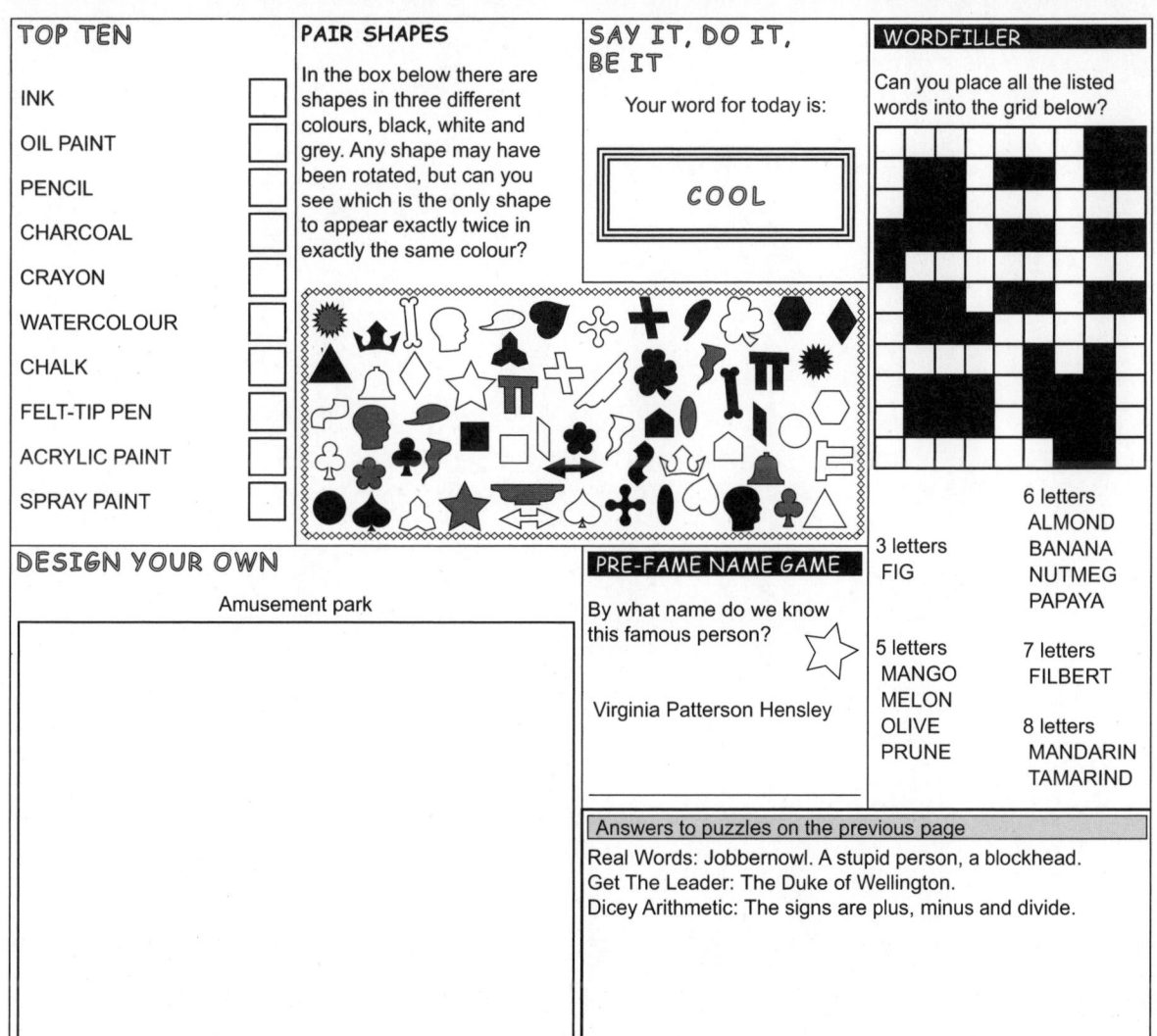

3 letters
FIG

5 letters
MANGO
MELON
OLIVE
PRUNE

6 letters
ALMOND
BANANA
NUTMEG
PAPAYA

7 letters
FILBERT

8 letters
MANDARIN
TAMARIND

DESIGN YOUR OWN

Amusement park

PRE-FAME NAME GAME

By what name do we know this famous person? ☆

Virginia Patterson Hensley

_____

Answers to puzzles on the previous page

Real Words: Jobbernowl. A stupid person, a blockhead.
Get The Leader: The Duke of Wellington.
Dicey Arithmetic: The signs are plus, minus and divide.

"She talks like a revolving door."

Anon

ARRANGING THINGS

If you fit six of these seven words into the grid below, the word left over will appear reading down the shaded squares.

ASHLEY   ALISON
BESSIE   DAMIAN
DWIGHT   GLADYS
        GORDON

LETTER TRACKER

Begin in the central shaded square and follow a continuous path which will track from square to square, up, down and sideways, but never diagonally.

Your trail should cover every letter once only, in order to find:

Sixteen volcanoes.

T	O	A	L	O	W	R	I	B	A	T
A	T	S	L	E	S	T	D	A	S	I
K	R	B	O	Y	T	S	E	N	T	N
A	O	M	L	I	O	U	I	V	U	I
R	K	N	O	S	N	E	V	E	S	P
T	J	E	E	R	C	O	T	O	P	A
N	O	F	F	I	O	T	T	A	A	G
G	M	O	I	L	K	E	E	C	X	A
E	A	S	C	A	I	A	N	A	I	N
N	G	R	A	M	J	N	G	O	F	I
O	T	G	N	I	U	F	R	E	H	S

CAPITALS

The capital of

BELIZE

is:

_____

SYMBOLISM

What whole number value between 1 and 9 should be allocated to each different symbol in order to reach the sum totals shown at the end of each row and column?

◇	○	△	□	=27
	◇	△		=11
○		□	◇	=21
	◇		□	=14

=12   =17   =21   =23

PLACE YOUR BETS

_____'s first words today will be:

"Where's my coffee?" ☐

"Late again?" ☐

"How lovely you could make it!" ☐

NAME THAT SONG

We give you the first line, you name the song: ♫

Life is bigger, it's bigger than you

Song: _____

Answers to puzzles on the previous page

Pre-Fame Name Game: Patsy Cline.
Pair shapes:

Wordfiller:

F	I	L	B	E	R	T	
I		A		A			
G		N	U	T	M	E	G
		A		A			
	M	A	N	D	A	R	I	N
P		A		I			
A		M	A	N	G	O	
P	R	U	N	E		D		L
A				L				I
Y				O				V
A	L	M	O	N	D			E

113

COMPLETE THIS LIMERICK:

A man from the Kent town, St Mary

Announced to his mates: "I'm a fairy,"

He had all sorts of things

But no wand nor wings

_____

DOMINADDITION

Can you place the remaining dominoes in their correct positions, so that the total number of spots in each of the four rows and five columns equals the sum at the end of that row or column?

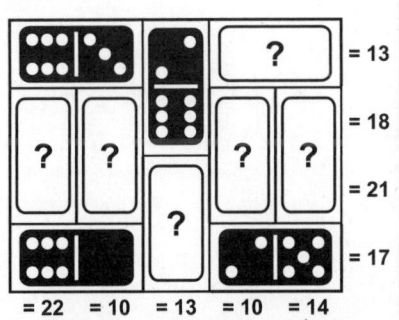

WORD LADDER

Change one letter at a time (but not the position of any letter) to make a new word – and move from the word at the top of the ladder to the word at the bottom using the exact number of rungs provided.

S L E E P

D R E A M

THIS WEEK'S PHOBIAS

Eleutherophobia – Fear of freedom
Ophthalmophobia – Fear of opening eyes
Geliophobia – Fear of laughter

THIN DIVIDING LINES

By using four straight lines, can you divide this grid into five sections, each containing five different numbers?

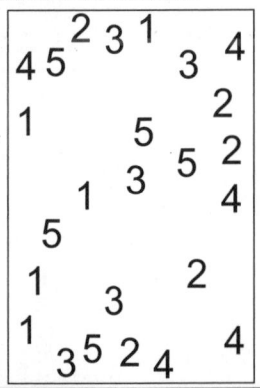

GET THE LEADER

Can you unscramble the anagram to reveal the leader?

Christ, will I scorn Hun!

Answer: _____

WHERE ON EARTH ?

Where on earth is Petting?

Answer: _____

EGG TIMER

Can you complete this puzzle in the time it takes to boil an egg? The answers to the clues are anagrams of the words immediately above and below, plus or minus a letter.

1 Unpredictable, eccentric
2 Opening at the top of a volcano
3 Draw by going over lines
4 Frequency
5 Gaze intently
6 Changes
7 Dressing for a wound

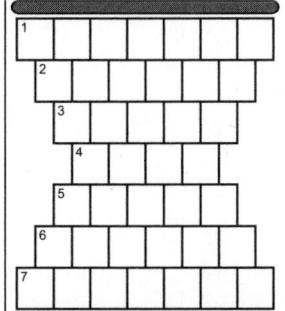

BALANCING THE SCALES

Given that scales A and B balance perfectly, how many squares are needed to balance scale C?

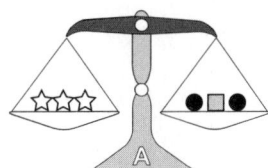

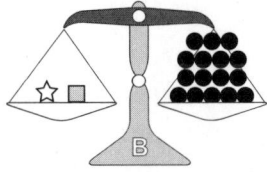

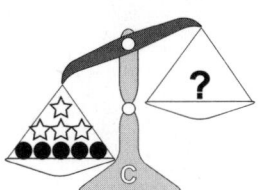

MIRROR WRITING

Write this word upside down:

IGNITED

_____

WHATEVER YOU DO, don't even THINK about...

Badly scratched records

Cold sores

Screeching car tyres

MISSING LETTERS

One letter of the alphabet is missing from each box. Find them all and place them in the order of the numbered boxes to reveal a six-letter word.

Word: _____

1	2	3
DEQXK	VINCH	MPATI
OITNA	OWRGZ	HBKVF
MBJFS	SBXMJ	OQUCZ
RUCZY	FEUPK	GJXLD
WHVGL	LTYQD	ERWNY

4	5	6
CHXOU	PSAQK	ZOCUP
RQJVY	BTJWF	DEWXK
KIWPD	CNXLG	NAITY
NAMSF	MVDRH	FBMSJ
BEZGL	EIZUY	VLHQG

TWO DOWN

Fit five of the seven listed words into the Across rows in the grid, so that the other two words read down the shaded columns numbered 2 and 3.

ABOUT   ACUTE
FORCE   FORTY
ORGAN   OTHER
       ROBOT

1	2		3	
4				
5				
6				
7				

TODAY'S GREATEST ACHIEVEMENT

Serenity ☐

Energy ☐

Spontaneity ☐

DO YOU KNOW...

...what happened on this date?

1 September 1939

AMAZING

Can you work your way from the entrance at the top to the exit at the bottom of this maze?

COUPLINGS

Apart from two, every word listed below can be coupled with one of the others to make another word or phrase. Rearrange the letters of the two which can't be paired together, to form one word, the name of a flower.

1 RAT	2 WEST
3 PUSSY	4 CATCHER
5 PIE	6 BOY
7 MERCHANT	8 WILD
9 PIN	10 APPLE
11 CAT	12 CUSHION
13 COW	14 MUSHY

Answer: _____

A IS TO B

   is to

A   B

as C   is to

D   E

F   G

WHAT DOES IT MEAN?

What is the meaning of the word

LUCUBRATION

Answer: _____
_____

MASS HYSTERIAS

Today we are all going to:

Put chicken wire over the windows so the monkey man can't get in.

WEATHER for PESSIMISTS

Today the weather will be:

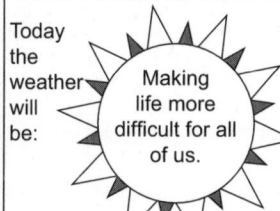

Making life more difficult for all of us.

USE YOUR IMAGINATION

Can you fill each of these boxes with a different bird's name?

PROVERBS & SAYINGS

The letters on the tiles were once all in place, but dropped out, falling in a straight line into the lower grid. Some tiles dropped earlier than others, so those on the lowest row aren't all from the same row in the grid above. Can you put them back into position in order to reveal a well-known proverb or saying?

L	F	T	N				A	M			L	H	
P	O	U	K	R	S	T	W	E	R	S		L	O	E
A	E	N	E	I	E	F	H	E	L	L	T	H	V	E	S
P	O	O	N	D	A	S	T	I	N	D	E	T	E	O	K

TOP FIVE

Best songs for planning a holiday:

1 _____
_____
2 _____
_____
3 _____
_____
4 _____
_____
5 _____
_____

WEATHER for OPTIMISTS

Today the weather will be:

Bright and sunny making anything possible.

LEARNING LINES

We give you a line, you tell us who said it and the film:

"I don't know . . . but some people without brains do an awful lot of talking... don't they?"

THOUGHT FOR THE DAY

The best time to do nothing is whenever, and as often as you can.

THINK ABOUT IT!

Can you picture this animal?

A tigerlope

Answers to puzzles on the previous page

What Does It Mean? Study or composition lasting late into the night. Couplings: 1/4, 3/11, 8/2, 9/12, 10/5, 13/6. The letters of 7 and 14 can be rearranged to form CHRYSANTHEMUM. A Is To B: G – Black shapes become white and white shapes become black, then the whole rotates anticlockwise by 60 degrees.

Amazing:

CODEWORD

This is a crossword puzzle in code. Every number represents a different letter of the alphabet and this number remains the same throughout the puzzle. Use the check-box to keep a track on your progress.

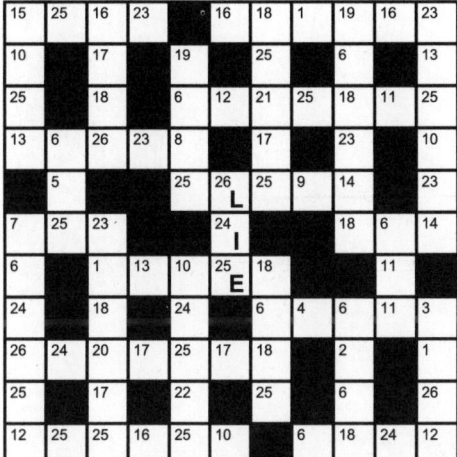

1	2	3	4	5	6	7	8	9	10	11	12	13

14	15	16	17	18	19	20	21	22	23	24	25	26

IN YOUR OWN LANGUAGE

Devise an Oriental-looking sign for your new restaurant.

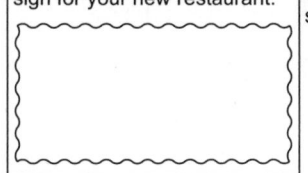

STARTING LINE

Which three letter word can be placed at the start, to form three seven-letter words?

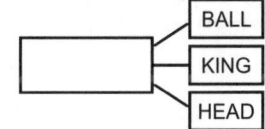

BALL
KING
HEAD

UNLIKELY CANDIDATE

PORN STAR

———————————

A MATCHING PAIR

Shirley wants a matching pair of shoes. Which two should she buy?

WHO AM I?

Ahoy! Belle at Ritz!

I am:

SECRET MISSION

Your secret mission (should you choose to accept it) is:

To say "maybe" every time someone asks you any question.

BRIEF SURVIVAL GUIDE

DIVORCE:

1 Be awarded a large sum of money
2 Be awarded the house and all its contents
3 Have lots of cosmetic surgery and look a million times better

SWEET BAD MUSIC

So who on earth was responsible for this lyric?

Open a soda pop, watch it fizz and pop.
The clock is tickin' and we can't stop.
Open a soda pop, bop-shi-bop-shi-bop.

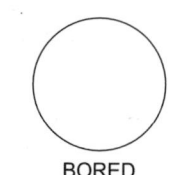

NAMED AND SHAMED

Boring

_____

Bland

_____

Bonkers

_____

GET THE LOOK

Make the face:

BORED

WAYS TO PASS THE TIME

Sewing ☐

Sausage-making ☐

Sitting ☐

WORDWHEEL

Using only the letters in the Wordwheel above, you have ten minutes to find as many words as possible, none of which may be plurals, foreign words or proper nouns. Each word must be of three letters or more, all must contain the central letter and letters can only be used once in every word. There is at least one nine-letter word in the wheel.

Nine-letter word: _____

HEXAGONY

Can you place the hexagons in the grid, so that where any triangle touches another along a straight line, the contents of both are the same? One triangle is already filled.

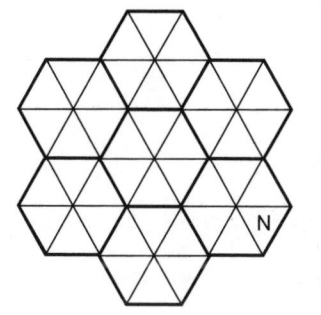

EYE-SPY

I spy with my little eye something beginning with:

_____

Answers to puzzles on the previous page

Who Am I? Elizabeth Taylor.
A Matching Pair: B and E.
Starting Line: PIN.

Codeword:

WORDSEARCH

Can you find all of the listed countries in the grid below? Words may run in either a forwards or backwards direction, horizontally, vertically or diagonally, but always in a straight, uninterrupted line.

```
C O L O M B I A A A P B P
S G J Z C A N I I A A A N
A N H D L A N R L B K R D
M O U O W O A E F E I B N
A C G S D G U M B L S A A
H N T E L Z G Z V I T D L
A O C U E B A J N Z A O I
B A B N R A R G O E N S Z
M Y E A I N A U H T I L A
P V Z B O P C A N A D A W
N I M B O A I N A B L A S
L A A R H O N D U R A S U
G G E A I D O B M A C R I
```

ALBANIA

ANGOLA

BAHAMAS

BARBADOS

BELIZE

BOTSWANA

BRAZIL

BULGARIA

CAMBODIA   GAMBIA

CANADA   HONDURAS   PAKISTAN

COLOMBIA   LITHUANIA   SINGAPORE

CONGO   MACEDONIA   SWAZILAND

GABON   NICARAGUA   VENEZUELA

CLOCKWORDS

It's a race against the clock…
How many common words of three or more different letters can you make from those on the clockface (without using plurals, proper nouns or abbreviations) in ten minutes? All words must contain BOTH the letters indicated by the hands on the clock.

UNFINISHED PICTURE

Can you complete the left half of this picture?

MATCH THAT

Use nine of these matches to make six squares.

EXCUSES FOR

Your family:

_____

_____

_____

_____

REAL WORDS

Which is the real word?

LOLLYGOTIOUS   ☐

LOLLYGAG   ☐

LOLLYNOXIOUS   ☐

NAME THAT SONG

We give you the first line, you name the song: 🎵

Won't you scratch my itch, sweet Annie Rich?

Song: _____

Answers to puzzles on the previous page

Sweet Bad Music: Britney Spears, *Soda Pop.*
Wordwheel: The nine-letter word is FLOWERPOT.

Hexagony:

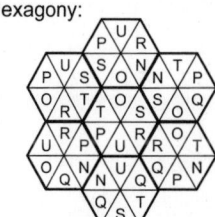

MISSING LINKS

Which word links the one on the left with the one on the right? We've done the first one, and when you've finished them all, the first letters of the link words will spell another word.

AGENT	ORANGE	PEEL
SNOW		MADE
THERE		NOON
SECOND		PICKED
ADAM'S		PIE

CELEBRITY WRESTLING

JERRY SPRINGER

-v-

OPRAH WINFREY

DICE-SECTION

Printed onto every one of the six numbered dice below are six letters (one per side), which can be rearranged to form the answer to each clue: however, some sides are invisible to you. Use the clues and write every answer into the grid. When correctly filled, the letters in the shaded squares, reading in the order 1 to 6, will spell out a woman's name.

Centre

Blossom, bloom

Infertile

Slight wind

Country of which Athens is the capital city

Small box for strawberries

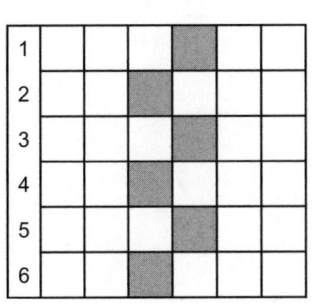

PRE-FAME NAME GAME

By what name do we know this famous person?

Richard Starkey

PICK 'N' MIX

Choose three words to describe a first date:

Drink	Fun
Interesting	Food
Sexy	Hopeful
Scary	Loving
Happy	Laughing

INSULT OF THE DAY

"America is a country that doesn't know where it is going, but is determined to set a speed record getting there."

Peter Lawrence

MONEY, MONEY, MONEY

The

YUAN RENMINBI

is the currency of

_____

Answers to puzzles on the previous page

Real Words: Lollygag. To fool around; to spend time aimlessly; to dawdle.
Name That Song: *Return Of The Grievous Angel*, Gram Parsons.
Match That:
A cube has six square faces

121

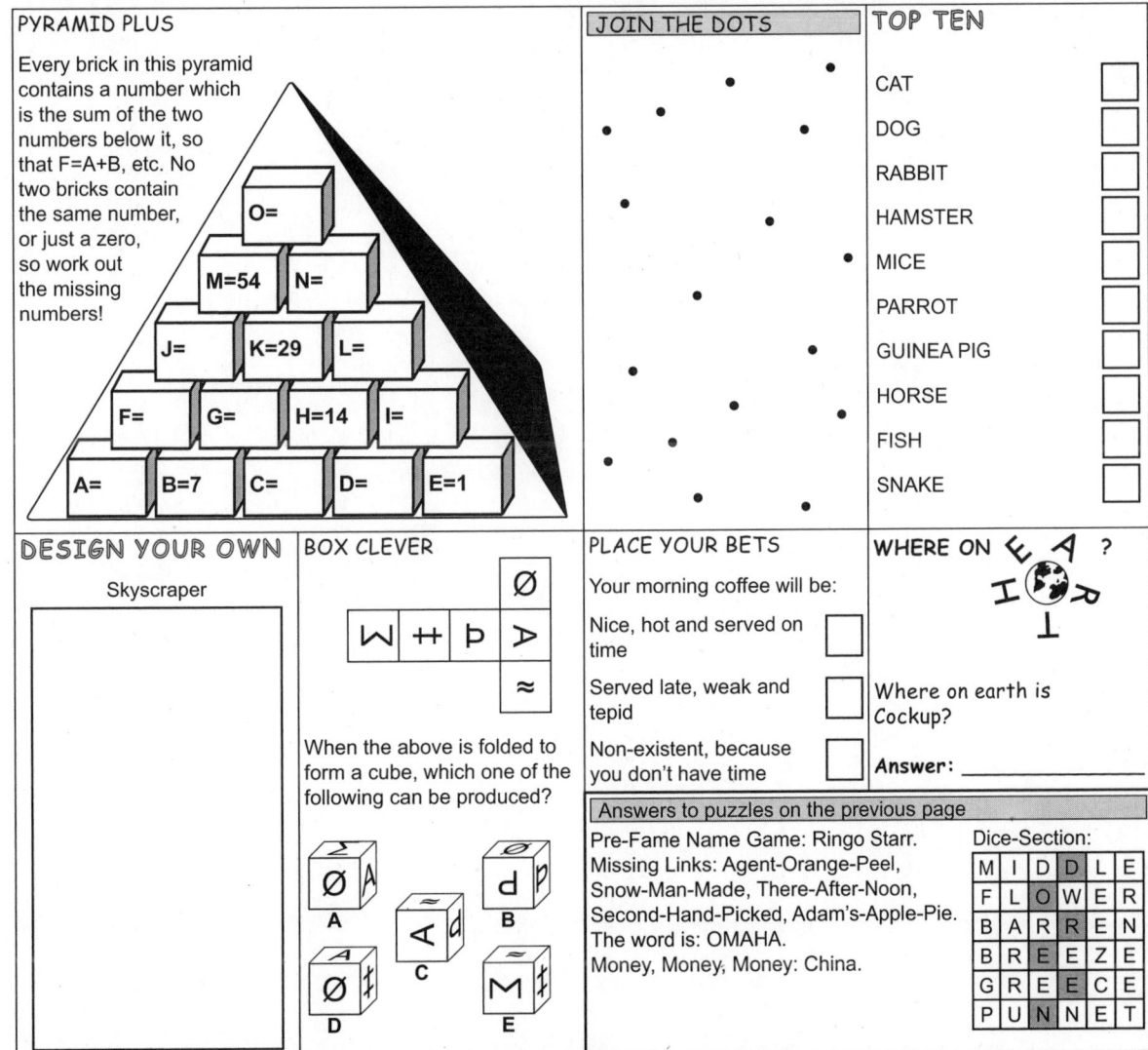

PYRAMID PLUS

Every brick in this pyramid contains a number which is the sum of the two numbers below it, so that F=A+B, etc. No two bricks contain the same number, or just a zero, so work out the missing numbers!

O=

M=54 N=

J= K=29 L=

F= G= H=14 I=

A= B=7 C= D= E=1

JOIN THE DOTS

TOP TEN

CAT ☐
DOG ☐
RABBIT ☐
HAMSTER ☐
MICE ☐
PARROT ☐
GUINEA PIG ☐
HORSE ☐
FISH ☐
SNAKE ☐

DESIGN YOUR OWN

Skyscraper

BOX CLEVER

When the above is folded to form a cube, which one of the following can be produced?

A B C D E

PLACE YOUR BETS

Your morning coffee will be:

Nice, hot and served on time ☐

Served late, weak and tepid ☐

Non-existent, because you don't have time ☐

WHERE ON EARTH?

Where on earth is Cockup?

Answer: _____

122

DICEY ARITHMETIC

Using three of the arithmetical signs ÷, −, x and +, can you achieve the correct total?

    =

LETTER TRACKER

Begin in the central shaded square and follow a continuous path which will track from square to square, up, down and sideways, but never diagonally.

Your trail should cover every letter once only, in order to find:

Seventeen countries.

T	N	I	X	E	E	C	E	E	R	G
I	E	C	Y	M	I	G	E	R	I	A
N	G	O	L	A	T	I	N	A	T	S
A	R	A	D	A	N	N	I	R	A	I
M	J	O	R	R	T	S	U	A	Q	K
O	A	I	L	A	B	A	N	G	P	A
Z	B	I	Q	U	A	L	I	L	H	S
A	M	P	O	E	I	C	E	A	D	E
C	A	I	I	E	D	H	T	E	I	N
H	E	P	H	T	N	T	S	I	A	K
I	L	E	R	U	I	E	N	T	W	U

JIGSAW CROSSWORD

Fit the blocks into the empty grid to form a complete crossword which, when finished, will be symmetrical, similar to the example seen here:

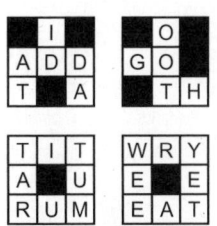

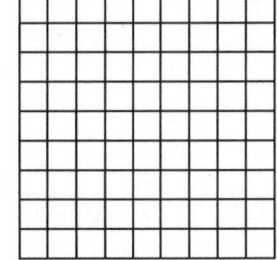

GET THE LEADER

Can you unscramble the anagram to reveal the leader?

Zap: rifle ends enjoyed trend, knight

Answer: _____

WHAT DOES IT MEAN?

What is the meaning of the word

HECATOMB

Answer: _____

_____

Answers to puzzles on the previous page

Where On Earth? Cumbria, England.
Box Clever: C.
Pyramid Plus: A=3, B=7, C=8, D=6, E=1, F=10, G=15, H=14, I=7, J=25, K=29, L=21, M=54, N=50, O=104.

123

LUCKY NUMBER

Discover your lucky number for today by following these instructions:

1 Think of your age and add the digits together;
2 Think of a number between eight and sixty-seven;
3 Add the result of 1 above to the result of 2 above;
4 Reverse the digits in this number.

Now you have your lucky number for today. Don't lose it – write it down:

_____

ON TARGET

The answers to the clues read from the outer circle to the centre, all ending with the same letter. When you've finished, the letters in the shaded ring will give a word.

1 Popular fruit
2 Dried plum
3 Wallet
4 Plenty
5 Untrue
6 Topic

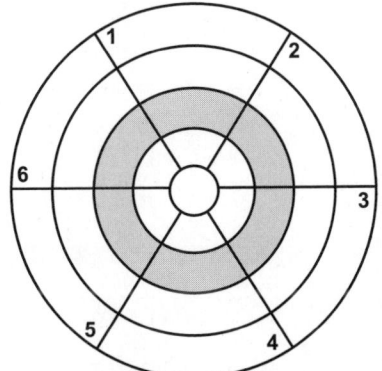

MASS HYSTERIAS

Today we are all going to:

> Build a wicker man and burn it at midnight.

NAME THAT SONG

We give you the first line, you name the song:

Young man, there's no need to feel down.

Song: _____

POTATOE OR POTATO?

RECOMMEND

OR

RECCOMEND

TWO-WORD HOROSCOPES

Aries – Why me?

Taurus – Great expectations.

Gemini – Funny bones.

Cancer – Little mistakes…

Leo – Work it!

Virgo – Last gasps.

Libra – Out there.

Scorpio – Nosy neighbours.

Sagittarius – Gossip merchant.

Capricorn – Last attempt.

Aquarius – Best practice.

Pisces – Beautiful outfit.

FOR SALE

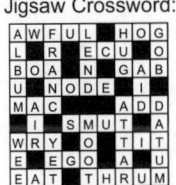

This is worth the asking price

of _____ because it

once belonged to _____

_____,

who used it for _____

_____

Answers to puzzles on the previous page

What Does It Mean? A large sacrifice or slaughter.
Get The Leader: President John Fitzgerald Kennedy.
Dicey Arithmetic: The signs are minus, divide and plus.
Letter Tracker: Bangladesh, Pakistan, Iraq, Australia, Jordan, Nigeria, Greece, Italy, Mexico, Argentina, Mozambique, Ethiopia, Chile, Peru, India, Liechtenstein, Kuwait.

Jigsaw Crossword:

A	W	F	U	L		H	O	G
L		R		E	C	U		O
B	O	A		N		G	A	B
U		N	O	D	E		I	
M	A	C				A	D	D
	I		S	M	U	T		A
W	R	Y		O		T	I	T
E		E	G	O		A		U
E	A	T		T	H	R	U	M

MIRROR WRITING

Write this word upside down:

IRONING

_____

MISSING LETTERS

One letter of the alphabet is missing from each box. Find them all and place them in the order of the numbered boxes to reveal a six-letter word.

Word: _____

1	2	3
RJPAY	FZUIE	IUDYM
QSBKX	NHYQB	NCHZT
ILOFW	CGXMT	OVXFB
MTDGZ	JRWDS	JKQAG
HNUEV	LAVPK	ERWLS

4	5	6
JTCXM	PYGDX	ATXOI
GDRWL	KQMBJ	HUWBP
BZSQK	AUZHW	MCVJQ
NEPVF	LSRFC	ZRDFK
HYUOA	ETOVI	LSYNE

WORD LADDER

Change one letter at a time (but not the position of any letter) to make a new word – and move from the word at the top of the ladder to the word at the bottom using the exact number of rungs provided.

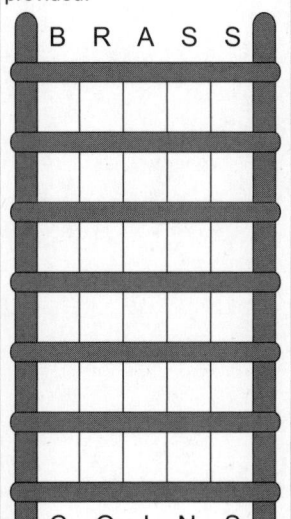

B R A S S

C O I N S

CAKE DECORATING

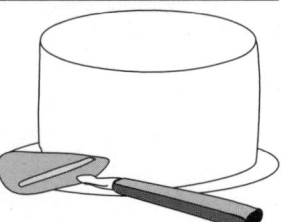

TWO DOWN

Fit five of the seven listed words into the Across rows in the grid, so that the other two words read down the shaded columns numbered 2 and 3.

ABOVE   BEVEL
DAIRY   NEVER
ORDER   OZONE
        ZEBRA

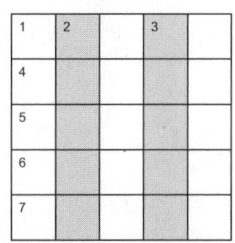

ARRANGING THINGS

If you fit six of these seven words into the grid below, the word left over will appear reading down the shaded squares.

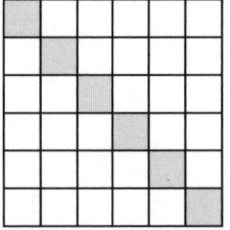

BANKER   DANCER
DRIVER   GAUCHO
MATRON   SAILOR
        SENTRY

TODAY'S GREATEST ACHIEVEMENT

Winning the argument ☐

Not having the argument ☐

Dispelling the argument ☐

WEATHER for PESSIMISTS

Today the weather will be:

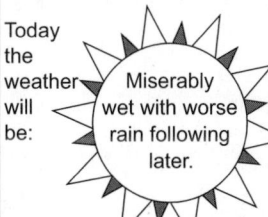

Miserably wet with worse rain following later.

DO YOU KNOW...

...what happened on this date?

1 February 1790

COMPLETE THIS LIMERICK:

There once was a girl called Louise

Who had very thin, bony knees

She tried padding them out

But that made her look stout

_____

ANTONYM WALL

Pair up these set of letters correctly to spell out two words of the same length but with opposite meanings.

NEC	ELA	CON
TED	UNR	TED

_____ & _____

SYMBOLISM

What whole number value between 1 and 9 should be allocated to each different symbol in order to reach the sum totals shown at the end of each row and column?

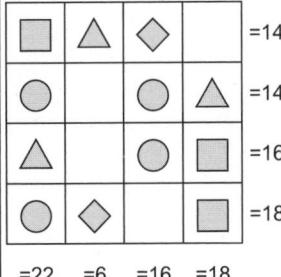

DOMINADDITION

Can you place the remaining dominoes in their correct positions, so that the total number of spots in each of the four rows and five columns equals the sum at the end of that row or column?

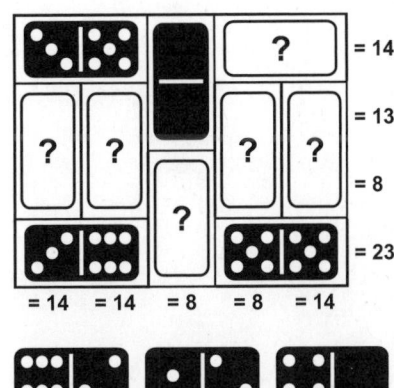

WHATEVER YOU DO, don't even THINK about...

Anything described as "cute"

Rotting meat

The thing that lives in the wardrobe

THIS WEEK'S PHOBIAS

Genuphobia – Fear of knees
Ereuthophobia – Fear of the colour red
Trichopathophobia – Fear of hair

WEATHER for OPTIMISTS

Today the weather will be:

Cold and bleak but perhaps with a lovely sunset.

LEARNING LINES

We give you a line, you tell us who said it and the film:

"Hasta la vista, baby."

BALANCING THE SCALES

Given that scales A and B balance perfectly, how many squares are needed to balance scale C?

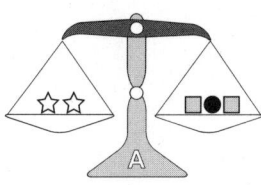

A

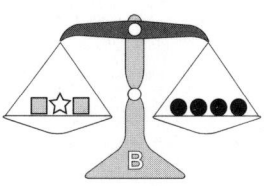

B

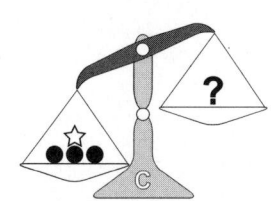

C

COUPLINGS

Apart from two, every word listed below can be coupled with one of the others to make another word or phrase. Rearrange the letters of the two which can't be paired together, to form one word, the name of an Asian country.

1 IRON	2 KETTLE
3 SAUCE	4 NIGHT
5 COPPER	6 MARE
7 BLADES	8 HANG
9 CURRY	10 CLUBS
11 SHAKE	12 MILK
13 GOLF	14 FILINGS

Answer: _____

PROVERBS & SAYINGS

The letters on the tiles were once all in place, but dropped out, falling in a straight line into the lower grid. Some tiles dropped earlier than others, so those on the lowest row aren't all from the same row in the grid above. Can you put them back into position in order to reveal a well-known proverb or saying?

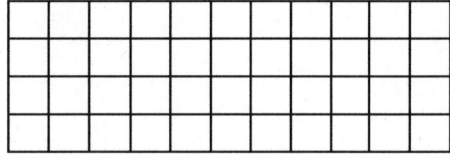

A	N			W	S				F		
T	O			E	H	S	A	E			
I	O		G	L	R	E	R	U	E	A	
F	N	O	T	L	E	R	D	S	H	R	

THOUGHT FOR THE DAY

"Beer is living proof that God loves us and wants to see us happy."

Benjamin Franklin

GET THE LOOK

Make the face:

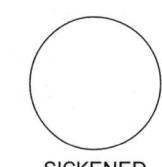

SICKENED

SECRET MISSION

Your secret mission (should you choose to accept it) is:

To close all doors behind you and tap three times on each one.

PRE-FAME NAME GAME

By what name do we know this famous person?

Nathaniel Adams Coles

_____

Answers to puzzles on the previous page

Learning Lines: The Terminator (Arnold Schwarzenegger), *Terminator 2: Judgement Day* (1991).
Antonym Wall: Connected and Unrelated.
Symbolism: Circle=6, Diamond=4, Square=8, Triangle=2.

Dominaddition:

3	5	0	1	5
6	1	0	2	4
2	2	4	0	0
3	6	4	5	5

THE TANGLED TRAIL

Which of these anglers has landed the fish?

A   B   C

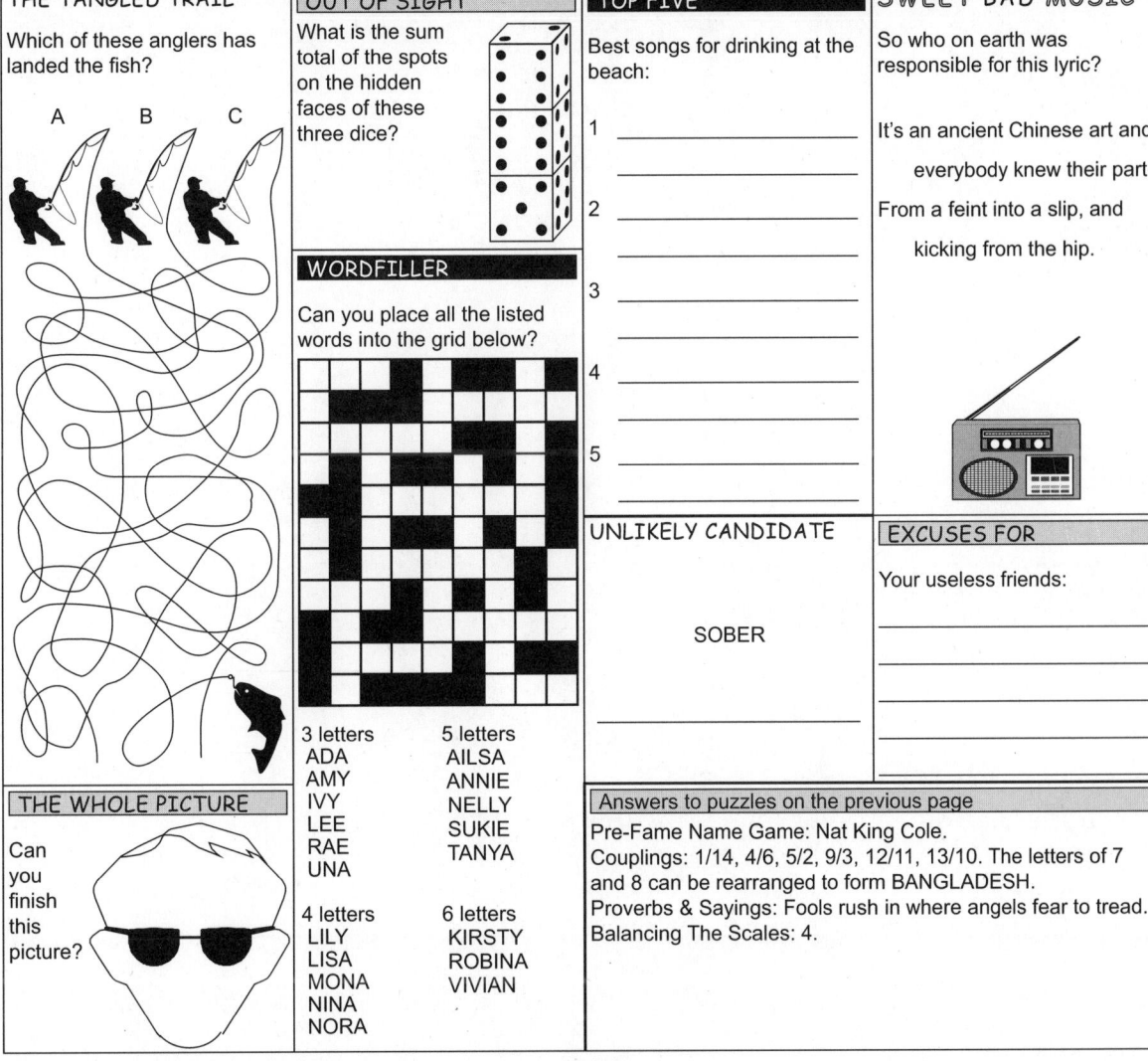

THE WHOLE PICTURE

Can you finish this picture?

OUT OF SIGHT

What is the sum total of the spots on the hidden faces of these three dice?

WORDFILLER

Can you place all the listed words into the grid below?

3 letters
ADA
AMY
IVY
LEE
RAE
UNA

4 letters
LILY
LISA
MONA
NINA
NORA

5 letters
AILSA
ANNIE
NELLY
SUKIE
TANYA

6 letters
KIRSTY
ROBINA
VIVIAN

TOP FIVE

Best songs for drinking at the beach:

1 _____

_____

2 _____

_____

3 _____

_____

4 _____

_____

5 _____

_____

UNLIKELY CANDIDATE

SOBER

_____

SWEET BAD MUSIC

So who on earth was responsible for this lyric?

It's an ancient Chinese art and

everybody knew their part,

From a feint into a slip, and

kicking from the hip.

EXCUSES FOR

Your useless friends:

_____

_____

_____

_____

Answers to puzzles on the previous page

Pre-Fame Name Game: Nat King Cole.
Couplings: 1/14, 4/6, 5/2, 9/3, 12/11, 13/10. The letters of 7 and 8 can be rearranged to form BANGLADESH.
Proverbs & Sayings: Fools rush in where angels fear to tread.
Balancing The Scales: 4.

Write down one each of the listed items, all of which must begin with the starter letter:

M

Country	
Tree	
Boy's name	
Girl's name	
River	
City	
Animal	
Make of car	
Drink	

NAMED AND SHAMED

Bankroll

_____

Bank robber

_____

Bank clerk

_____

REAL WORDS

Which is the real word?

MACILENT ☐

MACILICTIOUS ☐

MACILONGENITY ☐

WAYS TO PASS THE TIME

Boring ☐

Blessing ☐

Beginning ☐

WORDWHEEL

Using only the letters in the Wordwheel, you have ten minutes to find as many words as possible, none of which may be plurals, foreign words or proper nouns. Each word must be of three letters or more, all must contain the central letter and letters can only be used once in every word. There is at least one nine-letter word in the wheel.

Nine-letter word: _____

Wordwheel letters: U, T, A, P, R, E, N, R, (central) K

PATCHWORK

Fit the numbers 1, 2, 3, 4, 5, 6 and 7 into the grid below, so that every horizontal row, every vertical column and the two long diagonal lines of six smaller squares contain six different numbers. Some are already in place.

			7			3
	6			4		
	3		6		5	
2						7
		5			6	
5	7			2		
		1	2			

DESIGN YOUR OWN

Neighbourhood

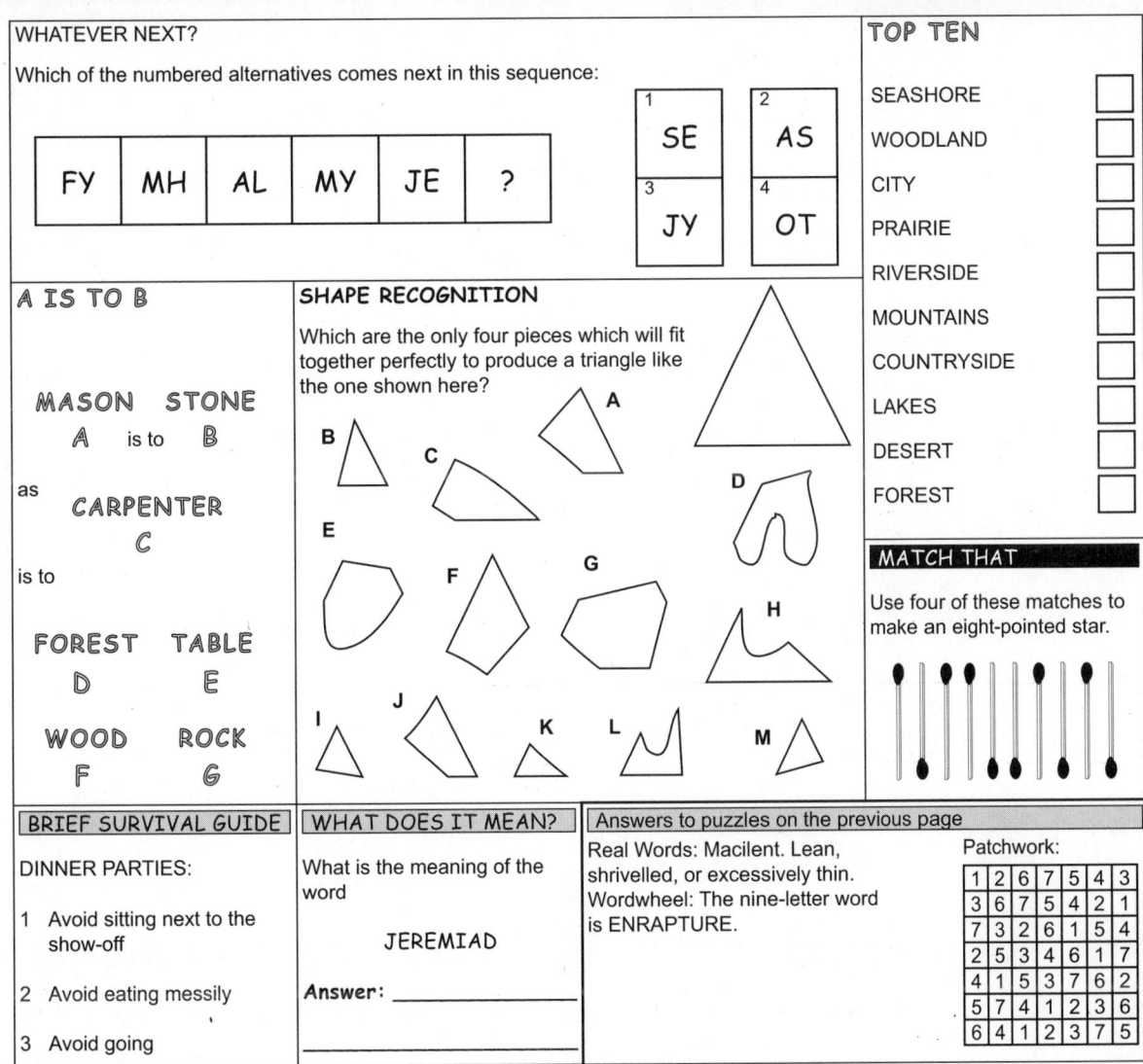

WHATEVER NEXT?

Which of the numbered alternatives comes next in this sequence:

| FY | MH | AL | MY | JE | ? |

1. SE
2. AS
3. JY
4. OT

TOP TEN

- SEASHORE ☐
- WOODLAND ☐
- CITY ☐
- PRAIRIE ☐
- RIVERSIDE ☐
- MOUNTAINS ☐
- COUNTRYSIDE ☐
- LAKES ☐
- DESERT ☐
- FOREST ☐

A IS TO B

MASON STONE
A is to B

as

CARPENTER
C

is to

FOREST TABLE
D E

WOOD ROCK
F G

SHAPE RECOGNITION

Which are the only four pieces which will fit together perfectly to produce a triangle like the one shown here?

A B C D E F G H I J K L M

MATCH THAT

Use four of these matches to make an eight-pointed star.

BRIEF SURVIVAL GUIDE

DINNER PARTIES:

1. Avoid sitting next to the show-off

2. Avoid eating messily

3. Avoid going

WHAT DOES IT MEAN?

What is the meaning of the word

JEREMIAD

Answer: _____

_____

Answers to puzzles on the previous page

Real Words: Macilent. Lean, shrivelled, or excessively thin.
Wordwheel: The nine-letter word is ENRAPTURE.

Patchwork:

1	2	6	7	5	4	3
3	6	7	5	4	2	1
7	3	2	6	1	5	4
2	5	3	4	6	1	7
4	1	5	3	7	6	2
5	7	4	1	2	3	6
6	4	1	2	3	7	5

130

PICK 'N' MIX

Choose three words to describe a job interview:

Calm	Fear
Taxing	Capable
Confidence	Clever
Hopeless	Horrible
Humiliating	Panic

STARTING LINE

Which three letter word can be placed at the start, to form three seven-letter words?

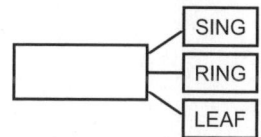

- SING
- RING
- LEAF

EYE-SPY

I spy with my little eye something beginning with:

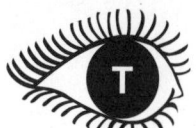

_____

MY FAVOURITE THINGS

These are a few of my favourite things:

My favourite meal is:

_____

My favourite cheese is:

_____

My favourite soup is:

_____

My favourite pudding is:

_____

LOOSE VOWELS

Someone has taken all the vowels out of what was once a completed crossword. Can you put them all back in again? You should use only those letters beneath the grid.

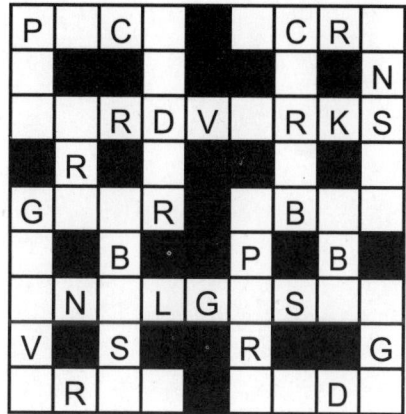

A A A A A A A A A A A A A

E E E E E E E E E

I I I

O O O

U U

GET THE LEADER

Can you unscramble the anagram to reveal the leader?

A darn long era

Answer: _____

WHERE ON EARTH?

Where on earth is Effin?

Answer: _____

HEXAGONY

Can you place the hexagons in the grid, so that where any triangle touches another along a straight line, the contents of both are the same? One triangle is already filled.

DOMINOLOGICAL

What is the value of the question mark?

= 21
= 51
= 54
= ?

NAME THAT SONG

We give you the first line, you name the song:

♫

Do you still remember how we used to be?

Song: _____

MASS HYSTERIAS

Today we are all going to:

◇◇◇◇◇◇◇◇◇◇◇◇◇◇◇◇◇◇◇◇◇◇

Renounce all worldly possessions and move to the South American jungle.

◇◇◇◇◇◇◇◇◇◇◇◇◇◇◇◇◇◇◇◇◇◇

SAY IT, DO IT, BE IT

Your word for today is:

GRASPING

CHARACTER ASSIGNATION

Fill in the answers to the clues, across the grid. Then read down the diagonal line of eight squares, to reveal:
A character from William Shakespeare's *King Henry VIII*.

1 Place selling novels, etc

2 Country, capital Tirana

3 Orange root vegetable

4 Jewish religious leader

5 Country road

6 Achieve victory

7 Abbreviation denoting the Pope's faith

8 Compass point abbreviation, opposite west

CHARACTER: _____

Answers to puzzles on the previous page

Where On Earth? Limerick, Ireland.
Get The Leader: Ronald Reagan.
Starting Line: TEA.

Loose Vowels:

P	A	C	E			A	C	R	E
E			I				A		N
A	A	R	D	V	A	R	K	S	
	R		E				O		U
G	E	A	R			O	B	O	E
U		B				P		B	
A	N	A	L	G	E	S	I	A	
V		S				R			G
A	R	E	A			A	I	D	E

132

WORDSEARCH

Can you find all of the listed colours in the grid below? Words may run in either a forwards or backwards direction, horizontally, vertically or diagonally, but always in a straight, uninterrupted line.

```
V T E J E A A C A T B H K
E E E T N N R U U M E A A
R L N I A I I R B L B U Y
M A D I M L Q R I U B E T
I V V S R U O O E E R O R
L E O O O A T C R G C N T
I N L I C R M G O I N C U
O D S P O A I A R H O A N
N E H P P N D P R R C M T
E R E S E A A O K T C E S
E N I R A M A U Q A L L E
G O L D L O G I R A M U H
B L U E R I H P P A S E C
```

AMBER

ANIL

APPLE

APRICOT

AQUAMARINE

ASH

AUBERGINE

AUBURN

AVOCADO

BAY	CRIMSON	
BLUE	GOLD	SAPPHIRE
CAMEL	HELIOTROPE	TANGERINE
CHESTNUT	JET	TURQUOISE
CHOCOLATE	LAVENDER	ULTRAMARINE
CORK	MARIGOLD	VERMILION

LETTER TRACKER

Begin in the central shaded square and follow a continuous path which will track from square to square, up, down and sideways, but never diagonally.

Your trail should cover every letter once only, in order to find:

Fourteen English counties.

E	H	C	E	R	F	U	R	I	A	C
S	H	S	H	I	F	S	E	H	S	N
R	I	E	G	L	O	R	E	E	L	A
E	O	I	D	K	H	I	W	R	I	H
F	X	R	B	D	S	K	I	L	T	S
O	R	A	M	O	**B**	R	O	E	S	R
S	D	C	S	R	E	D	Y	T	M	E
H	I	T	E	E	R	F	O	R	O	S
E	R	E	S	D	I	H	S	D	L	L
R	S	P	H	E	N	K	T	C	A	W
I	H	O	R	V	O	E	N	O	R	N

PLACE YOUR BETS

Your nice surprise today is:

A free holiday ☐

A pay rise ☐

You're sacked ☐

DO YOU KNOW...

...what happened on this date?

22 January 1901

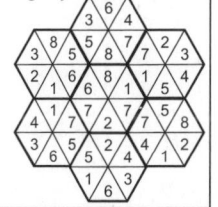

MONEY, MONEY, MONEY

The

COLON

is the currency of

_____

WORDS TO REMEMBER

With which company or organisation or product do you associate this slogan?

"You'll wonder where the yellow went, when you brush your teeth with…"

THINK ABOUT IT!

Can you picture this animal?

A hoat

MY NEXT HOBBY

What
_____

How
_____

Why
_____

SNAKES & LADDERS

This is a standard game, so when you land at the foot of a ladder, you climb it; and when you land on the head of a snake, you slide down its tail. You need to throw an exact number to land on 100 to win – counting backwards if you don't, eg if you land on 98 and throw a five, you will end up on 97. The dice is thrown for you and always lands in this recurring order: 1, 2, 3, 6, 5, 4, so you can start by immediately placing your counter on square 1. Good luck – hope you win!

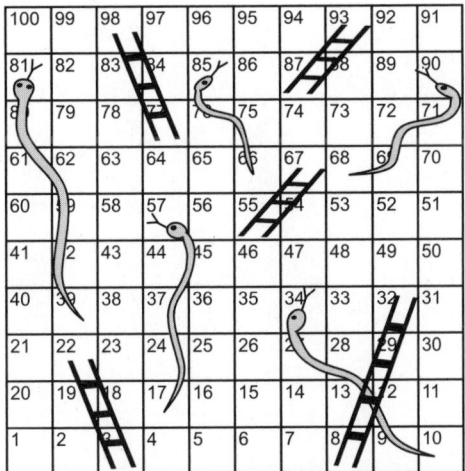

WEATHER for PESSIMISTS

Today the weather will be:

Dangerously spring-like but with a bite in the breeze.

PRE-FAME NAME GAME

By what name do we know this famous person?

Pierino Roland Como

_____

DICEY ARITHMETIC

Using three of the arithmetical signs ÷, −, x and +, can you achieve the correct total?

    =

Answers to puzzles on the previous page
Do You Know… Queen Victoria died.
Letter Tracker: Bedfordshire, Devon, Kent, Cornwall, Somerset, Yorkshire, Wiltshire, Lancashire, Suffolk, Dorset, Cambridgeshire, Cheshire, Oxfordshire, Shropshire.

BERMUDA TRIANGLE

Travel through the 'Bermuda Triangle' by visiting one room at a time and collecting a letter from each. You can enter the outside passageway as often as you like, but can only visit each room once. When you've completed your tour, rearrange the fifteen letters to spell out a word.

```
        /\
       /T \
      /A  I \
     /S  T  O \
    /O  I  A  N \
   /N  I  L  N  A \
```

MISSING LETTERS

One letter of the alphabet is missing from each box. Find them all and place them in the order of the numbered boxes to reveal a six-letter word.

Word: _____

1	2	3
XRHWA	MZHTE	UOWKD
KNVFB	QYBUL	GJPCN
CYSOU	NICXG	BVXTL
ZLGDP	ORDVJ	AHYRF
QMETI	PSFWK	IEQZM

4	5	6
LTCXH	NXSFD	YKSJA
MGSWD	LWOHB	LWIFB
NZBKR	VAZTM	QTVCM
OFIQV	QKIGC	ZNODG
JUEYA	RYUJP	PXUHE

IN YOUR OWN LANGUAGE

Devise an Oriental-looking sign for your new restaurant.

WHATEVER YOU DO, don't even THINK about...

Blisters on your feet

"I-ay-ay will always love yooooou"

Vomiting

DICE-SECTION

Printed onto every one of the six numbered dice below are six letters (one per side), which can be rearranged to form the answer to each clue; however, some sides are invisible to you. Use the clues and write every answer into the grid. When correctly filled, the letters in the shaded squares, reading in the order 1 to 6, will spell out a man's name.

Main meal of the day

Covered in pimples

Get on loan

Particular point in time

Canada's capital city

Blanket-like cloak

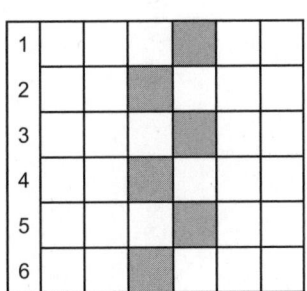

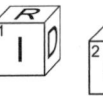

LEARNING LINES

We give you a line, you tell us who said it and the film:

"Houston, we have a problem."

ELIMINATION

Every oval shape contains a different letter from A to K inclusive. Use the clues to determine their locations. Reference in the clues to 'due' means in any location along the same horizontal or vertical line.

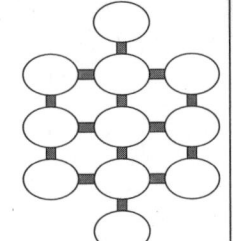

1 H is due north of G.
2 J is due north of F and due east of A.
3 B is due east of G and due north of K.
4 J is due west of I and due south of H.
5 D is due south of J and due east of C.

W—N—E—S (compass)

TOP FIVE

Best songs for relaxing with friends:

1 _____
 _____
2 _____
 _____
3 _____
 _____
4 _____
 _____
5 _____
 _____

JIGSAW CROSSWORD

Fit the blocks into the empty grid to form a complete crossword which, when finished, will be symmetrical, similar to the example seen here:

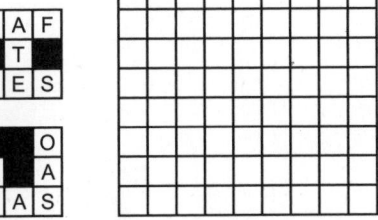

(blocks:)
I C A / A / B L E
R A F / T / C E S
F I C / A / H I P
O / S A / W A S
C / C U T / L
T E D / E / S P
I T / S / S P A L
H A T / H / L
D E D / I / M A R

TWO DOWN

Fit five of the seven listed words into the Across rows in the grid, so that the other two words read down the shaded columns numbered 2 and 3.

AMUSE   KAPUT
REPEL   RHYME
SHAPE   SPASM
        USUAL

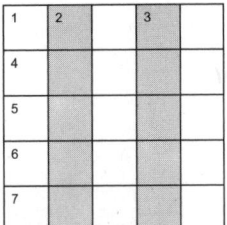

WEATHER for OPTIMISTS

Today the weather will be:

Thick fog causing severely reduced visibility but at least you won't be able to see ugly people.

MIRROR WRITING

Write this word upside down:

HOMELY

_____

GET THE LOOK

Make the face:

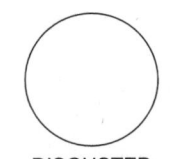

DISGUSTED

Answers to puzzles on the previous page

Learning Lines: Jim Lovell (Tom Hanks), *Apollo 13* (1995).
Bermuda Triangle: The word is NATIONALISATION.
Missing Letters: JASPER.

Dice-Section:

D	I	N	N	E	R
S	P	O	T	T	Y
B	O	R	R	O	W
M	O	M	E	N	T
O	T	T	A	W	A
P	O	N	C	H	O

DESIGN YOUR OWN

Shopping mall

CLOCKWORDS

It's a race against the clock...
How many common words of three or more different letters can you make from those on the clockface (without using plurals, proper nouns or abbreviations) in ten minutes? All words must contain BOTH the letters indicated by the hands on the clock.

Clockface letters: P A G, X, L, N, C, E, Y, I, O, T

COMPLETE THIS LIMERICK:

"Where there's a will, there's a way"

Johnnie often had heard people say

Then one day he felt ill

So he made out his will

_____

SECRET MISSION

Your secret mission (should you choose to accept it) is:

To stare at someone without blinking for at least three minutes.

UNLIKELY CANDIDATE

HEALTH GURU

_____

SWEET BAD MUSIC

So who on earth was responsible for this lyric?

I'm a cold Italian pizza,

I could use a lemon squeezer.

SYMBOLISM

What whole number value between 1 and 9 should be allocated to each different symbol in order to reach the sum totals shown at the end of each row and column?

☐	◇	◇	△	=14
△		△	○	=4
◇		◇	☐	=13
☐			○	=9

=18 =3 =7 =12

Answers to puzzles on the previous page
Two Down: Across:
1 Usual, 4 Rhyme,
5 Kaput, 6 Spasm,
7 Repel.
Down: 2 Shape,
3 Amuse.

Elimination:

Jigsaw Crossword:
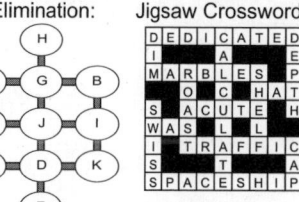

137

WHO AM I?

Don a man

I am:

_____

NAMED AND SHAMED

Obvious liar

_____

Worst nightmare

_____

Dictator

WORD LADDER

Change one letter at a time (but not the position of any letter) to make a new word – and move from the word at the top of the ladder to the word at the bottom using the exact number of rungs provided.

A MATCHING PAIR

Tom wants a couple of identical T-shirts. Which two should he buy?

A   B

C   D

E   F

DOMINADDITION

Can you place the remaining dominoes in their correct positions, so that the total number of spots in each of the four rows and five columns equals the sum at the end of that row or column?

WAYS TO PASS THE TIME

Tripping ☐

Trotting ☐

Telling ☐

EXCUSES FOR

An expensive lunch:

_____
_____
_____
_____
_____

USE YOUR IMAGINATION

Can you fill each of these boxes with a different colour?

SUM TOTAL

Place the digits 1-9, one per square, so that the sums are correct, according to the totals at the ends of the rows and columns. The calculations should be done in the order in which they appear, for example 6–2x5=20 should be read as 6–2(=4), then 4x5=20.

	+		x		=	96
–		x		+		
	x		–		=	19
+		+		x		
			x		=	10
=		=		=		
13		38		14		

THE LAST WORD

Which of the four lettered alternatives (a, b, c or d) should most logically fill the empty space? In other words, what have the listed words in common which is also shared by one of the alternatives?

ABBOT   BELLY

CHILLY   FLUX

GHOST   _____

a. Adept   b. Prime

c. Martyr   d. Shock

WORDWHEEL

Using only the letters in the Wordwheel, you have ten minutes to find as many words as possible, none of which may be plurals, foreign words or proper nouns. Each word must be of three letters or more, all must contain the central letter and letters can only be used once in every word. There is at least one nine-letter word in the wheel.

Nine-letter word: _____

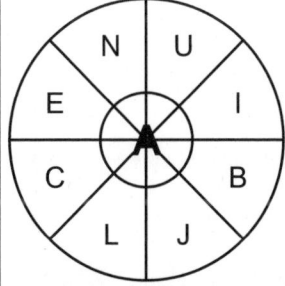

REAL WORDS

Which is the real word?

MUGDEMP ☐

MUGDINT ☐

MUGWUMP ☐

GET THE LEADER

Can you unscramble the anagram to reveal the leader?

Muddler of lands

Answer: _____

Answers to puzzles on the previous page

Who Am I? Madonna.
A Matching Pair: B and F.
Word Ladder: One solution is FOOT, font, fond, bond, band, bard, YARD.

Dominaddition:

3	0	2	3	3
1	2	6	6	5
5	2	5	5	0
6	6	2	2	4

ARRANGING THINGS

If you fit six of these seven words into the grid below, the word left over will appear reading down the shaded squares.

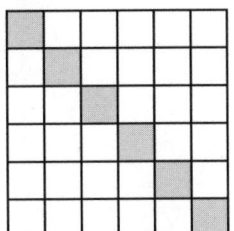

PACKET   PADDLE
PELVIC   PEOPLE
PILFER   PREACH
      PROFIT

PAIR SHAPES

In the box below there are shapes in three different colours, black, white and grey. Any shape may have been rotated, but can you see which is the only shape to appear exactly twice in exactly the same colour?

CAPITALS

The capital of

AUSTRALIA

is:

_____

UNFINISHED PICTURE

Can you complete the left half of this picture?

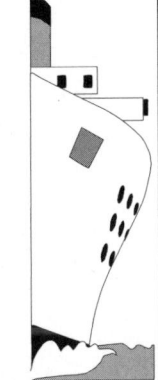

TOP TEN

CAR

AEROPLANE

BOAT

BICYCLE

WALKING

SCOOTERS

HORSEBACK

TRUCK

HOT-AIR BALLOON

CARAVAN

TODAY'S GREATEST ACHIEVEMENT

Breakfast

Lunch

Dinner

NAME THAT SONG

We give you the first line, you name the song: ♫

I met her in a club down in Old Soho

Song: _____

MATCH THAT

Using just twelve matches, make a hexagon and six triangles – and possibly even a circle!

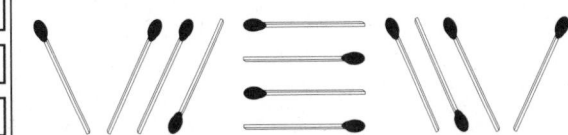

Answers to puzzles on the previous page

Real Words: Mugwump. A person who remains aloof from controversial issues.
Get The Leader: Donald Rumsfeld.
Wordwheel: The nine-letter word is JUBILANCE.
The Last Word: a. Adept – the letters in each word are in alphabetical order.

Sum Total:

9	+	7	x	6
–		x		+
4	x	5	–	1
+		+		x
8	–	3	x	2

COUPLINGS

Apart from two, every word listed below can be coupled with one of the others to make another word or phrase. Rearrange the letters of the two which can't be paired together, to form one word, the name of a European city.

1 MATTER	2 MOTH
3 HANDSHAKE	4 BREAK
5 BLOOD	6 BOTTLE
7 GOLDEN	8 RICE
9 RELATIVE	10 EATEN
11 WEEKEND	12 PUDDING
13 ROD	14 BLUE

Answer: _____

CODEWORD

This is a crossword puzzle in code. Every number represents a different letter of the alphabet and this number remains the same throughout the puzzle. Use the check-box to keep a track on your progress.

3	24	21	2			7	17	11	4 B	10 A	9 T
8			1	10	18			17		1	
21	24	11	4		13	17	12	24	18	9	
6			10			26		5		22	
	16	1	4	9		26	25	24	20	19	
4		6		17	7	1		1		13	
18	1	22	10	14		18	10	9	1		
1		18		10			20			7	
7	19	1	1	23	1		20	10	15	1	
1		9			1	2	1			10	
18	24	1	26	24	25		9	10	22	2	

1	2	3	4	5	6	7	8	9	10	11	12	13

14	15	16	17	18	19	20	21	22	23	24	25	26

JOIN THE DOTS

PICK 'N' MIX

Choose three words to describe your boss:

DICTATORIAL

DOMINEERING

UNDERSTANDING

CONSIDERATE

ANGRY

EGOTISTICAL

DAFT

INTELLIGENT

STUPID

SCARY

BRIEF SURVIVAL GUIDE

SPORTS DAY:

1 Fake a broken leg

2 Fake a debilitating illness

3 Fake mental incapacity

WHERE ON  ?

Where on earth is Humptulips?

Answer: _____

JUST A WORD

Can you find 'NIB' hidden in the grid, wordsearch-style?

```
A B A C H U S E R D S A L
O I N H I S E A H I U M P
S D I J U E R D C H J I S
E S B G H J I U K O I V C
E U H N R D T F G I O S E
E S U T Y H I M K S E R P
```

FOR SALE

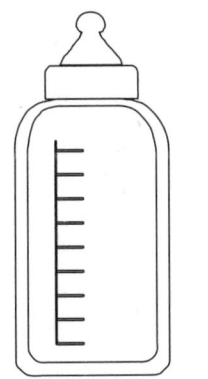

This is worth the asking price

of _____ because it

once belonged to _____

_____

who used it for _____

_____

WORDFILLER

Can you place all the listed words into the grid below?

3 letters	7 letters
NUN	EQUERRY
VET	

5 letters	8 letters
CLERK	HOTELIER
MASON	
NURSE	
TUTOR	9 letters
VALET	CARPENTER
	EXECUTIVE
6 letters	SECRETARY
SORTER	

EGG TIMER

Can you complete this puzzle in the time it takes to boil an egg? The answers to the clues are anagrams of the words immediately above and below, plus or minus a letter.

1 On display
2 Planting seeds
3 Oscillate
4 Chant
5 Sharp, stabbing pain
6 Lightweight cord
7 Gazing hard

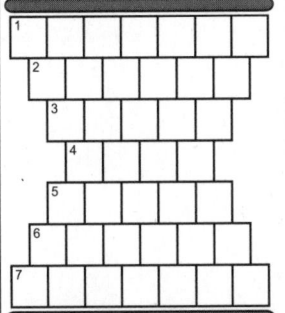

WEATHER for PESSIMISTS

Today the weather will be:

So hot and sunny your shoes will melt and your feet will burn.

TWO-WORD HOROSCOPES

Aries – Losing bet.

Taurus – Later fun.

Gemini – No worries.

Cancer – Not now.

Leo – Keep out.

Virgo – Isolated incident.

Libra – Crawl in.

Scorpio – Not clever.

Sagittarius – Happy trousers.

Capricorn – Telephone them.

Aquarius – Be organised.

Pisces – New shoes.

PRE-FAME NAME GAME

By what name do we know this famous person?

Frank James Cooper

ON TARGET

The answers to the clues read from the outer circle to the centre, all ending with the same letter. When you've finished, the letters in the shaded ring will give a word.

1 Citrus fruit

2 Unadorned

3 Fabric made from flax fibres

4 Grieve the loss of

5 Tarnish

6 Bird's hooked claw

1
2
3
4
5
6

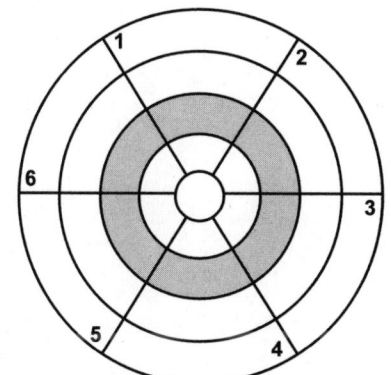

CHARACTER ASSIGNATION

Fill in the answers to the clues, across the grid. Then read down the diagonal line of eight squares, to reveal:
A character from Charles Kingsley's *Hereward The Wake*.

1
2
3
4
5
6
7
8

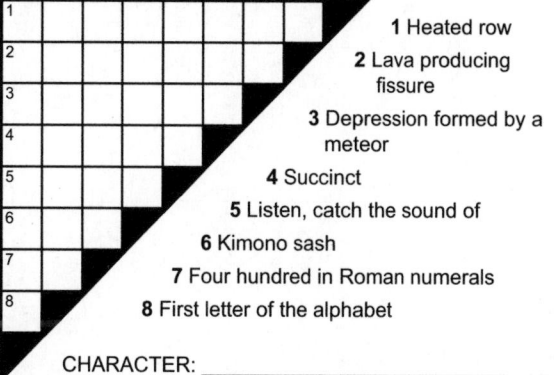

1 Heated row

2 Lava producing fissure

3 Depression formed by a meteor

4 Succinct

5 Listen, catch the sound of

6 Kimono sash

7 Four hundred in Roman numerals

8 First letter of the alphabet

CHARACTER: ____________________

TOP FIVE

Best songs for a break-up:

1 ____________________

____

2 ____________________

____

3 ____________________

____

4 ____________________

____

5 ____________________

____

PLACE YOUR BETS

__________'s wedding will be:

Sleek, expensive and stylish ☐

Raucous, drunken and wild ☐

Quiet, boring and uninspired ☐

STARTING LINE

Which three letter word can be placed at the start, to form three seven-letter words?

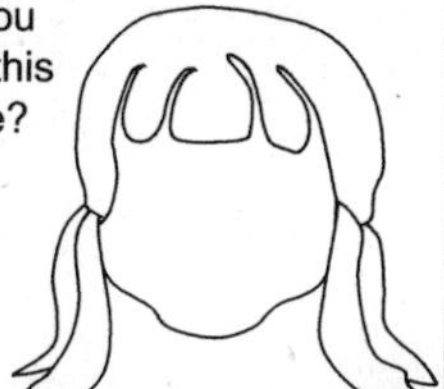

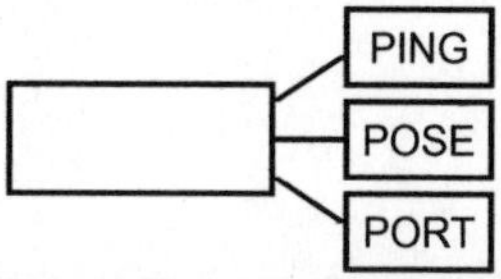

PING
POSE
PORT

THE WHOLE PICTURE

Can you finish this picture?

WHAT DOES IT MEAN?

What is the meaning of the word

MUMPSIMUS

Answer: ____________________

____

Answers to puzzles on the previous page

Pre-Fame Name Game: Gary Cooper.

Egg Timer:
1 Showing,
2 Sowing,
3 Swing,
4 Sing,
5 Sting,
6 String,
7 Staring.

Just A Word:

A	B	A	C	H	U	S	E	R	D	S	A	L
O	I	**N**	H	I	S	E	A	H	I	U	M	P
S	D	**I**	J	U	E	R	D	C	H	J	I	S
E	S	**B**	G	H	J	I	U	K	O	I	V	C
E	U	H	N	R	D	T	F	G	I	O	S	E
E	S	U	T	Y	H	I	M	K	S	E	R	P

Wordfit:

M		C	L	E	R	K		
A		A		X				
S	O	R	T	E	R			S
O		P		C		H		E
N		E		U		O		C
		N		T	U	T	O	R
V	E	T		I		E		E
		E		V	A	L	E	T
N	U	R	S	E		I		A
U						E		R
N		E	Q	U	E	R	R	Y

EYE-SPY

I spy with my little eye something beginning with:

P

DOMINO PUZZLE

Which domino (A, B, C, D or E) should fill the empty space?

?

 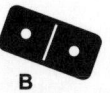  

A   B   C   D   E

SHADOWLAND

Test your skills of observation. Only one of the five shadows is that of the push bike. Which one?

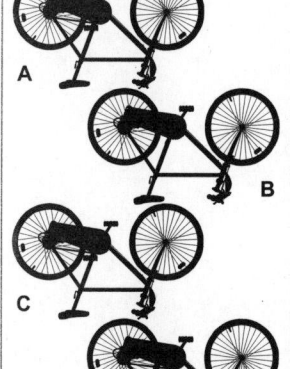

A

B

C

D

E

NUMB-SKULL

Fit the listed numbers into the grid, crossword-fashion.

2 digits
34
65

3 digits
125
128
183
226
231
465
492
493
495
541
732
912
964

4 digits
1273
3690
4449
5463
6496

5 digits
25808
55434
65780
79320

6 digits
860767

7 digits
9204513

9

MASS HYSTERIAS

Today we are all going to:

Wear orange dresses, shake our bells and tambourines and dance in the street.

DO YOU KNOW...

...what happened on this date?

1 January 45 BC

EXCUSES FOR

A new car:

Answers to puzzles on the previous page

What Does It Mean? A view stubbornly held even when shown to be wrong.
Starting Line: SUP.
On Target: 1 Lemon, 2 Plain, 3 Linen, 4 Mourn, 5 Stain, 6 Talon. Shaded word: Manual.
Character Assignation: 1 Argument, 2 Volcano, 3 Crater, 4 Brief, 5 Hear, 6 Obi, 7 CD, 8 A. Character: Torfrida.

144

POTATOE OR POTATO?

INDISPENSABLE

OR

INDISPENSIBLE

BOX CLEVER

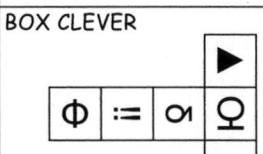

When the above is folded to form a cube, which one of the following can be produced?

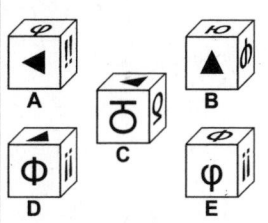

BROKEN-HEARTED

Don't be half-hearted in your attempts to get these couples back together again! Match both sides of each heart, to reveal their names.

___ & ___   ___ & ___   ___ & ___

___ & ___   ___ & ___   ___ & ___

GE JUL
A

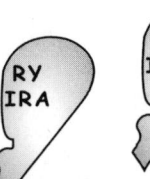
IAN IE
C

RY IRA
B

AS RAH
D

HYW DO
E

LUC SA
F

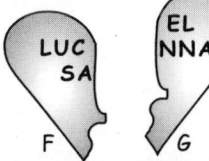
EL NNA
G

FL HEI
H

BAR MO
I

OFF IA
J

BR JOD
K

OYD DI
L

CELEBRITY WRESTLING

BOY GEORGE

-v-

MARILYN MANSON

LEARNING LINES

We give you a line, you tell us who said it and the film:

"Nature, Mr Allnut, is what we are put in this world to rise above."

DICEY ARITHMETIC

Using three of the arithmetical signs ÷, −, x and +, can you achieve the correct total? Afterwards, see if you can spot an alternative way to do this.

    =

Answers to puzzles on the previous page

Do You Know… New Year's Day was celebrated for the first time as the Julian calendar took effect in Rome.
Shadowland: C.
Domino Puzzle: E – The number of spots on the top alternates between six and three each time, whilst the number on the bottom increases by one each time.

Numb-Skull:

145

THIN DIVIDING LINES

By using two straight lines, can you divide this teeshirt into three parts, each containing four different forms of the letter 'T'?

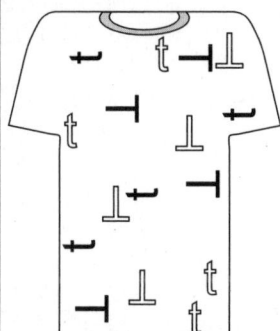

DESIGN YOUR OWN

Football ground

WEATHER for OPTIMISTS

Today the weather will be:

Heavy showers, perfect for splashing in puddles like Gene Kelly.

SWEET BAD MUSIC

So who on earth was responsible for this lyric?

All the cops in the donut shop say,
Ay oh whey oh, ay oh whey oh.

TOTAL CONCENTRATION

Can you fill in the missing numbers so that each row, each column and two longest diagonal lines meet the totals given?

							172
67	6		7		76	8	278
	3	60	9	31		78	229
26	50	11			20	6	148
	45	28		51	36	35	274
61	5	66	49	63			364
56			74	37	17	55	300
19	18	16	73		23	19	187
307	153	263	261	272	273	251	198

WAYS TO PASS THE TIME

Wandering ☐

Wilfully ☐

Wistfully ☐

| Answers to puzzles on the previous page |

Learning Lines: Rose Sayer (Katharine Hepburn), *The African Queen* (1951).
Dicey Arithmetic: The signs are times, divide and minus or minus, times and plus.
Broken-Hearted: A and J, E and G, F and D, H and L, I and B, K and C.
Box Clever: E.
Potatoe or Potato? Indispensable.

DOMINADDITION

Can you place the remaining dominoes in their correct positions, so that the total number of spots in each of the four rows and five columns equals the sum at the end of that row or column?

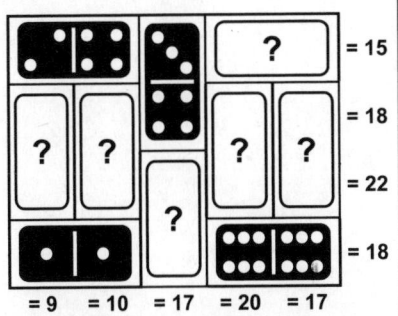

= 15
= 18
= 22
= 18

= 9   = 10   = 17   = 20   = 17

LETTER TRACKER

Begin in the central shaded square and follow a continuous path which will track from square to square, up, down and sideways, but never diagonally.

Your trail should cover every letter once only, in order to find:

Twenty things to eat.

E	S	E	L	P	A	N	C	N	O	C
H	A	A	L	A	E	K	A	E	B	A
C	L	P	I	R	S	E	R	G	D	U
I	A	D	D	R	C	S	O	L	E	F
U	Q	E	G	O	A	S	A	D	C	H
T	S	S	O	P	B	R	E	S	E	E
I	B	S	U	Y	A	L	O	E	M	A
U	I	T	P	R	T	E	C	O	H	C
C	S	U	P	R	U	P	A	S	C	A
K	E	N	A	S	C	Z	I	T	I	R
A	C	Y	R	T	A	Z	P	A	N	O

GET THE LOOK

Make the face:

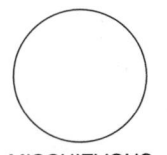

MISCHIEVOUS

UNLIKELY CANDIDATE

COSMETIC SURGEON

_____

SECRET MISSION

Your secret mission (should you choose to accept it) is:

To ask those around you not to speak to you until noon.

REAL WORDS

Which is the real word?

OCTONOCITY ☐

OCTOTHORPE ☐

OCTOBUCCULUS ☐

COMPLETE THIS LIMERICK:

There was a young lady in Leeds

Who swallowed a packet of seeds

Within half an hour

They started to flower

_____

CITY SEARCH

Here's a puzzle to test your skills! Fit the shapes into the grid so that the completed puzzle shows six six-letter cities. Three letters are already in place, to get you off to a good start…

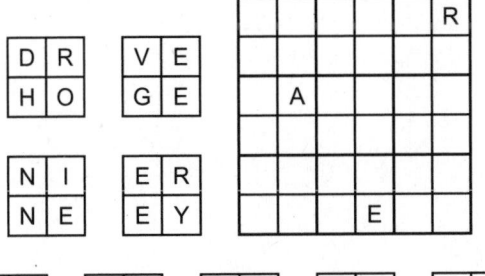

WORD LADDER

Change one letter at a time (but not the position of any letter) to make a new word – and move from the word at the top of the ladder to the word at the bottom using the exact number of rungs provided.

S O A P

D I S H

THOUGHT FOR THE DAY

MISSING LETTERS

One letter of the alphabet is missing from each box. Find them all and place them in the order of the numbered boxes to reveal a six-letter word.

Word: _____

1	2	3
WKOAJ	EXUOH	RZWHD
NVBIG	ZLBJP	QMJCF
LYCRF	NYGQC	LSVGB
ZDSPM	KTWDF	NYUAI
EXHUQ	MSVAI	EXTPK

4	5	6
OVHTC	KUGXD	PFUKA
KULDG	NZQBF	TBSYO
BMSQI	PRSMJ	IMWCG
NXFYE	OYWHC	JRZDH
PWARZ	LVETI	QVXLE

GET THE LEADER

Can you unscramble the anagram to reveal the leader?

This American-born led plan

Answer: _____

NAME THAT SONG

We give you the first line, you name the song: ♪

Load up on guns and bring your friends

Song: _____

Answers to puzzles on the previous page

Real Words: Octothorpe. Another name for the telephone handset symbol #.
Letter Tracker: Bread, Cheese, Macaroni, Chocolate, Pasta, Pizza, Curry, Porridge, Soup, Pastry, Cake, Nuts, Biscuits, Quiche, Salad, Paella, Pancakes, Casserole, Fudge, Bacon.

Dominaddition:

2	4	3	5	1
0	3	4	6	5
6	2	6	3	5
1	1	4	6	6

WHAT'S IN THE BOTTLE?

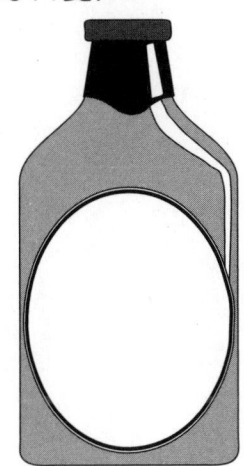

WORDWHEEL

Using only the letters in the Wordwheel, you have ten minutes to find as many words as possible, none of which may be plurals, foreign words or proper nouns. Each word must be of three letters or more, all must contain the central letter and letters can only be used once in every word. There is at least one nine-letter word in the wheel.

Nine-letter word: _____

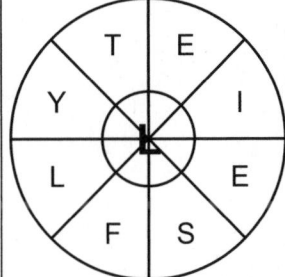

TWO DOWN

Fit five of the seven listed words into the Across rows in the grid, so that the other two words read down the shaded columns numbered 2 and 3.

ESTOP   INGOT
MINIM   ONION
SKUNK   STINK
     STONE

1	2		3	
4				
5				
6				
7				

OUT OF SIGHT

What is the sum total of the spots on the hidden faces of these three dice?

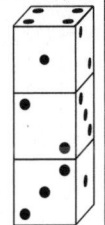

SHAPE RECOGNITION

Which are the only four pieces which will fit together in order to make this shape?

A B C D E F G

H I J K  L M

LEARNING LINES

We give you a line, you tell us who said it and the film:

"Oh Jerry, don't let's ask for the moon. We have the stars."

THIS WEEK'S PHOBIAS

Hypnophobia – Fear of sleep
Ichthyophobia – Fear of fish
Ostraconophobia – Fear of shellfish

EXCUSES FOR

An untidy house:

_____
_____
_____
_____
_____

Answers to puzzles on the previous page

Name That Song: *Smells Like Teen Spirit*, Nirvana.
Get The Leader: President Abraham Lincoln.
Word Ladder: One solution is SOAP, slap, flap, flat, fiat, fist, fish, DISH.
Missing Letters: TROJAN.

City Search:

N	A	P	I	E	R
S	Y	D	N	E	Y
M	A	D	R	I	D
L	A	H	O	R	E
V	E	N	I	C	E
G	E	N	E	V	A

By what name do we know this famous person?

Vincent Damon Furnier

TOP TEN

PIES ☐

CAKES ☐

COOKIES ☐

JELLIES ☐

TRIFLES ☐

MERINGUES ☐

ICE-CREAMS ☐

PUDDINGS ☐

PASTRIES ☐

TARTS ☐

TODAY'S GREATEST ACHIEVEMENT

No headaches ☐

Cured headache ☐

Buying milk ☐

SNAKES & LADDERS

This is a standard game, so when you land at the foot of a ladder, you climb it; and when you land on the head of a snake, you slide down its tail. You need to throw an exact number to land on 100 to win – counting backwards if you don't, eg if you land on 98 and throw a five, you will end up on 97. The dice is thrown for you and always lands in this recurring order: 6, 1, 2, 3, 4, 5, so you can start by immediately placing your counter on square 6. Good luck – hope you win!

100	99	98	97	96	95	94	93	92	91
81	82	83	84	85	86	87	88	89	90
80	79	78	77	76	75	74	73	72	71
61	62	63	64	65	66	67	68	69	70
60	59	58	57	56	55	54	53	52	51
41	42	43	44	45	46	47	48	49	50
40	39	38	37	36	35	34	33	32	31
21	22	23	24	25	26	27	28	29	30
20	19	18	17	16	15	14	13	12	11
1	2	3	4	5	6	7	8	9	10

ARRANGING THINGS

If you fit six of these seven words into the grid below, the word left over will appear reading down the shaded squares.

DEBBIE DOREEN
HELENA HESTER
JOANNE SANDRA
SYLVIA

MATCH THAT

Using just sixteen matches, can you make twelve triangles and six squares?

DESIGN YOUR OWN

Kitchen

ODD ONE OUT

Which one is different to the rest?

A

B

C

D

E

TOP FIVE

Best songs for travelling by train:

1 _____
_____

2 _____
_____

3 _____
_____

4 _____
_____

5 _____
_____

PICK 'N' MIX

Choose three words to describe your relationship:

Friendly

Masochistic

Sensual

Sadistic

Fighting

Committed

Loving

Understanding

Fun

Argumentative

WORDS TO REMEMBER

With which company or organisation or product do you associate this slogan?

"All the news that's fit to print."

MONEY, MONEY, MONEY

The

SUCRE

is the currency of

_____

Answers to puzzles on the previous page

Pre-Fame Name Game: Alice Cooper.
Arranging Things: Across (from the top): Hester, Debbie, Sylvia, Doreen, Joanne, Sandra. Down: Helena.
Match That: (there's also a rotated square in the centre).

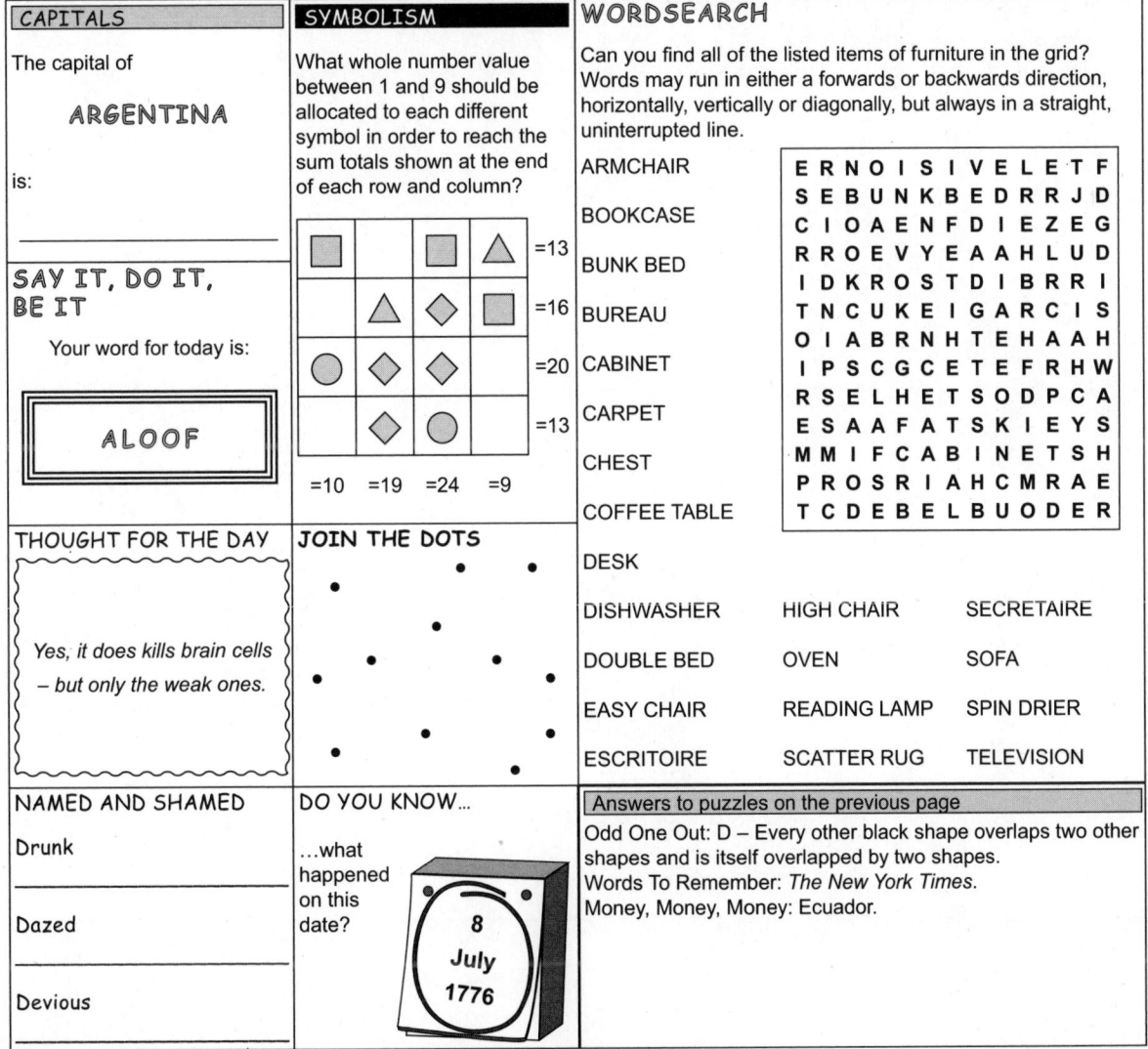

CAPITALS

The capital of

ARGENTINA

is:

_____

SAY IT, DO IT, BE IT

Your word for today is:

ALOOF

THOUGHT FOR THE DAY

Yes, it does kills brain cells – but only the weak ones.

NAMED AND SHAMED

Drunk

_____

Dazed

_____

Devious

_____

SYMBOLISM

What whole number value between 1 and 9 should be allocated to each different symbol in order to reach the sum totals shown at the end of each row and column?

☐		☐	△	=13
	△	◇	☐	=16
○	◇	◇		=20
	◇	○		=13

=10 =19 =24 =9

JOIN THE DOTS

DO YOU KNOW...

...what happened on this date?

8 July 1776

WORDSEARCH

Can you find all of the listed items of furniture in the grid? Words may run in either a forwards or backwards direction, horizontally, vertically or diagonally, but always in a straight, uninterrupted line.

ARMCHAIR

BOOKCASE

BUNK BED

BUREAU

CABINET

CARPET

CHEST

COFFEE TABLE

DESK

E	R	N	O	I	S	I	V	E	L	E	T	F
S	E	B	U	N	K	B	E	D	R	R	J	D
C	I	O	A	E	N	F	D	I	E	Z	E	G
R	R	O	E	V	Y	E	A	A	H	L	U	D
I	D	K	R	O	S	T	D	I	B	R	R	I
T	N	C	U	K	E	I	G	A	R	C	I	S
O	I	A	B	R	N	H	T	E	H	A	A	H
I	P	S	C	G	C	E	T	E	F	R	H	W
R	S	E	L	H	E	T	S	O	D	P	C	A
E	S	A	A	F	A	T	S	K	I	E	Y	S
M	M	I	F	C	A	B	I	N	E	T	S	H
P	R	O	S	R	I	A	H	C	M	R	A	E
T	C	D	E	B	E	L	B	U	O	D	E	R

DISHWASHER	HIGH CHAIR	SECRETAIRE
DOUBLE BED	OVEN	SOFA
EASY CHAIR	READING LAMP	SPIN DRIER
ESCRITOIRE	SCATTER RUG	TELEVISION

PROVERBS & SAYINGS

The letters on the tiles were once all in place, but dropped out, falling in a straight line into the lower grid. Some tiles dropped earlier than others, so those on the lowest row aren't all from the same row in the grid above. Can you put them back into position in order to reveal a well-known proverb or saying?

M		D		W			P		
A	L	D		S	L		A	C	K
A	A	K	U	N	O	J	K	O	A
A	N	L	E	L	O	R	B	L	Y	Y

WHO AM I?

Nigel, fetch an iron leg

I am:

UNLIKELY CANDIDATE

FASHION DESIGNER

_____

PLACE YOUR BETS

Your mother phones you because:

You owe her money ☐

You stole her jewellery ☐

She's been arrested ☐

GET THE LOOK

Make the face:

HUNGRY

COUPLINGS

Apart from two, every word listed below can be coupled with one of the others to make another word or phrase. Rearrange the letters of the two which can't be paired together, to form one word, the name of a sweet-smelling flower.

1 SCOTCH	2 LUNCHES
3 WEDDING	4 COAT
5 YOKE	6 LOOSE
7 MIST	8 CARDBOARD
9 WAND	10 BOX
11 MAGIC	12 BELLS
13 OVER	14 CANNON

Answer: _____

BAKING DAY

Five neighbours (from Nos 7, 8, 9, 11 and 12 Cook Close) did some baking yesterday. What did each make and what is her house number?

1   The woman (maybe Amy, maybe not!) who made jam tarts lives in a house with a number three higher than that of the woman who made a Swiss roll.

2   The scones were made by the woman who lives at No 7 and the sponge cake was made by the woman who lives at a number two higher than that of Joyce's house. Joyce didn't make the scones or apple pie.

3   Lynn's house has a number one lower than that of the woman who made apple pie.

4   Mandy (whose house has a number one higher than that of Sue's house) didn't make a Swiss roll.

REAL WORDS

Which is the real word?

OBNUBILATE ☐

OBNUBICINE ☐

OBNOSCIENT ☐

MISSING LINKS

Which word links the one on the left with the one on the right? We've done the first one, and when you've finished them all, the first letters of the link words will spell a colour.

FOOL'S	**GOLD**	RING
RED		DOLL
DEAD		GAME
FAR		ANGLIA
CREW		TIE

SECRET MISSION

Your secret mission (should you choose to accept it) is:

To find a garden or verandah with several pot plants and rearrange them without being seen.

IN YOUR OWN LANGUAGE

Devise an Oriental-looking sign for your cat.

HEXAGONY

Can you place the hexagons in the grid, so that where any triangle touches another along a straight line, the contents of both are the same? One triangle is already filled.

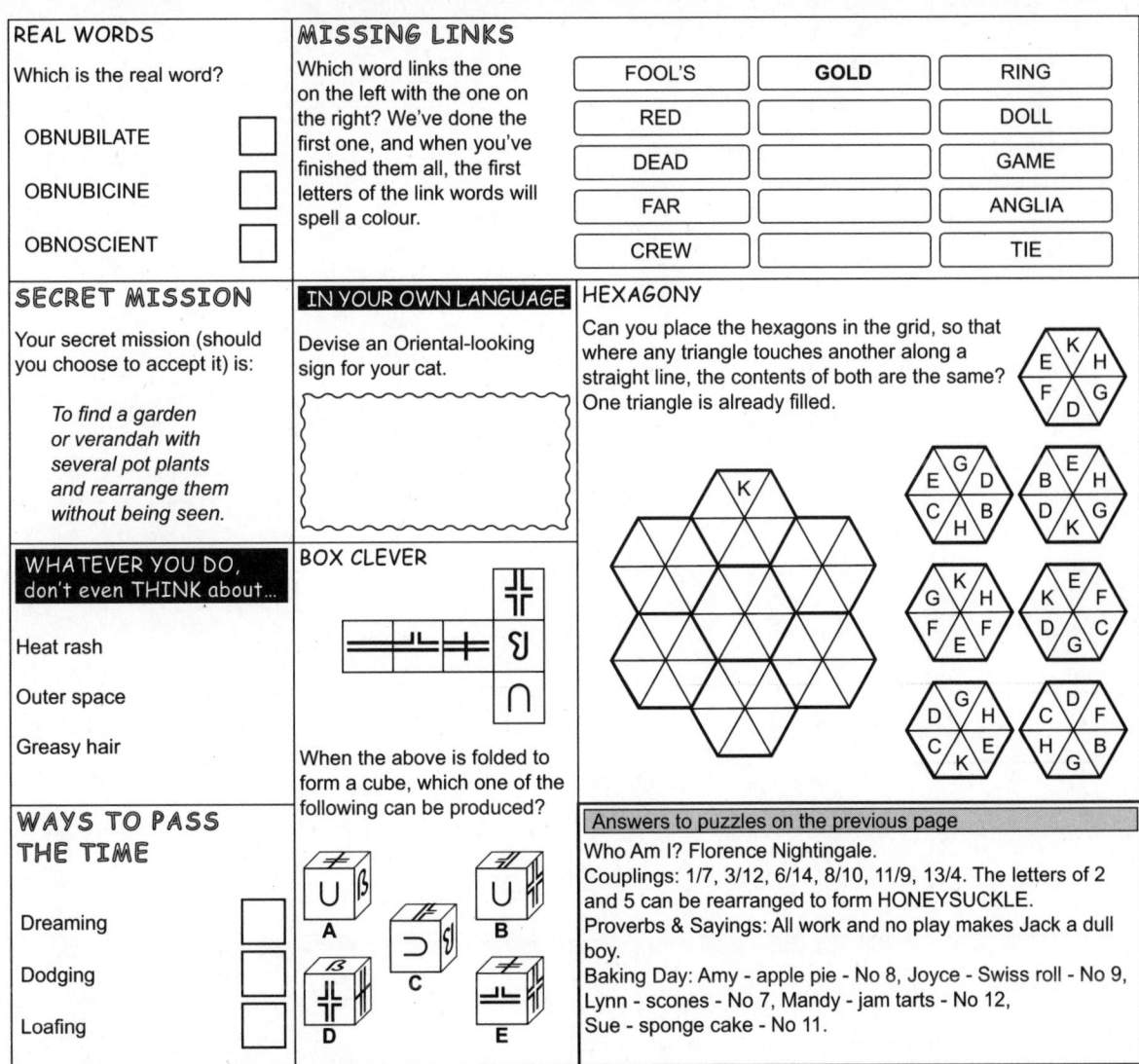

WHATEVER YOU DO, don't even THINK about...

Heat rash

Outer space

Greasy hair

BOX CLEVER

When the above is folded to form a cube, which one of the following can be produced?

WAYS TO PASS THE TIME

Dreaming ☐

Dodging ☐

Loafing ☐

WHATEVER NEXT?

Which of the numbered alternatives comes next in this sequence:

| BMA | LEL | TTI | LAD | AHY | ? |

1 MAR
2 RAM
3 ARM
4 MRA

BRIEF SURVIVAL GUIDE

JOB INTERVIEW:

1 Rehearse over-eager workaholic personality the night before
2 Try to remember what the job description is
3 Wash and dress before going

DICE-SECTION

Printed onto every one of the six numbered dice below are six letters (one per side), which can be rearranged to form the answer to each clue; however, some sides are invisible to you. Use the clues and write every answer into the grid. When correctly filled, the letters in the shaded squares, reading in the order 1 to 6, will spell out a woman's name.

Native of ancient Troy — 1
Acquired knowledge — 2
Lent out — 3
Linger (with intent!) — 4
Package — 5
Dairy product — 6

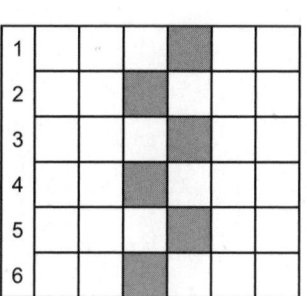
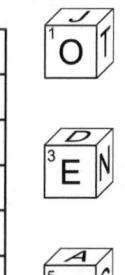

SWEET BAD MUSIC

So who on earth was responsible for this lyric?

There were plants and birds and rocks and things,
There was sand and hills and rings.
The first thing I met was a fly with a buzz

MIRROR WRITING

Write this word upside down:

JACKALS

CELEBRITY WRESTLING

BAMBI

-v-

MICKEY MOUSE

Answers to puzzles on the previous page

Real Words: Obnubilate. To darken, cloud over, or obscure.
Box Clever: D.
Missing Links: Fool's-Gold-Ring, Red-Rag-Doll, Dead-End-Game, Far-East-Anglia, Crew-Neck-Tie.
The word is: GREEN.

Hexagony:

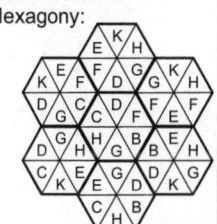

LUCKY NUMBER

Discover your lucky number for today by following these instructions:

1 Think of your house number and add fifteen to this figure;
2 Think of a number between twenty and seventy-two;
3 Add the result of 1 above to the result of 2 above;
4 Reverse the digits in this number.

Now you have your lucky number for today. Don't lose it – write it down:

_____

THINK ABOUT IT!

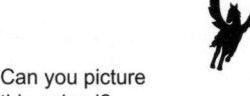

Can you picture this animal?

Sheeow

STARTING LINE

Which three letter word can be placed at the start, to form three seven-letter words?

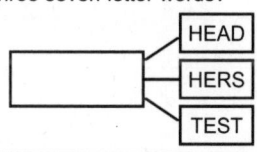

HEAD
HERS
TEST

DICEY ARITHMETIC

Using three of the arithmetical signs ÷, −, x and +, can you achieve the correct total?

    =

CHARACTER ASSIGNATION

Fill in the answers to the clues, across the grid. Then read down the diagonal line of eight squares, to reveal:
A character from Henry James's *The Ambassadors*.

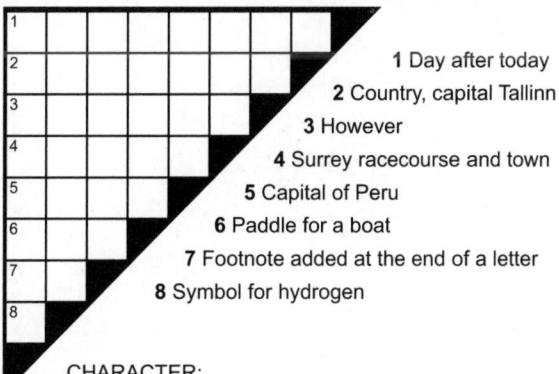

1 Day after today
2 Country, capital Tallinn
3 However
4 Surrey racecourse and town
5 Capital of Peru
6 Paddle for a boat
7 Footnote added at the end of a letter
8 Symbol for hydrogen

CHARACTER: _____

JUST A WORD

Can you find 'RAG' hidden in the grid, wordsearch-style?

```
D E F O I M N F E A C F D
S A A I J K G O P R G E F
G H I L O A W R E G V B R
R E I O R P M G R W A I O
D G H I R A E D F R A I O
S F H I J K L O P W S E F
```

WEATHER for PESSIMISTS

Today the weather will be:

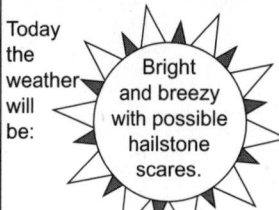

Bright and breezy with possible hailstone scares.

WEATHER for OPTIMISTS

Today the weather will be:

Sub-zero temperatures will make you dance in the street.

NAME THAT SONG

We give you the first line, you name the song: ♪

I was born in a cross-fire hurricane

Song: _____

Answers to puzzles on the previous page

Sweet Bad Music: America, *Horse With No Name*.
Whatever Next? 2 – the groups of three letters can be read backwards as "Mary had a little lamb".

Dice-Section:

T	R	O	J	A	N
L	E	A	R	N	T
L	O	A	N	E	D
L	O	I	T	E	R
P	A	R	C	E	L
C	H	E	E	S	E

THIS WEEK'S PHOBIAS

Ideophobia – Fear of ideas
Linonophobia – Fear of string
Melophobia – Fear of music

A IS TO B

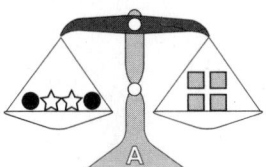

A is to B

as C is to

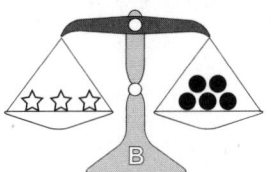

D   E

F   G

BALANCING THE SCALES

Given that scales A and B balance perfectly, how many squares are needed to balance scale C?

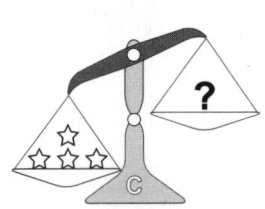

LETTER TRACKER

Begin in the central shaded square and follow a continuous path which will track from square to square, up, down and sideways, but never diagonally.

Your trail should cover every letter once only, in order to find:

Twenty-two things to drink.

T	R	E	F	F	O	E	T	A	U	Q
I	A	E	J	U	C	A	H	S	M	S
N	M	E	C	I	R	I	E	R	U	R
I	L	D	Y	S	P	T	Z	M	O	A
M	E	N	E	R	W	A	T	I	C	O
O	N	A	G	A	L	R	E	L	K	C
D	A	R	B	N	I	W	S	K	O	R
E	V	O	D	K	G	H	I	Y	P	T
P	M	A	H	A	E	N	I	W	A	S
A	G	C	C	S	A	N	G	R	I	H
E	N	A	N	G	O	C	Y	R	R	E

MASS HYSTERIAS

Today we are all going to:

Climb to the top of a tall tree and stay there fasting for the next year.

WHAT DOES IT MEAN?

What is the meaning of the word

OMPHALOSKEPSIS

Answer: _____
_____

Answers to puzzles on the previous page

Name That Song: *Jumpin' Jack Flash*, Rolling Stones.
Starting Line: FAT.
Dicey Arithmetic: The signs are plus, minus and times.
Character Assignation:
1 Tomorrow, 2 Estonia,
3 Anyway, 4 Epsom, 5 Lima,
6 Oar, 7 PS, 8 H.
Character: Waymarsh.

Just A Word:

D	E	F	O	I	M	N	F	E	A	C	F	D
S	A	A	I	J	K	**G**	O	P	R	G	E	F
G	H	I	L	O	**A**	W	R	E	G	V	B	R
R	E	I	O	**R**	P	M	G	R	W	A	I	O
D	G	H	I	R	A	E	D	F	R	A	I	O
S	F	H	I	J	K	L	O	P	W	S	E	F

157

STARTER LETTER

Write down one each of the listed items, all of which must begin with the starter letter:

T

Country	
Tree	
Boy's name	
Girl's name	
River	
City	
Animal	
Make of car	
Drink	

MISSING LETTERS

One letter of the alphabet is missing from each box. Find them all and place them in the order of the numbered boxes to reveal a six-letter word.

Word: _____

1	2	3
ZRTAH	QIOVF	PTYGD
JYVMB	NWTBJ	FUMXJ
UGXSC	CSRPG	OSQIB
IKODF	ZKUHD	ZRKAH
QEWPL	MXYAL	EVNLW

4	5	6
NYUHC	IQVSD	KVUFA
LSMDG	MBXKG	PLTHB
QXBPI	RNWFL	OCYSN
ZRJEF	OYHCU	IMDZG
WKVOA	EZTPJ	QWJXE

CODEWORD

This is a crossword puzzle in code. Every number represents a different letter of the alphabet and this number remains the same throughout the puzzle. Use the check-box to keep a track on your progress.

8	13	19	23	21	10		1			2
13		11			25	9	12	15	19	14
15	24	20	21	22	12		21			21
10		21			15	14	5	25	11	18
12	19	22		17		15			21	
	25	12	3	21	10	26	19	1	21	
	12			10		11		25	18	21
2	15	14	22	25	11			13		14 L
14			10		15	23	21	10	1	21 E
15	14	16	15	14	19			22		6 G
7			6		14	19	16	21	14	4

1	2	3	4	5	6	7	8	9	10	11	12	13

14	15	16	17	18	19	20	21	22	23	24	25	26

DOMINOLOGICAL

What is the value of the question mark?

= 44
= 78
= 11
= ?

GET THE LEADER

Can you unscramble the anagram to reveal the leader?

Lean and solemn

Answer: _____

WHERE ON EARTH?

Where on earth is Fuku?

Answer: _____

WORDWHEEL

Using only the letters in the Wordwheel, you have ten minutes to find as many words as possible, none of which may be plurals, foreign words or proper nouns. Each word must be of three letters or more, all must contain the central letter and letters can only be used once in every word. There is at least one nine-letter word in the wheel.

Nine-letter word: _____

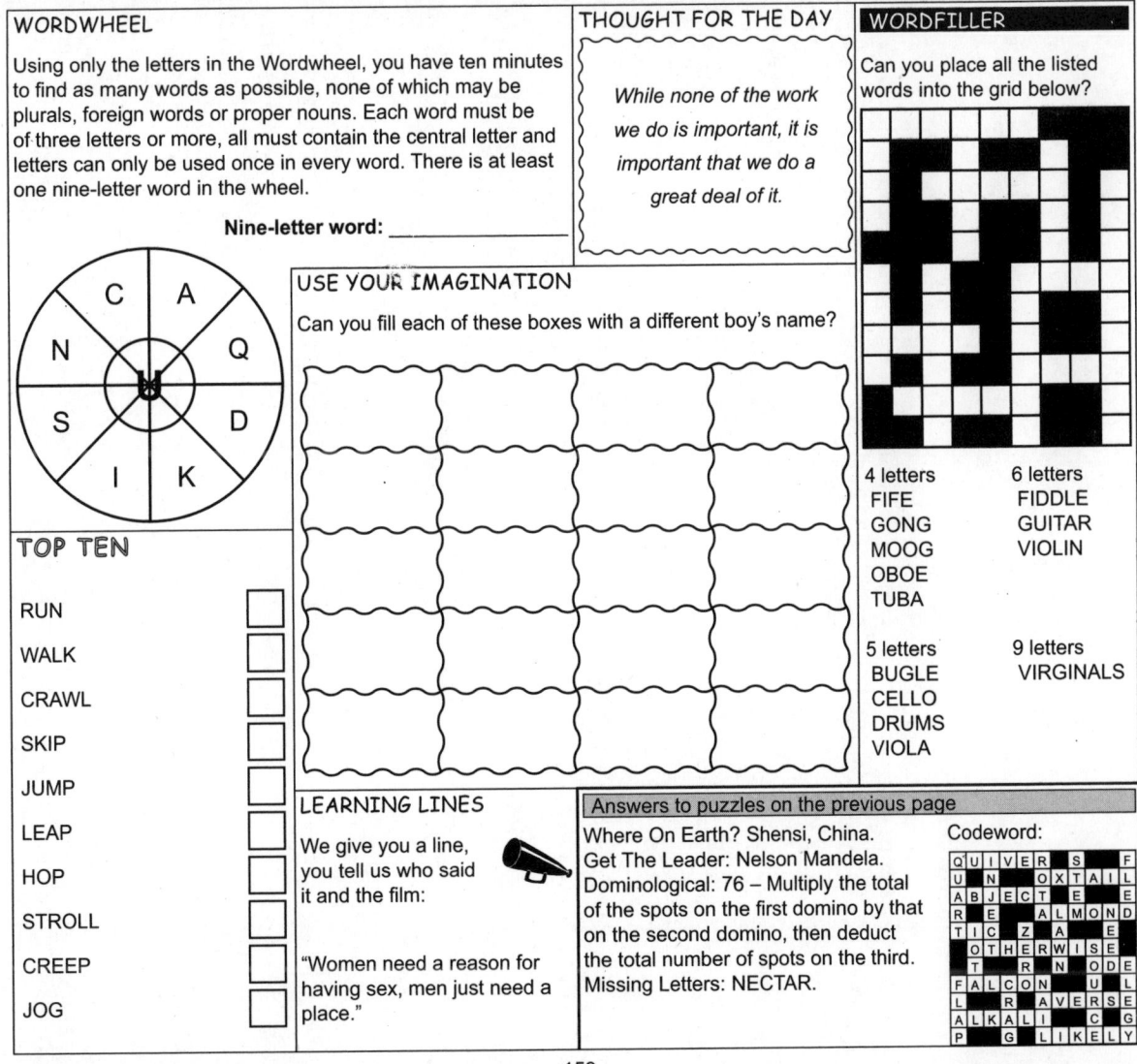

Letters in wheel: C, A, Q, D, K, I, S, N (centre: U)

TOP TEN

RUN ☐

WALK ☐

CRAWL ☐

SKIP ☐

JUMP ☐

LEAP ☐

HOP ☐

STROLL ☐

CREEP ☐

JOG ☐

USE YOUR IMAGINATION

Can you fill each of these boxes with a different boy's name?

LEARNING LINES

We give you a line, you tell us who said it and the film:

"Women need a reason for having sex, men just need a place."

WORDFILLER

Can you place all the listed words into the grid below?

4 letters
FIFE
GONG
MOOG
OBOE
TUBA

5 letters
BUGLE
CELLO
DRUMS
VIOLA

6 letters
FIDDLE
GUITAR
VIOLIN

9 letters
VIRGINALS

ARRANGING THINGS

If you fit six of these seven words into the grid below, the word left over will appear reading down the shaded squares.

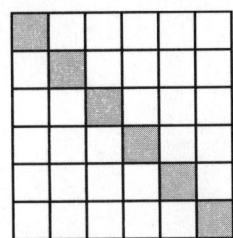

CANADA   CYPRUS
ISRAEL   MONACO
RWANDA   TAIWAN
        ZAMBIA

PATCHWORK

Fit the numbers 1, 2, 3, 4, 5, 6 and 7 into the grid below, so that every horizontal row, every vertical column and the two long diagonal lines of six smaller squares contain six different numbers. Some are already in place.

	2	7		4		
			2			1
3					4	
		6		5		4
	1					2
		5			1	
2			4	7		

MATCH THAT

Move one match to make this sum correct:

DESIGN YOUR OWN

Beach resort

THE WHOLE PICTURE

Can you finish this picture?

TOP FIVE

Best songs for travelling by car:

1 _____
  _____
2 _____
  _____
3 _____
  _____
4 _____
  _____
5 _____
  _____

PICK 'N' MIX

Choose three words to describe your schooldays:

Pointless   Useless
Educational   Forgettable
Enjoyable   Brutal
Brilliant   Painful
Purposeful   Boring

MY FAVOURITE THINGS

These are a few of my favourite things:

My favourite ice-cream is:

_____

My favourite cake is:

_____

My favourite fruit is:

_____

My favourite vegetable is:

_____

BERMUDA TRIANGLE

Travel through the 'Bermuda Triangle' by visiting one room at a time and collecting a letter from each. You can enter the outside passageway as often as you like, but can only visit each room once. When you've completed your tour, rearrange the fifteen letters to spell out a word.

D
S E
B T T
N U A A
U S N T I

PRE-FAME NAME GAME

By what name do we know this famous person?

Declan Patrick McManus

_____

TODAY'S GREATEST ACHIEVEMENT

Parking space ☐

Right choice of alcohol ☐

Avoided getting wet ☐

UNLIKELY CANDIDATE

CELEBRITY CHEF

_____

FOR SALE

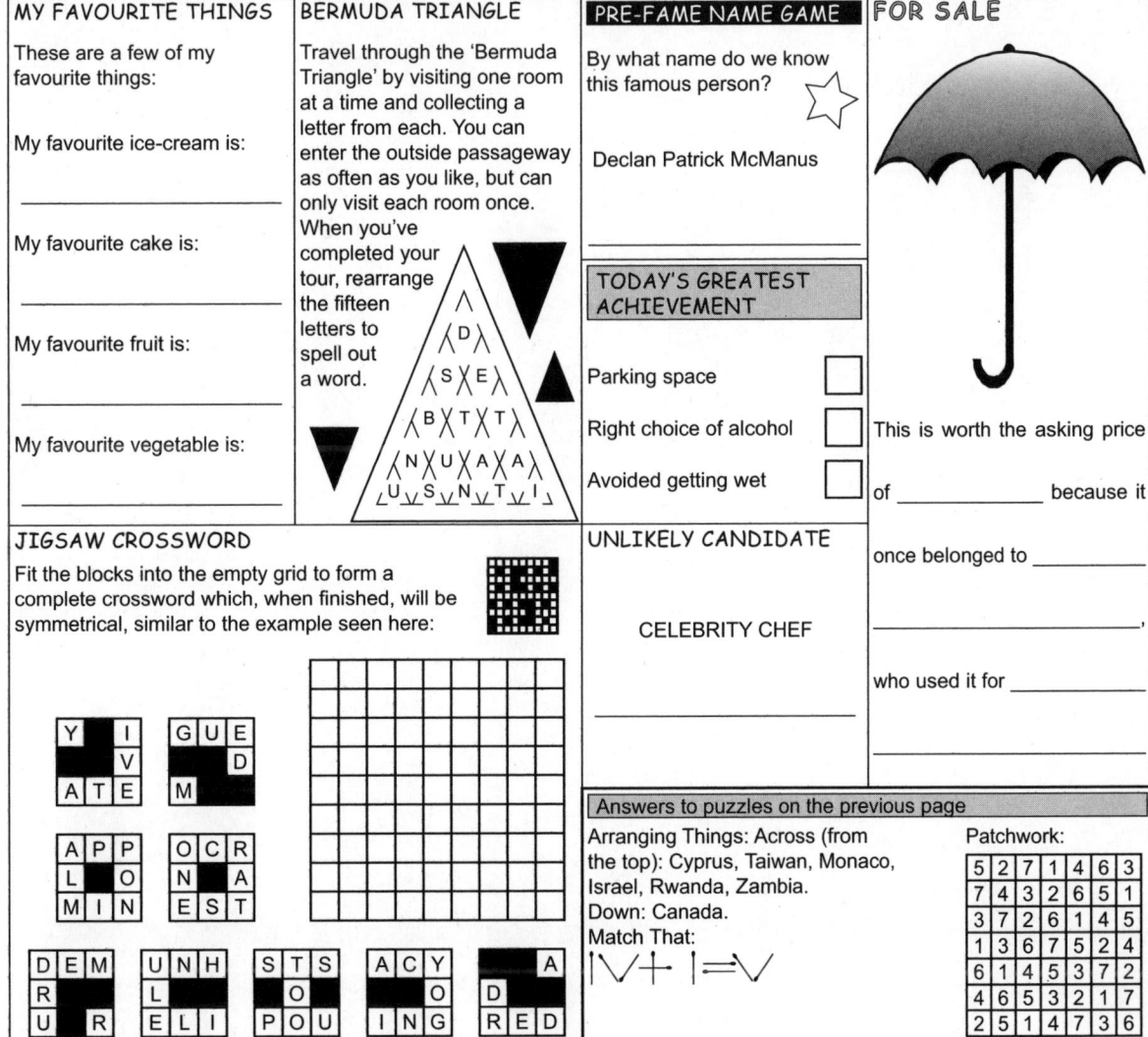

This is worth the asking price

of _____ because it

once belonged to _____

_____,

who used it for _____

_____

JIGSAW CROSSWORD

Fit the blocks into the empty grid to form a complete crossword which, when finished, will be symmetrical, similar to the example seen here:

```
Y   I   G U E
    V       D
A T E   M
```

```
A P P   O C R
L   O   N   A
M I N   E S T
```

```
D E M   U N H   S T S   A C Y       A
R       L       O       O   D
U   R   E L I   P O U   I N G   R E D
```

Answers to puzzles on the previous page

Arranging Things: Across (from the top): Cyprus, Taiwan, Monaco, Israel, Rwanda, Zambia.
Down: Canada.
Match That:

Patchwork:

5	2	7	1	4	6	3
7	4	3	2	6	5	1
3	7	2	6	1	4	5
1	3	6	7	5	2	4
6	1	4	5	3	7	2
4	6	5	3	2	1	7
2	5	1	4	7	3	6

161

DOMINADDITION

Can you place the remaining dominoes in their correct positions, so that the total number of spots in each of the four rows and five columns equals the sum at the end of that row or column?

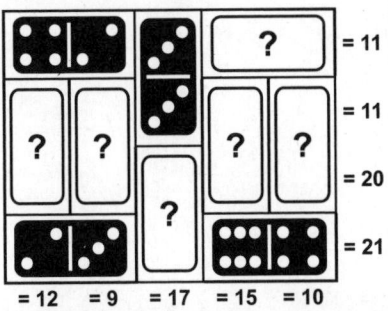

= 11
= 11
= 20
= 21

= 12   = 9   = 17   = 15   = 10

WORD LADDER

Change one letter at a time (but not the position of any letter) to make a new word – and move from the word at the top of the ladder to the word at the bottom using the exact number of rungs provided.

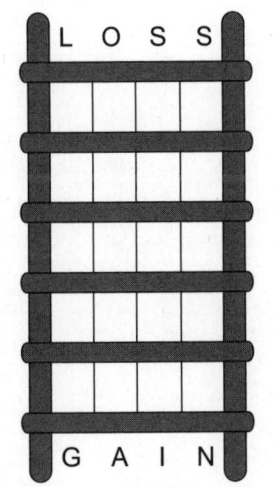

L O S S

G A I N

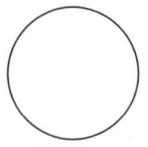
DO YOU KNOW...

...what happened on this date?

1 August 1914

PAIR SHAPES

In the box below there are shapes in three different colours, black, white and grey. Any shape may have been rotated, but can you see which is the only shape to appear exactly twice in exactly the same colour?

WAYS TO PASS THE TIME

Hiding

Hollering

Hounding

NAME THAT SONG

We give you the first line, you name the song: ♪

Once upon a time you dressed so fine

Song: _____

PLACE YOUR BETS

_____'s party outfit will be:

Cheap, sparkly and ridiculous ☐

Cool, elegant and tasteful ☐

Mutton-dressed-as-lamb ☐

PYRAMID PLUS

Every brick in this pyramid contains a number which is the sum of the two numbers below it, so that F=A+B, etc. No two bricks contain the same number, or just a zero, so work out the missing numbers!

O=92

M=   N=

J=   K=   L=26

F=   G=9   H=   I=14

A=   B=5   C=   D=   E=

COMPLETE THIS LIMERICK:

An old man who once lived in Devon

One day thought that he'd gone to heaven

He tried to complain

That his cloud held rain

_____

TWO DOWN

Fit five of the seven listed words into the Across rows in the grid, so that the other two words read down the shaded columns numbered 2 and 3.

AFIRE   FOLIO
LICIT   LOCAL
RAPID   ROWDY
        SLOPE

1	2		3	
4				
5				
6				
7				

SYMBOLISM

What whole number value between 1 and 9 should be allocated to each different symbol in order to reach the sum totals shown at the end of each row and column?

○	◇	■	△	=21
■		○	■	=19
	◇		■	=13
○	△	△	△	=22

=11 =15 =17 =32

EYE-SPY

I spy with my little eye something beginning with:

B

_____

Answers to puzzles on the previous page

Do You Know... The First World War began.
Word Ladder: One solution is LOSS, lost, loot, loon, loin, lain, GAIN.
Pair Shapes:

Dominaddition:

4	2	3	1	1
1	2	3	4	1
5	2	5	4	4
2	3	6	6	4

163

A MATCHING PAIR

Tom wants a couple of identical T-shirts. Which two should he buy?

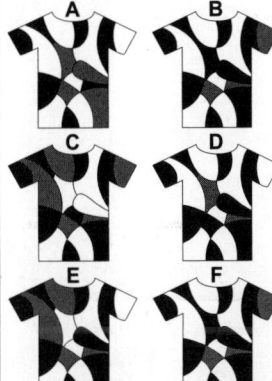

HEXAGONY

Can you place the hexagons in the grid, so that where any triangle touches another along a straight line, the contents of both are the same? One triangle is already filled.

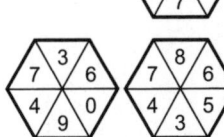

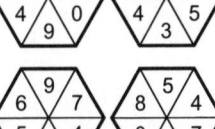

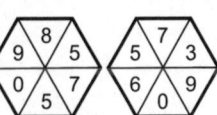

TONGUE TWISTER

Get your tongue around this one, if you can!

Betty Botter had some butter,
"But," she said, "this butter's bitter.
If I bake this bitter bit o' butter,
It would make my batter bitter.
But a bit of better butter...
Ah, that would make my batter better."

So she bought a bit o' butter,
Better than her bitter butter,
And she baked it in her batter,
Thus the batter was not bitter.
So 'twas better Betty Botter
Bought a better bit o' butter.

WHATEVER YOU DO, don't even THINK about...

Axe murderers

Fairground rides

Sunburn

SWEET BAD MUSIC

So who on earth was responsible for this lyric?

Plant a seed, plant a flower,
Plant a rose, you can plant any one of those,
Keep planting to find out which one grows.

CLOCKWORDS

It's a race against the clock...
How many common words of three or more different letters can you make from those on the clockface (without using plurals, proper nouns or abbreviations) in ten minutes? All words must contain BOTH the letters indicated by the hands on the clock.

WEATHER for OPTIMISTS

Today the weather will be:

Cloudy and dull with a certainty that it is going to be a beautiful day later.

SHAPE RECOGNITION

Which are the only four pieces from which this house can be constructed?

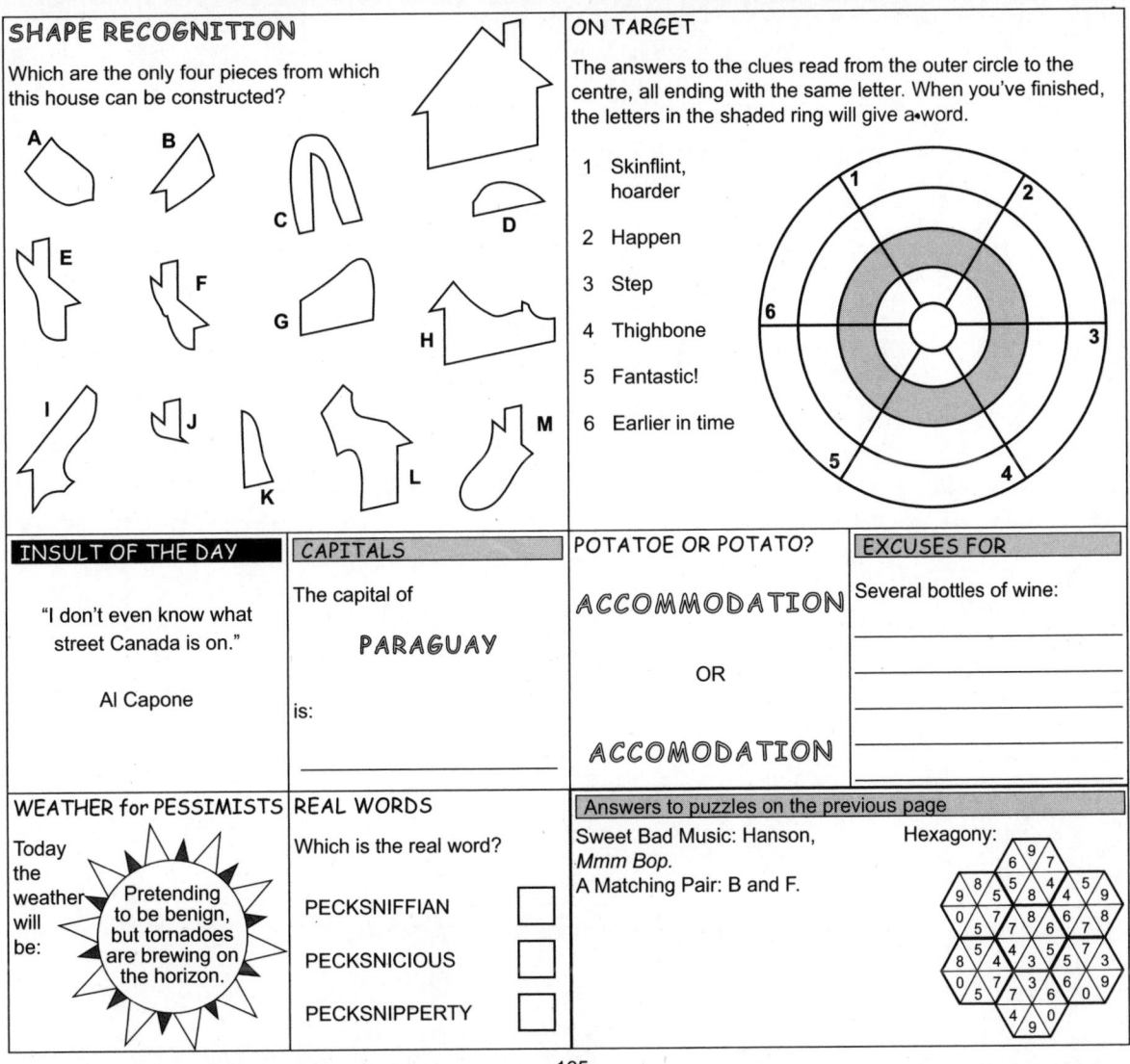

ON TARGET

The answers to the clues read from the outer circle to the centre, all ending with the same letter. When you've finished, the letters in the shaded ring will give a word.

1 Skinflint, hoarder
2 Happen
3 Step
4 Thighbone
5 Fantastic!
6 Earlier in time

INSULT OF THE DAY

"I don't even know what street Canada is on."

Al Capone

CAPITALS

The capital of

PARAGUAY

is:

_____

POTATOE OR POTATO?

ACCOMMODATION

OR

ACCOMODATION

EXCUSES FOR

Several bottles of wine:

_____
_____
_____
_____

WEATHER for PESSIMISTS

Today the weather will be:

Pretending to be benign, but tornadoes are brewing on the horizon.

REAL WORDS

Which is the real word?

PECKSNIFFIAN ☐

PECKSNICIOUS ☐

PECKSNIPPERTY ☐

Answers to puzzles on the previous page

Sweet Bad Music: Hanson, *Mmm Bop.*
A Matching Pair: B and F.

Hexagony:

WORDSEARCH

Can you find all of the listed girls' names in the grid?
Words may run in either a forwards or backwards direction, horizontally, vertically or diagonally, but always in a straight, uninterrupted line.

ADELE

ANTOINETTE

APRIL

CAROLINE

CASSANDRA

CATHERINE

CHRISTINE

CLEMENTINE

CONSTANCE

DANIELLE

DAWN

ELIZABETH

EMMA

FELICITY

GABRIELLE

```
E M M A E K C D E J A T H
L I A G T I A A C U J H T
L C G E T M R N N L E E E
E A E I E B O I A I N N B
I S R N N E L E T E I R A
R S A A I R I L S T R I Z
B A L H O L N L N T E E I
A N D P T E E E O E H T L
G D I E N Y M U C O T T E
I R N T A E Q Z Q Z A A L
V A E S L I R P A C C M E
Y T I C I L E F N W A D D
C H R I S T I N E T B J A
```

GAIL

GERALDINE

HENRIETTA

IVY

JACQUELINE

JULIETTE

KIMBERLEY

STEPHANIE

ZOE

COUPLINGS

Apart from two, every word listed below can be coupled with one of the others to make another word or phrase. Rearrange the letters of the two which can't be paired together, to form one word, that of something to watch.

1	2
UGLY	PLANNING
3	4
NIGHT	FORWARD
5	6
POTATOES	FIRE
7	8
FORT	INVITE
9	10
WORKS	SMOOTHING
11	12
SOLE	DUCKLING
13	14
IRON	ROAST

Answer: _____

JOIN THE DOTS

MASS HYSTERIAS

Today we are all going to:

Start a new religion worshipping pandas and bandicoots.

SECRET MISSION

Your secret mission (should you choose to accept it) is:

Find a cat or dog and have a conversation with it.

GET THE LEADER

Can you unscramble the anagram to reveal the leader?

All marines nod

Answer: _____

Answers to puzzles on the previous page

Real Words: Pecksniffian. Unctuously hypocritical.
On Target: 1 Miser, 2 Occur, 3 Stair, 4 Femur, 5 Super, 6 Prior.
Shaded word: Scampi.
Shape Recognition:

Potatoe or Potato?
Accommodation.
Capitals: Ascuncion.

THOUGHT FOR THE DAY

Never underestimate the power of human stupidity.

STARTING LINE

Which three letter word can be placed at the start, to form three seven-letter words?

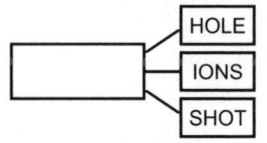

HOLE
IONS
SHOT

SNAKES & LADDERS

This is a standard game, so when you land at the foot of a ladder, you climb it; and when you land on the head of a snake, you slide down its tail. You need to throw an exact number to land on 100 to win – counting backwards if you don't, eg if you land on 98 and throw a five, you will end up on 97. The dice is thrown for you and always lands in this recurring order: 2, 4, 6, 3, 5, 1, so you can start by immediately placing your counter on square 2. Good luck – hope you win!

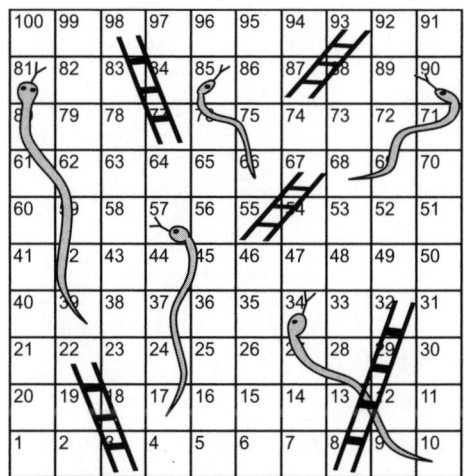

DICEY ARITHMETIC

Using three of the arithmetical signs ÷, −, x and +, can you achieve the correct total? Afterwards, see if you can spot an alternative way to do this.

    =

WHAT DOES IT MEAN?

What is the meaning of the word

PECCAVI

Answer: _____

_____

SPOT THE BALL

Place a cross where you imagine the centre of the ball to be.

Answers to puzzles on the previous page

Get The Leader: Admiral Nelson.
Couplings: 1/12, 4/2, 6/9, 7/3, 10/13, 14/5. The letters of 8 and 11 can be rearranged to form TELEVISION.

STARTER LETTER

Write down one each of the listed items, all of which must begin with the starter letter:

L

Country	
Tree	
Boy's name	
Girl's name	
River	
City	
Animal	
Make of car	
Drink	

MISSING LETTERS

One letter of the alphabet is missing from each box. Find them all and place them in the order of the numbered boxes to reveal a six-letter word.

Word: _____

1	2	3
QLVAI	KGTOE	WILAS
MXRFH	BWPZN	GZTPB
NWSJC	JHMCF	FKHNC
GTOZD	VXDUQ	DUYQJ
UYKEP	SYLAI	MXRVE

4	5	6
MWRIC	HSWDO	AXUPM
HSVDF	BVRNJ	JTVBI
PLQZB	ZAGQK	CGQZN
UYJEG	ITFPY	DRWKF
NXTKA	UMEXL	LSYOE

EGG TIMER

Can you complete this puzzle in the time it takes to boil an egg? The answers to the clues are anagrams of the words immediately above and below, plus or minus a letter.

1 Cockerel
2 List of names
3 Put aside for later
4 Fragrant flower
5 Achieve a goal
6 Old hags, witches
7 Estimates

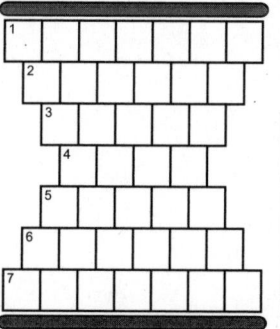

LEARNING LINES

We give you a line, you tell us who said it and the film:

"I don't feel I have to wipe everybody out, Tom. Just my enemies."

ANTONYM WALL

Pair up these set of letters correctly to spell out two words of the same length but with opposite meanings.

S S	R E	C A	C K
I O	U T	L E	U S

_____ & _____

DESIGN YOUR OWN

Hotel complex

WORDWHEEL

Using only the letters in the Wordwheel, you have ten minutes to find as many words as possible, none of which may be plurals, foreign words or proper nouns. Each word must be of three letters or more, all must contain the central letter and letters can only be used once in every word. There is at least one nine-letter word in the wheel.

Nine-letter word: _____

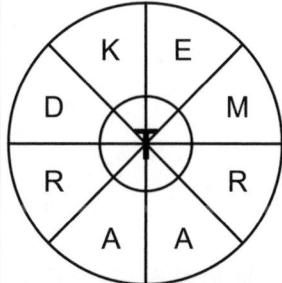

AMAZING

Can you work your way from the entrance at the top to the exit at the bottom of this maze?

MIRROR WRITING

Write this word upside down:

KITCHEN

_____

TOP FIVE

Best songs for writing a masterpiece:

1 _____

_____

2 _____

_____

3 _____

_____

4 _____

_____

5 _____

_____

UNLIKELY CANDIDATE

BEST-DRESSED
PERSON

_____

DO YOU KNOW...

...what happened on this date?

30 March 1981

Answers to puzzles on the previous page

Learning Lines: Michael Corleone (Al Pacino), *Godfather, Part II* (1974).
Egg Timer: 1 Rooster, 2 Roster, 3 Store, 4 Rose, 5 Score, 6 Crones, 7 Reckons.
Antonym Wall: Cautious and Reckless.
Missing Letters: BROOCH.

BALANCING THE SCALES

Given that scales A and B balance perfectly, how many squares are needed to balance scale C?

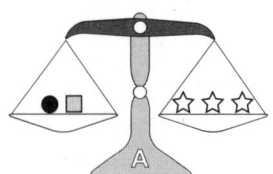

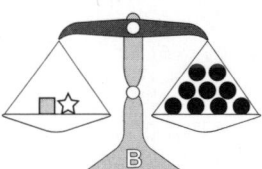

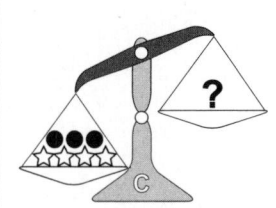

LUCKY NUMBER

Discover your lucky number for today by following these instructions:
1. Think of your house number, then add seventeen;
2. Think of a number between one and forty-one;
3. Add the result of 1 above to the result of 2 above;
4. Reverse the digits in this number.

Now you have your lucky number for today. Don't lose it – write it down: _____

MATCH THAT

How can you remove six matches to leave three squares of different sizes?

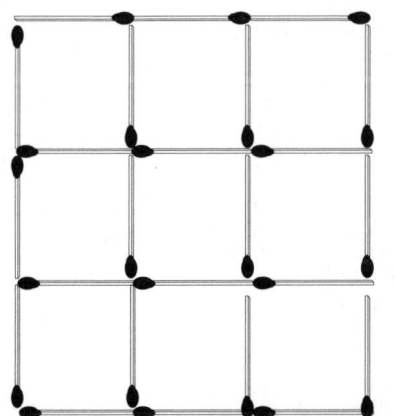

MY NEXT ARGUMENT

Who
_____

Why
_____

Where

ARRANGING THINGS

If you fit six of these seven words into the grid below, the word left over will appear reading down the shaded squares.

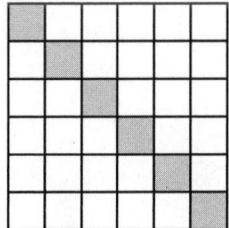

ARTHUR   CARRIE
GANDHI   GREASE
GO WEST   IMPACT
THE FLY

PICK 'N' MIX

Delete as appropriate:

Last weekend was fun/boring/bonkers. My mother-in-law/best friend/neighbour called round and we had a huge fight/party/discussion because I had won/lost/broken their favourite ring/potato chips/car.

NAME THAT SONG

We give you the first line, you name the song:

Over a bridge of sighs to rest my eyes

Song: _____

Answers to puzzles on the previous page

Do You Know... President Reagan of the USA was shot and injured.
Wordwheel: The nine-letter word is TRADEMARK.

Amazing:

170

PICTOWORD

Which well-known word or phrase is represented by the following?

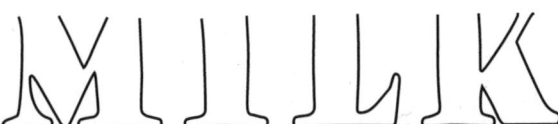

WORD LADDER

Change one letter at a time (but not the position of any letter) to make a new word – and move from the word at the top of the ladder to the word at the bottom using the exact number of rungs provided.

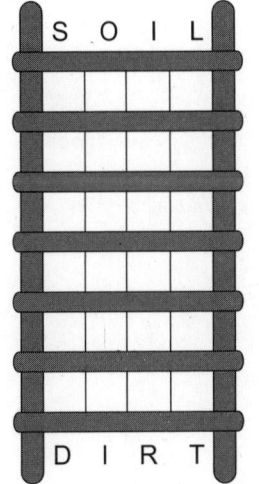

SUM TOTAL

Place the digits 1-9, one per square, so that the sums are correct, according to the totals at the ends of the rows and columns. The calculations should be done in the order in which they appear, for example 6–2x5=20 should be read as 6–2(=4), then 4x5=20.

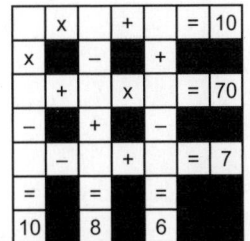

CHARACTER ASSIGNATION

Fill in the answers to the clues, across the grid. Then read down the diagonal line of eight squares, to reveal: A character from William Shakespeare's *King Lear*.

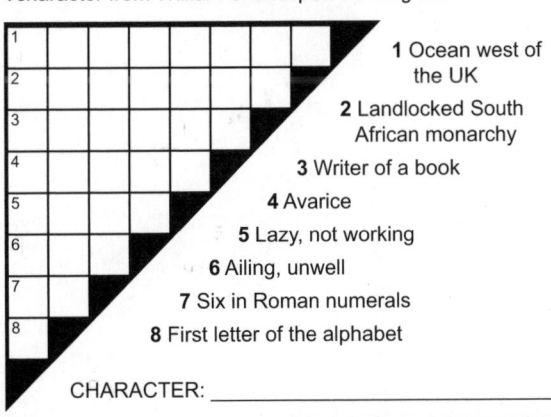

1 Ocean west of the UK
2 Landlocked South African monarchy
3 Writer of a book
4 Avarice
5 Lazy, not working
6 Ailing, unwell
7 Six in Roman numerals
8 First letter of the alphabet

CHARACTER: _____

PRE-FAME NAME GAME

By what name do we know this famous person?

Lucille LeSueur

NAMED AND SHAMED

Attention-seeker
_____

Spoiled brat
_____

Off the rails

Answers to puzzles on the previous page

Name That Song: *Itchycoo Park*, The Small Faces.
Arranging Things: Across (from the top): *Gandhi*, *Arthur*, *The Fly*, *Impact*, *Go West*, *Carrie*. Down: *Grease*. Match That:
Balancing The Scales: 2.

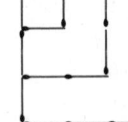

TELL THE TRUTH

Which (if any) of these numbered statements is true?

1 One of these statements is false.
2 Two of these statements are false.
3 Three of these statements are false.
4 Four of these statements are false.
5 Five of these statements are false.
6 Six of these statements are false.

CELEBRITY WRESTLING

SIGMUND FREUD

-v-

ANDREA DWORKIN

WHO AM I?

Read, shun Islam

I am:

_____

CODEWORD

This is a crossword puzzle in code. Every number represents a different letter of the alphabet and this number remains the same throughout the puzzle. Use the check-box to keep a track on your progress.

25	17	4	14	7		15	5	25	26 R	20
24		11		20		26			2 Y	
26		5		21	26	12	15	15	20 E	26
11	17	18		5		13		26		20
20		17	25	17	7	22	18	20	23	13
7		8			14			20		26
19	24	5	9	9	5	4	17	11		5
24		23		5		24		17	3	20
20	23	6	5	23	20	7		23		10
	20			6		22		4		20
1	20	11	11	2		2	5	20	11	16

1	2	3	4	5	6	7	8	9	10	11	12	13

14	15	16	17	18	19	20	21	22	23	24	25	26

BOX CLEVER

When the above is folded to form a cube, which one of the following can be produced?

A B C D E

TOP TEN

SHOUT
SING
TALK
LAUGH
YODEL
WHISPER
YELL
CRY
RECITE
SIGH

SWEET BAD MUSIC

So who on earth was responsible for this lyric?

We're heading for Venus

And still we stand tall

Cause maybe they've seen us

And welcome us all.

PLACE YOUR BETS

Today, _____ will eat:

Two dozen doughnuts ☐

A pie sandwich with chips ☐

Everything in sight, offered or not ☐

WHATEVER YOU DO, don't even THINK about...

Sewage

Aniseed-flavoured alcohol

Itchy wool

LOOSE VOWELS

Someone has taken all the vowels out of what was once a completed crossword. Can you put them all back in again? You should use only those letters beneath the grid.

D			S	■		N	T	
■	D			■	L			M
L		V		■	S			P
	■		N		■	K		■
	V		L			■	R	
			■	R	S		■	C
S			R		■		T	H
	■		■			■		
N		V		■	Z		R	

A A A A A A A

E E E E E E E E E E E E

I I I I I I

O O O O O O

U U

COMPLETE THIS LIMERICK:

One fine day, a vicar from Reading

Was giving advice at a wedding

He said to the groom

"If you own a large broom

_____."

IN YOUR OWN LANGUAGE

Devise an Oriental-looking sign for your sister.

WAYS TO PASS THE TIME

Enjoying ☐

Complaining ☐

Grumbling ☐

Answers to puzzles on the previous page

Who Am I? Salman Rushdie.
Box Clever: C.
Tell The Truth: Statement number 5 is true.

Codeword:

B	A	C	K	S	■	F	I	B	R	E
U	■	L	■	E	■	R	■	Y	■	
R	■	I	■	P	R	O	F	F	E	R
L	A	M	■	I	■	T	■	R	■	E
E	■	A	B	A	S	H	M	E	N	T
S	■	X	■	K	■	■	E	■	■	R
Q	U	I	Z	Z	I	C	A	L	■	I
U	■	N	■	I	■	U	■	A	W	E
E	N	G	I	N	E	S	■	N	■	V
■	E	■	G	■	H	■	C	■	E	■
J	E	L	L	Y	■	Y	I	E	L	D

HOW FULL IS YOUR GLASS?

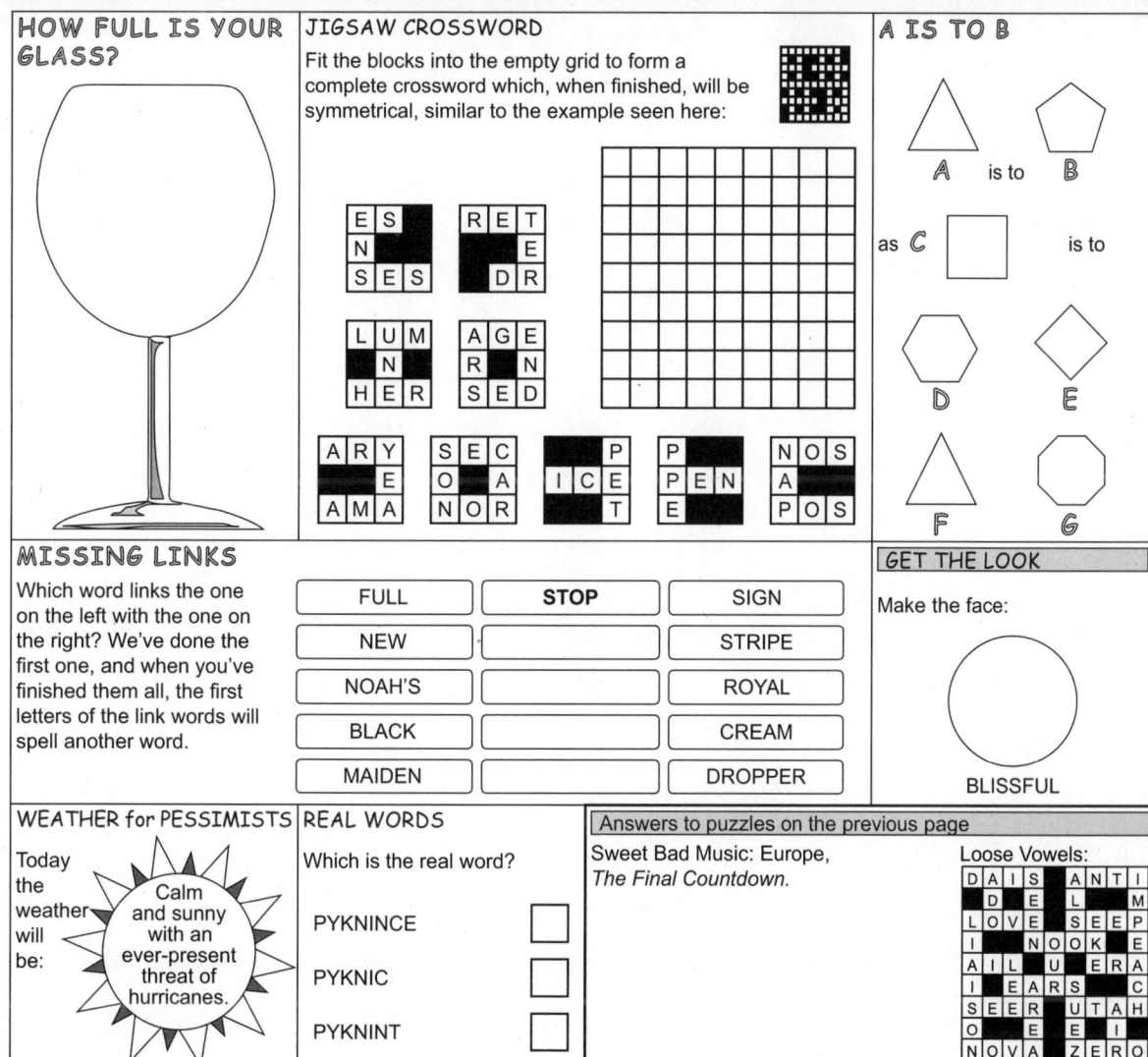

JIGSAW CROSSWORD

Fit the blocks into the empty grid to form a complete crossword which, when finished, will be symmetrical, similar to the example seen here:

Blocks:

```
E S      R E T
N          E
S E S    D R
```

```
L U M    A G E
  N      R   N
H E R    S E D
```

```
A R Y    S E C      P      P      N O S
    E    O   A    I C E    P E N   A
A M A    N O R      T      E      P O S
```

A IS TO B

A (triangle) is to B (pentagon)

as C (square) is to

D (hexagon)   E (diamond)

F (triangle)   G (octagon)

MISSING LINKS

Which word links the one on the left with the one on the right? We've done the first one, and when you've finished them all, the first letters of the link words will spell another word.

FULL	**STOP**	SIGN
NEW		STRIPE
NOAH'S		ROYAL
BLACK		CREAM
MAIDEN		DROPPER

GET THE LOOK

Make the face:

( )

BLISSFUL

WEATHER for PESSIMISTS

Today the weather will be:

Calm and sunny with an ever-present threat of hurricanes.

REAL WORDS

Which is the real word?

PYKNINCE ☐

PYKNIC ☐

PYKNINT ☐

Answers to puzzles on the previous page

Sweet Bad Music: Europe, *The Final Countdown.*

Loose Vowels:

```
D A I S   A N T I
  D   E   L     M
L O V E   S E E P
I   N O O K     E
A I L   U   E R A
I   E A R S     C
S E E R   U T A H
O   E   E   E   I
N O V A   Z E R O
```

SYMBOLISM

What whole number value between 1 and 9 should be allocated to each different symbol in order to reach the sum totals shown at the end of each row and column?

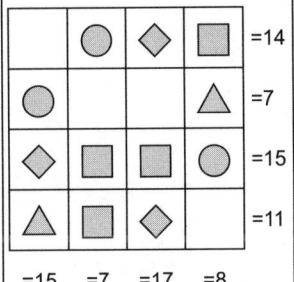

	○	◇	▢	=14
○			△	=7
◇	▢		○	=15
△	▢	◇		=11

=15 =7 =17 =8

DOMINADDITION

Can you place the remaining dominoes in their correct positions, so that the total number of spots in each of the four rows and five columns equals the sum at the end of that row or column?

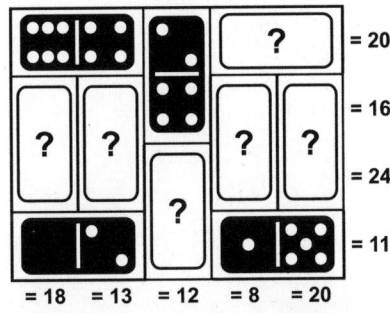

= 20
= 16
= 24
= 11

= 18 = 13 = 12 = 8 = 20

PATCHWORK

Fit the numbers 1, 2, 3, 4, 5, 6 and 7 into the grid below, so that every horizontal row, every vertical column and the two long diagonal lines of six smaller squares contain six different numbers. Some are already in place.

	3		6		
2	1				5
		5		2	
4		3		5	
				7	6
3		4	1		
		1			4

THE WHOLE PICTURE

Can you finish this picture?

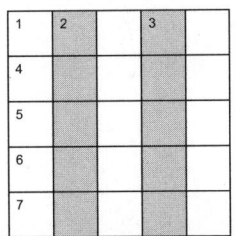

TWO DOWN

Fit five of the seven listed words into the Across rows in the grid, so that the other two words read down the shaded columns numbered 2 and 3.

ABODE   ASIAN
BASTE   DEATH
DELHI   STATE
    TAKEN

1	2		3	
4				
5				
6				
7				

MASS HYSTERIAS

Today we are all going to:

Buy only fruit grown by monks in the mountains and drink mediæval ale.

WEATHER for OPTIMISTS

Today the weather will be:

Rain later but it shouldn't spoil your day.

WHERE ON E A I R ?

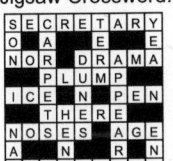

Where on earth is Climax?

Answer: _____

COUPLINGS

Apart from two, every word listed below can be coupled with one of the others to make another word or phrase. Rearrange the letters of the two which can't be paired together, to form one word, the name of something to eat.

1 EGG	2 MILK
3 BED	4 MOTH
5 RAGING	6 PEN
7 BREED	8 PUDDING
9 YOLK	10 TIGER
11 MEDAL	12 LINEN
13 BRONZE	14 BALLPOINT

Answer: _____

WORDFILLER

Can you place all the listed words into the grid below?

4 letters
LENA
NILE
ODER

5 letters
RHONE
SOMME
VOLGA
YUKON

6 letters
MEKONG
ORANGE
TIGRIS

7 letters
YENISEY
ZAMBEZI

9 letters
EUPHRATES

WORDS TO REMEMBER

With which company or organisation or product do you associate this slogan?

"Because I'm worth it."

DESIGN YOUR OWN

Village

DO YOU KNOW...

...what happened on this date?

1 October 1936

Answers to puzzles on the previous page

Where On Earth? Colorado, USA.
Two Down: Across: 1 Abode, 4 Taken, 5 Asian, 6 State, 7 Delhi.
Down: 2 Baste, 3 Death.
Symbolism: Circle=5, Diamond=8, Square=1, Triangle=2.

Dominaddition:

6	4	2	3	5
6	1	4	0	5
6	6	3	4	5
0	2	3	1	5

Patchwork:

7	3	2	5	6	4	1
2	1	6	7	4	3	5
1	4	5	6	7	2	3
4	6	3	2	5	1	7
5	2	4	1	3	7	6
3	5	7	4	1	6	2
6	7	1	3	2	5	4

FOR SALE

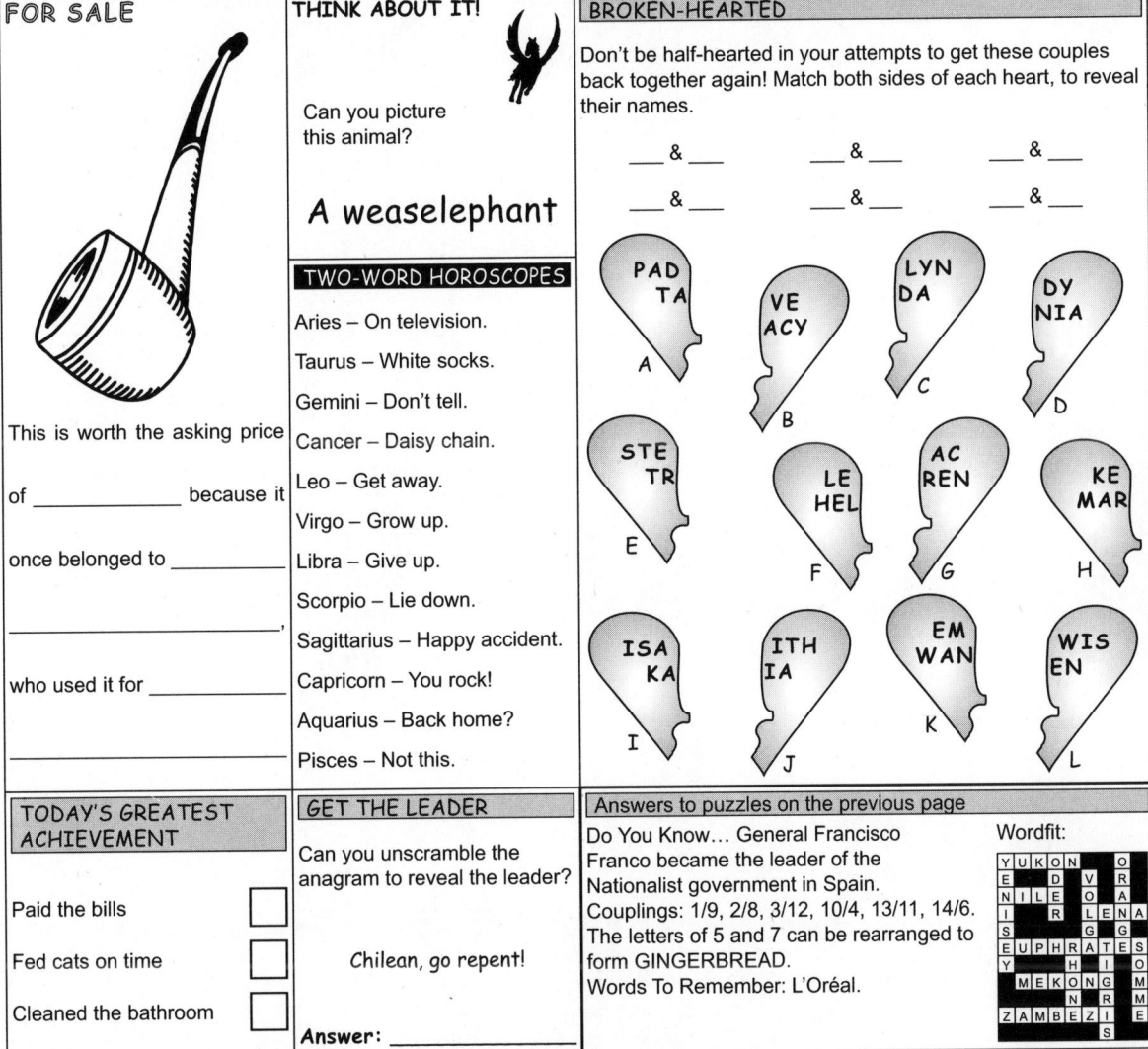

This is worth the asking price

of _____ because it

once belonged to _____

_____,

who used it for _____

_____

TODAY'S GREATEST ACHIEVEMENT

Paid the bills ☐

Fed cats on time ☐

Cleaned the bathroom ☐

THINK ABOUT IT!

Can you picture this animal?

A weaselephant

TWO-WORD HOROSCOPES

Aries – On television.

Taurus – White socks.

Gemini – Don't tell.

Cancer – Daisy chain.

Leo – Get away.

Virgo – Grow up.

Libra – Give up.

Scorpio – Lie down.

Sagittarius – Happy accident.

Capricorn – You rock!

Aquarius – Back home?

Pisces – Not this.

GET THE LEADER

Can you unscramble the anagram to reveal the leader?

Chilean, go repent!

Answer: _____

BROKEN-HEARTED

Don't be half-hearted in your attempts to get these couples back together again! Match both sides of each heart, to reveal their names.

___ & ___   ___ & ___   ___ & ___

___ & ___   ___ & ___   ___ & ___

PAD TA — A

VE ACY — B

LYN DA — C

DY NIA — D

STE TR — E

LE HEL — F

AC REN — G

KE MAR — H

ISA KA — I

ITH IA — J

EM WAN — K

WIS EN — L

MY FAVOURITE THINGS

These are a few of my favourite things:

My favourite book is:

_____

My favourite city is:

_____

My favourite animal is:

_____

My favourite nursery rhyme is:

_____

EYE-SPY

I spy with my little eye something beginning with:

_____

CLOCKWORDS

It's a race against the clock…
How many common words of three or more different letters can you make from those on the clockface (without using plurals, proper nouns or abbreviations) in ten minutes? All words must contain BOTH the letters indicated by the hands on the clock.

MISSING LETTERS

One letter of the alphabet is missing from each box. Find them all and place them in the order of the numbered boxes to reveal a six-letter word.

Word: _____

1	2	3
HRLSA	QTYEI	IMZDN
MXYZB	NXSJB	FTCLV
GQNTI	CPRKH	HSBOW
ODUWJ	DUWLF	AJXGQ
FPKVE	MVGAZ	EUYKP

4	5	6
SCHZF	GDXIP	OVCGJ
LDMYR	JBWFT	BPKRS
ITGXB	NYAHL	LAUZE
JPUEQ	QCVSK	HMDIR
KVAWO	MRZOU	NWYXQ

TOP FIVE

Best songs for eating dinner:

1 _____

_____

2 _____

_____

3 _____

_____

4 _____

_____

5 _____

_____

THOUGHT FOR THE DAY

Do not adjust your mind, there is a fault in reality.

DICEY ARITHMETIC

Using three of the arithmetical signs ÷, −, x and +, can you achieve the correct total?

BRIEF SURVIVAL GUIDE

FAMILY CHRISTMAS:

1 Start early on the sherry

2 Finish late with the whisky

3 Stuff enough food into your mouth to avoid having to speak

Answers to puzzles on the previous page

Get The Leader: General Pinochet.
Broken-Hearted: A and D, E and B, F and L, H and J, I and G, K and C.

178

MATCH THAT

Change the position of three matches to leave four squares.

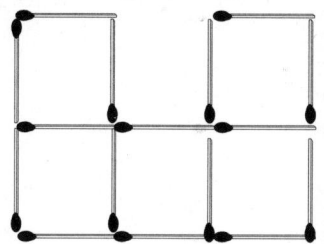

WORDWHEEL

Using only the letters in the Wordwheel, you have ten minutes to find as many words as possible, none of which may be plurals, foreign words or proper nouns. Each word must be of three letters or more, all must contain the central letter and letters can only be used once in every word. There is at least one nine-letter word in the wheel.

Nine-letter word: _____

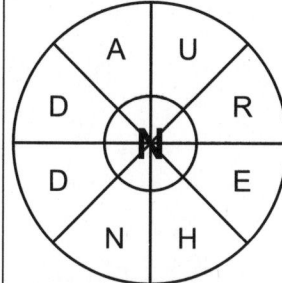

UNLIKELY CANDIDATE

NATIONAL POLITICIAN

_____

WORDSEARCH

Can you find all of the listed pub-related words in the grid? Words may run in either a forwards or backwards direction, horizontally, vertically or diagonally, but always in a straight, uninterrupted line.

```
Y X I H F B L E R R A B S
N C S O R R O U N D A H O
N L E S U O H E E R F A D
E I O T I W O L B G T N A
P G N E T N C I X I H D W
A H I L J A L V M N G P A
H T M R U L A E O G I U T
E A O Y I E P M O E N M E
V L D A C L K U R R Z P R
O E R K E L A S P A I S E
H D P A T N O I A L U Q D
S P S I R C M C T E Q K I
W E L B A T L O O P N R C
```

ALCOHOL

BAR BILLIARDS

BARREL

BROWN ALE

CIDER

CRISPS

DOMINOES

FREE HOUSE

FRUIT JUICE   LIVE MUSIC

GINGER ALE   ON TAP

SHOVE HA'PENNY

HANDPUMPS   POOL TABLE   SODA WATER

HOSTELRY   QUIZ NIGHT   TAP ROOM

LIGHT ALE   ROUND   TIME PLEASE

LEARNING LINES

We give you a line, you tell us who said it and the film:

"You're like the thief who isn't the least bit sorry he stole, but is terribly, terribly sorry he's going to jail."

EXCUSES FOR

Unkempt hair:

_____
_____
_____
_____
_____

WHATEVER YOU DO, don't even THINK about...

Boils

Sex change operations

Raw liver

PICK 'N' MIX

Choose three words to describe your cooking:

Gourmet   Burnt
Flavoursome   Inedible
Scrumptious   Pitiful
Delicious   Awful
Palatable   Tasty

LETTER TRACKER

Begin in the central shaded square and follow a continuous path which will track from square to square, up, down and sideways, but never diagonally.

Your trail should cover every letter once only, in order to find:

Seventeen British Prime Ministers.

H	E	H	A	N	L	I	M	C	N	A
I	A	T	D	A	L	C	A	A	M	H
L	E	A	D	C	H	L	L	L	A	G
V	A	R	I	R	I	L	O	N	S	Q
E	L	S	N	U	H	S	T	E	A	U
C	D	I	G	T	C	D	A	L	T	I
R	O	P	L	O	N	G	L	E	T	T
E	L	W	A	B	N	E	T	E	A	H
P	E	G	L	A	E	D	H	A	T	C
N	I	N	F	O	L	P	R	A	M	H
N	A	C	R	U	E	E	O	J	R	E

STARTING LINE

Which three letter word can be placed at the start, to form three seven-letter words?

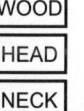

WOOD
HEAD
NECK

PRE-FAME NAME GAME

By what name do we know this famous person?

Harry Lillis Crosby

NUMB-SKULL

Fit the listed numbers into the grid, crossword-fashion.

2 digits
25
29
43
45
46
56
62
90
96

3 digits
230
245
323
464
490
494

577
715
765
971

4 digits
2766
6234
7645

5 digits
55555
67300

7 digits
4514326

8 digits
45356487
53215312

Answers to puzzles on the previous page

Learning Lines: Rhett Butler (Clark Gable), *Gone With The Wind* (1939).
Wordwheel: The nine-letter word is UNDERHAND.

Match That:

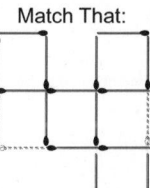

180

BALANCING THE SCALES

Given that scales A and B balance perfectly, how many squares are needed to balance scale C?

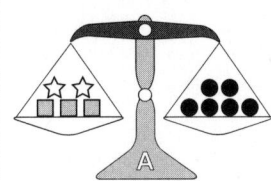

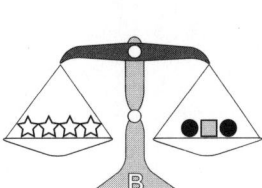

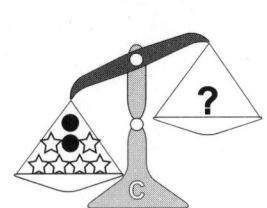

The

NAKFA

is the currency of

_____

MIRROR WRITING

Write this word upside down:

LEMONS

USE YOUR IMAGINATION

Can you fill each of these boxes with a different occupation?

TOP TEN

BOOK ☐

MAGAZINE ☐

LEAFLET ☐

POSTER ☐

NEWSPAPER ☐

COMIC ☐

PAMPHLET ☐

PICTURE BOOK ☐

LETTER ☐

POSTCARD ☐

NAME THAT SONG

We give you the first line, you name the song: ♫

I am an antichrist

Song: _____

THIN DIVIDING LINES

By using three straight lines, can you divide this star into five parts, each containing six different shapes?

Answers to puzzles on the previous page

Pre-Fame Name Game: Bing Crosby.
Starting Line: RED.
Letter Tracker: Churchill, Callaghan, MacMillan, Addington, Gladstone, Asquith, Attlee, Thatcher, Major, Peel, Eden, Balfour, Canning, Walpole, Perceval, Disraeli, Heath.

Numb-Skull:

SWEET BAD MUSIC

So who on earth was responsible for this lyric?

Well you can terraplane
In the fallin' rain.
I drive a Rolls Royce
'Cos it's good for my voice.

NAMED AND SHAMED

Psychobabbler

_____

New Age shyster

_____

Hippy-dippy hanger-on

_____

WAYS TO PASS THE TIME

Gossiping ☐

Gallivanting ☐

Gambling ☐

PROVERBS & SAYINGS

The letters on the tiles were once all in place, but dropped out, falling in a straight line into the lower grid. Some tiles dropped earlier than others, so those on the lowest row aren't all from the same row in the grid above. Can you put them back into position in order to reveal a well-known proverb or saying?

Y	R			M	A	N						
W	O	T	H	O	E	L	G		E			
A	I	U	O	C	I	N	E	O	T	G	M	A
B	N	E	A	K	U	T	N	T	T	E	G	S	K	E

SHADOWLAND

Test your skills of observation.
Only one of the five shadows is that of the tree. Which one?

A   B   C   D   E

OUT OF SIGHT

What is the sum total of the spots on the hidden faces of these three dice?

STARTER LETTER

Write down one each of the listed items, all of which must begin with the starter letter:

N

Country	
Tree	
Boy's name	
Girl's name	
River	
City	
Animal	
Make of car	
Drink	

COMPLETE THIS LIMERICK:

There was a young laddie from Leith

Who at night would not clean his teeth

In time they turned bad

Which was terribly sad

_____

POTATOE OR POTATO?

INOCULATE

OR

INNOCULATE

Make the face:

CONCERNED

HEXAGONY

Can you place the hexagons in the grid, so that where any triangle touches another along a straight line, the contents of both are the same? One triangle is already filled.

CHARACTER ASSIGNATION

Fill in the answers to the clues, across the grid. Then read down the diagonal line of eight squares, to reveal:
A character from J R R Tolkien's *Lord Of The Rings*.

1 Edible fungus
2 Consider to be true
3 Shade or hue
4 Prickly plants
5 Qatar's capital
6 Supreme being, deity
7 Carry out an action
8 One hundred in Roman numerals

CHARACTER: _____

REAL WORDS

Which is the real word?

RHAPSODOMANCY ☐

RHAPSODONITE ☐

RHAPSODOBITULIST ☐

PLACE YOUR BETS

_____'s wedding dress will be:

A big, white, fluffy meringue ☐

A minimal, designer affair ☐

Made by her granny ☐

WORD LADDER

Change one letter at a time (but not the position of any letter) to make a new word – and move from the word at the top of the ladder to the word at the bottom using the exact number of rungs provided.

F L E S H

B L O O D

WHATEVER NEXT?

Which of the lettered alternatives comes next in this sequence:

| 23 | 16 | 20 | 13 | 17 | ? |

A	B
21	22

C	D
9	10

POOR LITTLE MITE!

Decide the fate of Little Red Riding Hood – granny's house or wolf's lunch?

LRRH's HOUSE

WOLF's HOUSE

GRANNY's HOUSE

PAIR SHAPES

In the box below there are shapes in three different colours, black, white and grey. Any shape may have been rotated, but can you see which is the only shape to appear exactly twice in exactly the same colour?

WEATHER for PESSIMISTS

Today the weather will be:

Colder than you can ever imagine and twice as vicious.

WHAT DOES IT MEAN?

What is the meaning of the word

PILGARLICK

Answer: _____

_____

Answers to puzzles on the previous page

Real Words: Rhapsodomancy. The seeking of guidance through the chance selection of a passage in literature.
Character Assignation: 1 Mushroom, 2 Believe, 3 Colour, 4 Cacti, 5 Doha, 6 God, 7 Do, 8 C.
Character: Meriadoc.
Potatoe or Potato? Inoculate.

Hexagony:

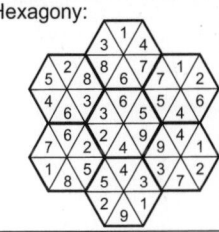

BERMUDA TRIANGLE

Travel through the 'Bermuda Triangle' by visiting one room at a time and collecting a letter from each. You can enter the outside passageway as often as you like, but can only visit each room once. When you've completed your tour, rearrange the fifteen letters to spell out a word.

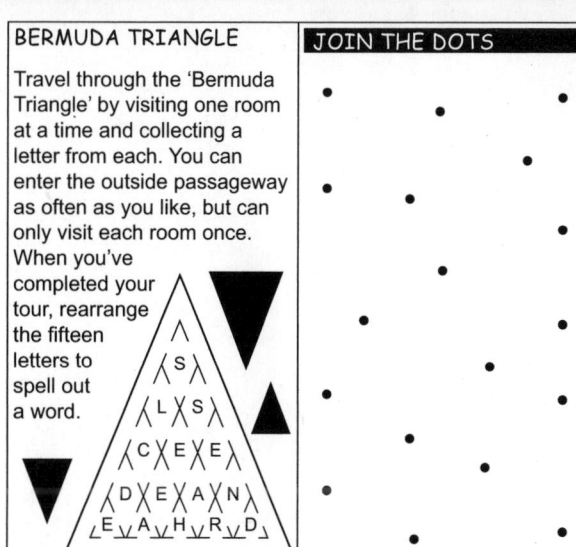

JOIN THE DOTS

DOMINOLOGICAL

What is the value of the question mark?

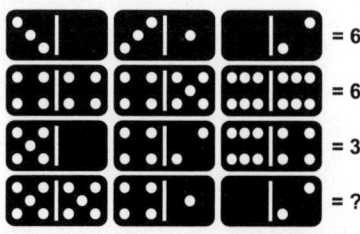

= 6
= 6
= 3
= ?

ARRANGING THINGS

If you fit six of these seven words into the grid below, the word left over will appear reading down the shaded squares.

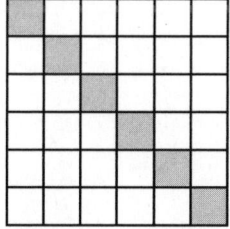

BASKET   BEAKER
BUCKET   CARAFE
GOBLET   TEAPOT
VESSEL

MASS HYSTERIAS

Today we are all going to:

Wear our coats inside out as a representation of our internal thoughts.

WHERE ON  ?

Where on earth is Shag Island?

Answer: _____

DESIGN YOUR OWN

Swimming pool

Answers to puzzles on the previous page

What Does It Mean? A poor wretch; used self-pityingly to refer to oneself.
Word Ladder: One solution is FLESH, flash, flask, flank, blank, bland, blond, BLOOD.
Whatever Next? D – take seven from the first number, then add four to the next, take seven from the next, add four to the next, etc.

Pair Shapes:

ELIMINATION

Every oval shape contains a different letter from A to K inclusive. Use the clues to determine their locations. Reference in the clues to 'due' means in any location along the same horizontal or vertical line.

1. J is due west of K and due north of C.
2. G is due north of F and due east of J.
3. E is due north of A and due east of B.
4. I is due south of D and due west of A.
5. B is due north of G and due east of H.

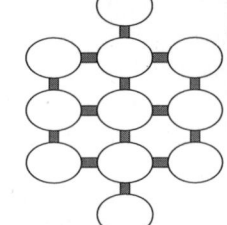

A MATCHING PAIR

Mr Holliday would like a matching pair of cases. Which two should he buy?

A  B

C  D

E  F

JIGSAW CROSSWORD

Fit the blocks into the empty grid to form a complete crossword which, when finished, will be symmetrical, similar to the example seen here:

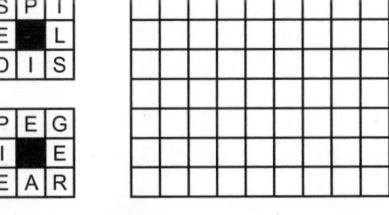

TWO DOWN

Fit five of the seven listed words into the Across rows in the grid, so that the other two words read down the shaded columns numbered 2 and 3.

AITCH   AVAIL
AVERT   BASTE
CANAL   TRACT
     PLUTO

PRE-FAME NAME GAME

By what name do we know this famous person?

Bernard Schwartz

CAPITALS

The capital of

ZIMBABWE

is:

_____

BRIEF SURVIVAL GUIDE

THROWING A PARTY:

1. Invite only friends you like and who like each other
2. Invite all your exes and then leave them to it
3. Don't invite anyone at all

Answers to puzzles on the previous page

Where On Earth? Indian Ocean.
Arranging Things: Across (from the top): Beaker, Carafe, Vessel, Bucket, Goblet, Teapot. Down: Basket.
Bermuda Triangle: The word is CLEARHEADEDNESS.
Dominological: 25 – Multiply the total number of spots on the first domino by the total number on the second domino, then divide this by the total number of spots on the third domino.

EGG TIMER

Can you complete this puzzle in the time it takes to boil an egg? The answers to the clues are anagrams of the words immediately above and below, plus or minus a letter.

1 Least hirsute
2 Housing for a horse
3 Explosion
4 Pierce with a knife
5 Wild animal
6 Front part of the chest
7 Flat-topped straw hats

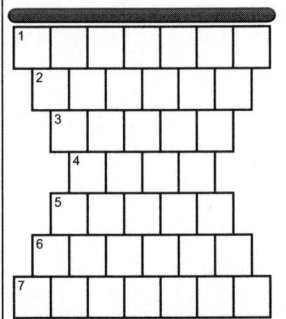

THE TANGLED TRAIL

Which of these women is walking the dog?

A
B
C

SNAKES & LADDERS

This is a standard game, so when you land at the foot of a ladder, you climb it; and when you land on the head of a snake, you slide down its tail. You need to throw an exact number to land on 100 to win – counting backwards if you don't, eg if you land on 98 and throw a five, you will end up on 97. The dice is thrown for you and always lands in this recurring order: 3, 5, 1, 4, 2, 6, so you can start by immediately placing your counter on square 3. Good luck – hope you win!

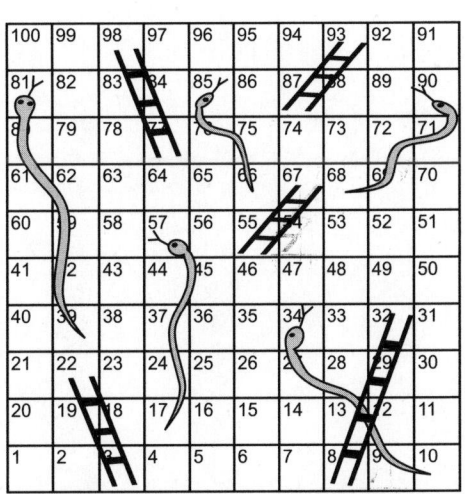

SECRET MISSION

Your secret mission (should you choose to accept it) is:

To ask "Why?" every time someone asks you to do/for anything.

DO YOU KNOW...

...what happened on this date?

1 May 1997

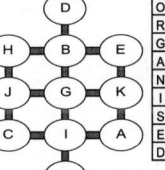

ON TARGET

The answers to the clues read from the outer circle to the centre, all ending with the same letter. When you've finished, the letters in the shaded ring will give a word.

1 Drinking chocolate
2 Allocation
3 Ball-shaped, Dutch cheese
4 Country, capital Damascus
5 Shaped and dried dough
6 'Laughing' African animal

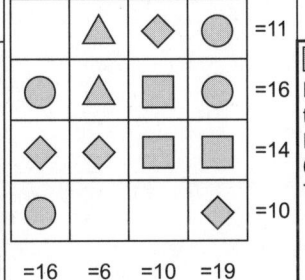

DOMINADDITION

Can you place the remaining dominoes in their correct positions, so that the total number of spots in each of the four rows and five columns equals the sum at the end of that row or column?

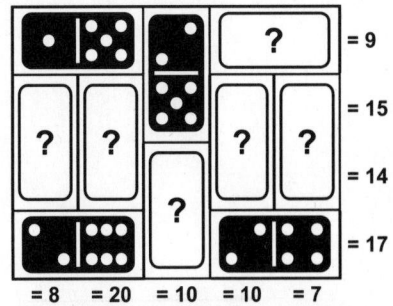

UNLIKELY CANDIDATE

LOWBROW

_____

TODAY'S GREATEST ACHIEVEMENT

Saving energy ☐

Saving money ☐

Saving your soul ☐

SYMBOLISM

What whole number value between 1 and 9 should be allocated to each different symbol in order to reach the sum totals shown at the end of each row and column?

	△	◇	◯	=11
◯	△	▢	◯	=16
◇	◇	▢	▢	=14
◯			◇	=10
=16	=6	=10	=19	

INSULT OF THE DAY

"A pretentious fad-chaser... the pom-pom girl of American letters."

Edward Abbey of Tom Wolfe (attributed)

WHO AM I?

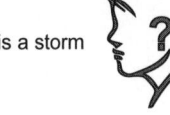

Screen is a storm

I am:

_____

Answers to puzzles on the previous page

Do You Know… The Labour Party, led by Tony Blair, returned to power in the UK after 18 years of Conservative government.
Egg Timer: 1 Baldest, 2 Stable, 3 Blast, 4 Stab, 5 Beast, 6 Breast, 7 Boaters.
The Tangled Trail: Woman B.

WORDWHEEL

Using only the letters in the Wordwheel, you have ten minutes to find as many words as possible, none of which may be plurals, foreign words or proper nouns. Each word must be of three letters or more, all must contain the central letter and letters can only be used once in every word. There is at least one nine-letter word in the wheel.

Nine-letter word: _____

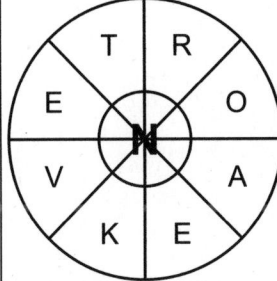

Wheel letters: T, R, O, A, E, V, K, E (centre: N)

A HELPING HAND

Give Incey Wincey Spider a web.

TOP TEN

DRAMA ☐

SOAP OPERA ☐

DOCUMENTARY ☐

NEWS ☐

MUSIC ☐

GAMESHOW ☐

CHAT SHOW ☐

TALENT SHOW ☐

REALITY TV ☐

FILM ☐

EXCUSES FOR

Guitar solos:

_____

_____

_____

_____

_____

REAL WORDS

Which is the real word?

SABERMETRICULIST ☐

SABERMECTICULOUS ☐

SABERMETRICIAN ☐

COUPLINGS

Apart from two, every word listed below can be coupled with one of the others to make another word or phrase. Rearrange the letters of the two which can't be paired together, to form one word, the name of a drink.

1 STEP	2 WINNING
3 MOWER	4 PARK
5 POND	6 CHANGE
7 CAR	8 LAWN
9 SMILE	10 MAP
11 OPENER	12 FISH
13 BOTTLE	14 MOTHER

Answer: _____

SHAPE RECOGNITION

Can you mend an achy-breaky heart like this one, with just four pieces?

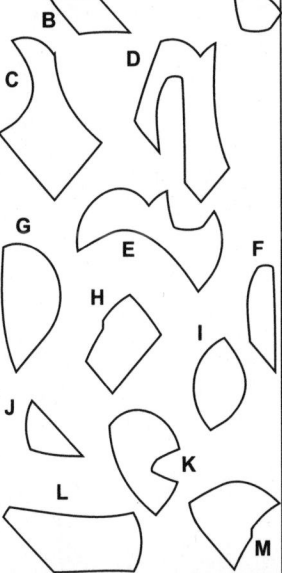

Answers to puzzles on the previous page

Who Am I? Martin Scorsese.
On Target: 1 Cocoa, 2 Quota, 3 Gouda, 4 Syria, 5 Pasta, 6 Hyena.
Shaded word: Course.
Symbolism: Circle=6, Diamond=4, Square=3, Triangle=1.

Dominaddition:

1	5	2	0	1
1	5	5	4	0
4	4	0	4	2
2	6	3	2	4

PICK 'N' MIX

A traumatic experience from your childhood, to relate at dinner parties, works outings, board meetings, whatever… – delete as appropriate:

I once got lost in a forest/ nightclub/supermarket. My mum/brother/Aunty Vi sent out a search-party and they eventually found me under a pile of apples/pile of newspapers/stack of bottles, where I had been hiding/ sleeping/crying for three days/ months/years.

MATCH THAT

Change the position of four matches to make three equilateral triangles. There are several ways to do this, but don't worry if you get stuck: one solution is on the next page…

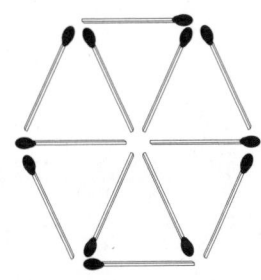

THOUGHT FOR THE DAY

Practice makes perfect, but no one's perfect, so why practise?

DICEY ARITHMETIC

Using three of the arithmetical signs ÷, −, x and +, can you achieve the correct total?

     =

TOTAL CONCENTRATION

Can you fill in the missing numbers so that each row, each column and two longest diagonal lines meet the totals given?

							400
44		55	45	29		31	252
11		84	34		46	78	303
		94	62	78	21		392
	27	63	59	37	91	7	368
12	39	83		68	44	2	270
85	91				59	44	511
12	68	47	30	1		9	249
293	352	513	348	286	356	197	359

MISSING LETTERS

One letter of the alphabet is missing from each box. Find them all and place them in the order of the numbered boxes to reveal a six-letter word.

Word: _____

1	2	3
MVIQA	FSWNJ	NVDUK
LWBRF	MRPBI	MWGHC
KXPHC	LXTCG	BYRZL
DNYUG	QYDUH	AOISF
OTZJE	ZKVOA	EXPTJ

4	5	6
LFXCI	DQPFJ	HMUOA
DTYPK	BYVKO	GXLZB
HNJBS	UGZNA	CYFKQ
ERWO	CXRLH	RWDSI
MZVGA	TWESM	VEPTJ

LEARNING LINES

We give you a line, you tell us who said it and the film:

"Most women use more brains picking a horse in the third at Belmont than they do picking a husband."

Answers to puzzles on the previous page

Real Words: Sabermetrician. A person who studies baseball statistics.
Wordwheel:
The nine-letter word is OVERTAKEN.
Couplings: 1/14, 2/9, 7/4, 8/3, 12/5, 13/11. The letters of 6 and 10 can be rearranged to form CHAMPAGNE.

Shape Recognition:

LETTER TRACKER

Begin in the central shaded square and follow a continuous path which will track from square to square, up, down and sideways, but never diagonally.

Your trail should cover every letter once only, in order to find:

Fifteen American states.

O	N	T	A	N	A	U	I	A	N	S
M	E	E	N	I	L	O	S	N	N	Y
E	S	S	G	M	W	A	I	A	E	L
N	N	E	T	O	Y	M	K	A	P	V
R	N	I	A	A	B	A	S	A	N	A
O	F	I	A	L	N	E	B	R	I	A
E	G	L	A	N	E	K	S	A	S	K
R	O	N	C	T	U	D	A	H	N	A
O	E	D	T	U	C	I	C	O	R	A
A	R	E	I	C	K	Y	O	L	O	D
W	A	L	T	C	E	N	N	O	C	O

THINK ABOUT IT!

Can you picture this animal?

A pandormouse

NAMED AND SHAMED

Least trustworthy

_____

Least likeable

_____

Least loveable

_____

SWEET BAD MUSIC

So who on earth was responsible for this lyric?

I feel inclined to blow my mind,
Get hung up, feed the ducks with a bun.
They all come out to groove about
Be nice and have fun in the sun.

UNFINISHED PICTURE

Can you complete the left half of this picture?

CLOCKWORDS

It's a race against the clock…
How many common words of three or more different letters can you make from those on the clockface (without using plurals, proper nouns or abbreviations) in ten minutes? All words must contain BOTH the letters indicated by the hands on the clock.

WORDFILLER

Can you place all the listed words into the grid below?

3 letters	5 letters
ASH	BOWER
ELM	LEMON
LOG	MANGO
NUT	PLANE
OAK	
YEW	6 letters
	PAWPAW
	WATTLE
4 letters	
PEAR	7 letters
ROOT	AVOCADO
TEAK	
WOOD	8 letters
	HORNBEAM

WORDSEARCH

Can you find all of the listed creepy-crawlies in the grid? Words may run in either a forwards or backwards direction, horizontally, vertically or diagonally, but always in a straight, uninterrupted line.

```
K U H S I F R E V L I S S
R E P P O H G O R F J A P
E Y G R A S S H O P P E R
F L H B W E S M O I L E I
A F T I Z D T I N T V B N
H S O T V G A T E E A E G
C I M I O E G E L G P L T
K D S N S B B V H N O B A
C D S G R G E E X A U M I
O A U I N T E U E R R U L
C C P U A G T L L O E B Z
K T D N G F L E A B R C T
V A T S H I E L D B U G D
```

BITING

BLUEBOTTLE

BUMBLE BEE

CADDIS FLY

COCKCHAFER

DUNG BEETLE

EGGS

FLEA

FROGHOPPER

GRASSHOPPER

HEAD

HIVE BEE

LEGS

MITE

ORANGE TIP

PUSS MOTH

SEDGE

SHIELD BUG

SILVERFISH

SPRINGTAIL

STAG BEETLE

VAPOURER

VELVET ANT

STARTING LINE

Which three letter word can be placed at the start, to form three seven-letter words?

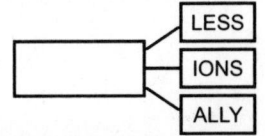

LESS
IONS
ALLY

IN YOUR OWN LANGUAGE

Devise an Oriental-looking sign for your favourite band.

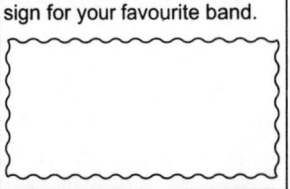

WHATEVER YOU DO, don't even THINK about...

Pigs' trotters

The smell of burnt hair

Ice burns

WEATHER for OPTIMISTS

Today the weather will be:

Bright, breezy and carefree even in the rain!

NAME THAT SONG

We give you the first line, you name the song: 🎵

She was more like a beauty queen from a movie scene

Song: _____

TOP DESIGNER

Decorate this spinning top for the children…

SUDOKU

Each heavily outlined box of nine smaller squares should contain the digits 1-9, as should every row of nine squares and every column of nine squares in the grid below. Only one number should be placed in every smaller square. Can you fill in the missing numbers?

4				1		5	2	
	5	6	3	7			8	
9	1	7			2			
3			4	9				
8		9				6		2
				8	6			3
			5			7	3	1
	2			6	7	9	4	
	8	1		4				6

COMPLETE THIS LIMERICK:

There was a young man, call him Paul

Who didn't date women at all

He said "I'm too shy"

"And they just make me cry"

_____

MIRROR WRITING

Write this word upside down:

MONDAY

_____

JUST A WORD

Can you find 'CAB' hidden in the grid, wordsearch-style?

```
N C R B E C G H J I O B M
B G C J E A C K I S E A N
H A K O P S E D W A B G H
I C U O C S R T E B A C I
G B I L O P C D E G V B R
R T Y I J H N D C E R S T
```

WAYS TO PASS THE TIME

Appropriating ☐

Accusing ☐

Asking ☐

PLACE YOUR BETS

You need some money because:

You need to make a quick getaway ☐

You need a drink ☐

You've never had any ☐

193

PATCHWORK

Fit the numbers 1, 2, 3, 4, 5, 6 and 7 into the grid below, so that every horizontal row, every vertical column and the two long diagonal lines of six smaller squares contain six different numbers. Some are already in place.

1				5		7
			1			4
	7				3	
		5		3		
			2			3
5					4	
		6				

MASS HYSTERIAS

Today we are all going to:

Collect cats in beer crates and use their fur to make trendy hot water bottle covers.

CODEWORD

This is a crossword puzzle in code. Every number represents a different letter of the alphabet and this number remains the same throughout the puzzle. Use the check-box to keep a track on your progress.

9	23	5	1	7	2	3		14	24	8
1		17		8		7		1		24
24	18	16	1	20		17	3	16	19	17
15		24		19	7	2		24		4
1	7	25	1	17		9	24	10	25	14
	6		19			13		7		
11	19	24	17	25		12	3	20	20	14
24		17		5 U	9 S	1 E		19		7
21	16	5	26	26		25	19	22	1	20
1		20		25		1		7		9
18	3	1		9	4	20	5	17	4	14

1	2	3	4	5	6	7	8	9	10	11	12	13

14	15	16	17	18	19	20	21	22	23	24	25	26

FOR SALE

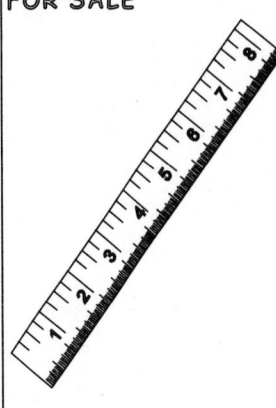

This is worth the asking price

of _____ because it

once belonged to _____

_____,

who used it for _____

WEATHER for PESSIMISTS

Today the weather will be:

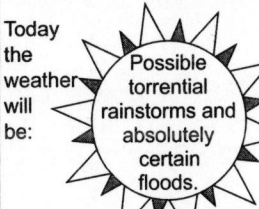

Possible torrential rainstorms and absolutely certain floods.

GET THE LEADER

Can you unscramble the anagram to reveal the leader?

Hated for ill

Answer: _____

Answers to puzzles on the previous page

Sudoku:

4	3	8	6	1	9	5	2	7
2	5	6	3	7	4	1	8	9
9	1	7	8	5	2	3	6	4
3	6	2	4	9	1	8	7	5
8	4	9	7	3	5	6	1	2
1	7	5	2	8	6	4	9	3
6	9	4	5	2	8	7	3	1
5	2	3	1	6	7	9	4	8
7	8	1	9	4	3	2	5	6

Just A Word:

```
N C R B E C G H J I O B M
B G C J E A C K I S E A N
H A K O P S E D W A B G H
I C U O C S R T E B A C I
G B I L O P C D E G V B R
R T Y I J H N D C E R S T
```

194

DICE-SECTION

Printed onto every one of the six numbered dice below are six letters (one per side), which can be rearranged to form the answer to each clue; however, some sides are invisible to you. Use the clues and write every answer into the grid. When correctly filled, the letters in the shaded squares, reading in the order 1 to 6, will spell out a man's name.

Flap of material under the laces of a shoe

Worldwide

Image reflector

Capital of Spain

Protection worn by a knight

Capital of England

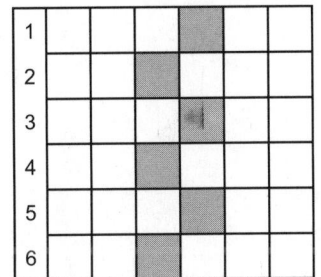

WORDS TO REMEMBER

With which company or organisation or product do you associate this slogan?

"When it absolutely, positively has to be there overnight."

EYE-SPY

I spy with my little eye something beginning with:

_____

THE WHOLE PICTURE

Can you finish this picture?

LEARNING LINES

We give you a line, you tell us who said it and the film:

"Why can't a woman be more like a man?"

THIS WEEK'S PHOBIAS

Nephophobia – Fear of clouds
Sitophobia – Fear of food
Phobophobia – Fear of fear

BRIEF SURVIVAL GUIDE

GETTING DRESSED:

1 Put your underwear on first
2 Try to make sure that your outfit matches
3 Try to make sure that your outfit fits

Answers to puzzles on the previous page

Get The Leader:
Adolf Hitler.

Patchwork:

1	6	4	3	5	2	7
2	3	7	1	6	5	4
6	7	2	5	4	3	1
7	4	5	6	3	1	2
4	5	1	2	7	6	3
5	2	3	7	1	4	6
3	1	6	4	2	7	5

Codeword:

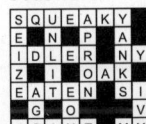

195

LUCKY NUMBER

Discover your lucky number for today by following these instructions:

1. Think of a number between seven and forty-six;
2. Think of the third and fourth digits of your telephone number;
3. Add the result of 1 above to the result of 2 above;
4. Reverse the digits in this number.

Now you have your lucky number for today. Don't lose it – write it down:

_____

ARRANGING THINGS

If you fit six of these seven words into the grid below, the word left over will appear reading down the shaded squares.

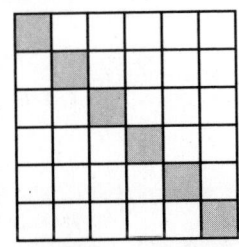

CORNET   HUMBUG
MOUSSE   NOUGAT
SORBET   SUNDAE
     TOFFEE

TODAY'S GREATEST ACHIEVEMENT

No cigarettes   ☐

No alcohol   ☐

No sense   ☐

SUM TOTAL

Place the digits 1-9, one per square, so that the sums are correct, according to the totals at the ends of the rows and columns. The calculations should be done in the order in which they appear, for example 6–2x5=20 should be read as 6–2(=4), then 4x5=20.

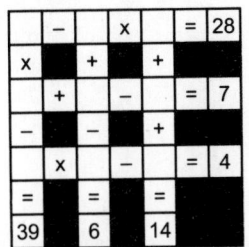

WHAT DOES IT MEAN?

What is the meaning of the word

SELCOUTH

Answer: _____

_____

SPOT THE BALL

Place a cross where you imagine the centre of the ball to be.

PROVERBS & SAYINGS

The letters on the tiles were once all in place, but dropped out, falling in a straight line into the lower grid. Some tiles dropped earlier than others, so those on the lowest row aren't all from the same row in the grid above. Can you put them back into position in order to reveal a well-known proverb or saying?

B	U	T			T			R	A	N	
H	O	U		Y	A	N		D	A	A	N	O	R
Y	A	R	E	E	I	U		C	W	I	T	K	A
M	O	K	S	C	O	T	O	L	E	N	D	E	T

TWO DOWN

Fit five of the seven listed words into the Across rows in the grid, so that the other two words read down the shaded columns numbered 2 and 3.

AGATE   BORAX
EGYPT   GOUGE
GUESS   PASTA
TEXAS

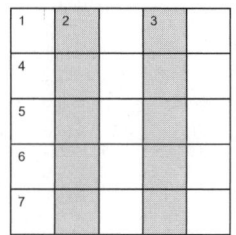

UNLIKELY CANDIDATE

HIGHBROW

_____

DOMINO PUZZLE

Which domino (A, B, C, D or E) should fill the empty space?

   ?

 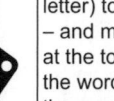

A   B   C   D   E

OCCUPATIONAL HAZARD

Here's a puzzle to test your skills! Fit the shapes into the grid so that the completed puzzle shows six six-letter occupations. Three letters are already in place, to get you off to a good start…

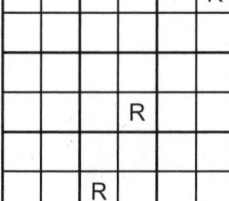

WORD LADDER

Change one letter at a time (but not the position of any letter) to make a new word – and move from the word at the top of the ladder to the word at the bottom using the exact number of rungs provided.

GET THE LOOK

Make the face:

CALM

DO YOU KNOW…

…what happened on this date?

1 April 1918

Answers to puzzles on the previous page

What Does It Mean? Something strange, unfamiliar and marvellous.
Arranging Things: Across (from the top): Sundae, Mousse, Cornet, Humbug, Toffee, Nougat. Down: Sorbet.
Proverbs & Sayings: You can lead a horse to water but you cannot make it drink.

Sum Total:

8	–	4	x	7
x		+		+
6	+	3	–	2
–		–		+
9	x	1	–	5

CHARACTER ASSIGNATION

Fill in the answers to the clues, across the grid. Then read down the diagonal line of eight squares, to reveal:
A character from Thomas Hughes's *Tom Brown's Schooldays*.

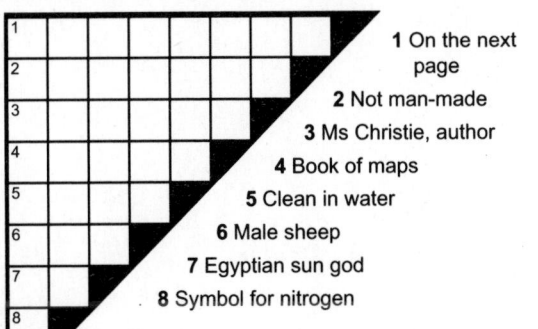

1 On the next page
2 Not man-made
3 Ms Christie, author
4 Book of maps
5 Clean in water
6 Male sheep
7 Egyptian sun god
8 Symbol for nitrogen

CHARACTER: _____

TONGUE TWISTER

Get your tongue around this one, if you can!

A tree toad loved a she-toad
Who lived up in a tree.
He was a two-toed tree toad
But a three-toed toad was she.
The two-toed tree toad tried to win
The three-toed she-toad's heart,
For the two-toed tree toad loved the ground
The three-toed tree toad trod.
But the two-toed tree toad tried in vain.
He couldn't please her whim.
From her tree toad bower
With her three-toed power
The she-toad vetoed him.

THOUGHT FOR THE DAY

It's a dangerous dog that doesn't bark.

WHERE ON

Where on earth is Slackbottom?

Answer: _____

DESIGN YOUR OWN

Cruise ship

PYRAMID PLUS

Every brick in this pyramid contains a number which is the sum of the two numbers below it, so that F=A+B, etc. No two bricks contain the same number, or just a zero, so work out the missing numbers!

O=90

M=   N=

J=27   K=   L=

F=14   G=   H=10   I=

A=   B=   C=   D=6   E=

Answers to puzzles on the previous page

Do You Know… The RAF (Royal Air Force) was founded in Britain.
Two Down: Across: 1 Egypt, 4 Borax, 5 Guess, 6 Agate, 7 Texas.
Down: 2 Gouge, 3 Pasta.
Word Ladder: BRIDE, brine, brink, brick, brock, brook, broom, GROOM.
Domino Puzzle: B – The total number of spots increases by two each time.

Occupational Hazard:

B	A	N	K	E	R
W	A	R	D	E	N
T	A	I	L	O	R
M	A	T	R	O	N
J	O	C	K	E	Y
B	U	R	S	A	R

198

PICTOWORD

Which well-known word or phrase is represented by the following?

BR EA ST KEA (box) / LU NC HE ON (box) / DI N ER N (box)

EXCUSES FOR

Killing flies:

_____
_____
_____
_____

MY NEXT PARTY

Where
_____

Who's there
_____

What occasion
_____

WORDWHEEL

Using only the letters in the Wordwheel, you have ten minutes to find as many words as possible, none of which may be plurals, foreign words or proper nouns. Each word must be of three letters or more, all must contain the central letter and letters can only be used once in every word. There is at least one nine-letter word in the wheel.

Nine-letter word: _____

Wordwheel letters: E, G, L, F, H, I, N, T

STARTER LETTER

Write down one each of the listed items, all of which must begin with the starter letter:

F

Country	
Tree	
Boy's name	
Girl's name	
River	
City	
Animal	
Make of car	
Drink	

REAL WORDS

Which is the real word?

SNOLLYGOSTER ☐

SNOLLYGOOSE ☐

SNOLLIGESTIC ☐

DOMINADDITION

Can you place the remaining dominoes in their correct positions, so that the total number of spots in each of the four rows and five columns equals the sum at the end of that row or column?

Row sums: = 16, = 11, = 22, = 14

Column sums: = 20, = 9, = 10, = 14, = 10

IN YOUR OWN LANGUAGE

Devise an Oriental-looking sign for your local pub.

PAIR SHAPES

In the box below there are shapes in three different colours, black, white and grey. Any shape may have been rotated, but can you see which is the only shape to appear exactly twice in exactly the same colour?

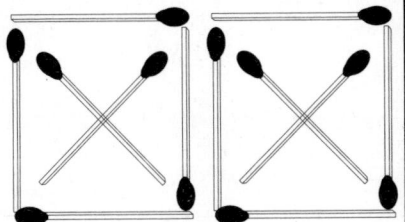

SYMBOLISM

What whole number value between 1 and 9 should be allocated to each different symbol in order to reach the sum totals shown at the end of each row and column?

	○	◇		=7
○	◇	□	□	=23
	△	△	◇	=14
△	□		○	=19

=11 =21 =16 =15

NAMED AND SHAMED

Celebrity skeleton

_____

Outrageous obesity

_____

Ridiculous haircut

_____

SWEET BAD MUSIC

So who on earth was responsible for this lyric?

Semolina pilchard, climbing
   up the Eiffel Tower.
Elementary penguin singing
   Hare Krishna.

COUPLINGS

Apart from two, every word listed below can be coupled with one of the others to make another word or phrase. Rearrange the letters of the two which can't be paired together, to form one word, a boy's name.

1	2
FUN	DICK
3	4
WORMHOLE	PALACE
5	6
TOP	TAB
7	8
HOLY	FAIR
9	10
MOBY	HAT
11	12
BIBLE	BRIDGE
13	14
LONDON	BUCKINGHAM

Answer: _____

MATCH THAT

Remove seven matches and leave nineteen!

Answers to puzzles on the previous page

Real Words: Snollygoster. A shrewd, unprincipled person, especially a politician.
Wordwheel: The nine-letter word is NIGHTLIFE.
Pictoword: Three square meals.

Dominaddition:

5	4	1	1	5
5	0	4	2	0
6	3	3	6	4
4	2	2	5	1

PRE-FAME NAME GAME

By what name do we know this famous person?

Doris Kappelhof

_____

SECRET MISSION

Your secret mission (should you choose to accept it) is:

Wear something blue and stroke it as if it is very special.

LETTER TRACKER

Begin in the central shaded square and follow a continuous path which will track from square to square, up, down and sideways, but never diagonally.

Your trail should cover every letter once only, in order to find:

Eighteen birds.

A	S	A	E	L	I	A	U	R	A	L
N	T	W	H	P	N	P	Q	K	D	Y
N	E	R	H	H	O	L	E	V	O	K
H	R	U	S	E	R	O	V	E	R	S
T	W	I	F	L	L	U	B	H	B	U
R	O	N	C	H	B	R	D	C	N	Z
R	R	A	F	C	L	I	B	F	I	Z
A	E	S	D	U	A	C	K	F	A	A
P	S	T	L	C	K	O	O	C	H	R
N	G	A	E	K	C	N	U	L	G	D
I	L	R	I	F	O	N	D	E	A	E

CELEBRITY WRESTLING

BRITNEY SPEARS

-v-

CHRISTINA AGUILERA

MISSING LETTERS

One letter of the alphabet is missing from each box. Find them all and place them in the order of the numbered boxes to reveal a six-letter word.

Word: _____

1	2	3
MVZHA	KSUPF	IRYND
PBWLG	LRYOB	FVKGC
CYSQN	QZXCI	QSOBZ
IJUFD	JMVDG	PWULA
OXTEK	ATNWH	HXMTE

4	5	6
MUHSC	ZHOVD	VXAJQ
ODRZJ	BYRNK	KBFNR
LYNBG	ISXAG	IWCOS
FTWIQ	FTQLJ	GLHZD
VKXPA	EUWMP	EUYMP

BOX CLEVER

When the above is folded to form a cube, which one of the following can be produced?

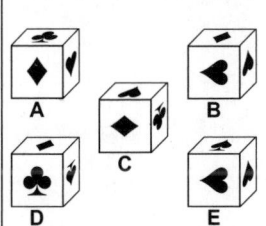

A B C D E

JOIN THE DOTS

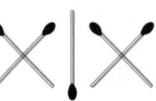

NAME THAT SONG

We give you the first line, you name the song: ♪

So true, funny how it seems always in time, but never in line for dreams.

Song: _____

PICK 'N' MIX

An interesting piece of personal information, to pass on to friends, neighbours, colleagues, etc – delete as appropriate:

My sister is a lunatic/lawyer/lazy girl. Last week she asked me to go with her to the cinema/shops/doctor's surgery, because she had stolen/lost/broken an old jar of pickles under her jeans/shirt/hat and wanted it surgically removed/mended/cosmetically enhanced.

WAYS TO PASS THE TIME

Stealing ☐

Chasing ☐

Accosting ☐

A IS TO B

A   is to   B

as C   is to

D   E

F   G

SNAKES & LADDERS

This is a standard game, so when you land at the foot of a ladder, you climb it; and when you land on the head of a snake, you slide down its tail. You need to throw an exact number to land on 100 to win – counting backwards if you don't, eg if you land on 98 and throw a five, you will end up on 97. The dice is thrown for you and always lands in this recurring order: 4, 3, 2, 5, 6, 1, so you can start by immediately placing your counter on square 4. Good luck – hope you win!

OUT OF SIGHT

What is the sum total of the spots on the hidden faces of these three dice?

THE WHOLE PICTURE

Can you finish this picture?

MIRROR WRITING

Write this word upside down:

NORMAL

PATCHWORK

Fit the numbers 1, 2, 3, 4, 5, 6 and 7 into the grid below, so that every horizontal row, every vertical column and the two long diagonal lines of six smaller squares contain six different numbers. Some are already in place.

		1		5		7
4			3	2		
	1					4
2				3		
	5				4	
1			6			
		7			2	

DICEY ARITHMETIC

Using three of the arithmetical signs ÷, −, x and +, can you achieve the correct total?

PLACE YOUR BETS

A dark sky means:

A storm is brewing ☐

It's night time ☐

You're wearing sunglasses ☐

LEARNING LINES

We give you a line, you tell us who said it and the film:

"They're here."

COMPLETE THIS LIMERICK:

There was a young maiden called Jill

Who ran to the top of a hill

To be nearer the sky

(We do not know why!)

_____

USE YOUR IMAGINATION

Can you fill each of these boxes with a different drink?

JIGSAW CROSSWORD

Fit the blocks into the empty grid to form a complete crossword which, when finished, will be symmetrical, similar to the example seen here:

Blocks:

```
S   C
 LO
S   A
```
```
U M S
 S   T
P E A
```
```
C U P
L   R
A X I
```
```
U N G
A   H
L A T
```
```
E   L
C K
T   F
```
```
  R
C A L
  D
```
```
A
U R N
S   I
```
```
I   S
M U M
    S
```
```
    I
K N O
    G
```

ON THE CARDS

These cards follow a particular pattern. Discover the trick and work out what value the joker should be.

TOP FIVE

Best songs for happy memories:

1 _____

_____

2 _____

_____

3 _____

_____

4 _____

_____

5 _____

_____

A MATCHING PAIR

Sean wants two identical pairs of shorts. Which should he buy?

TOP TEN

BOOK STORE ☐

CLOTHES SHOP ☐

NEWS-STAND ☐

GROCER ☐

BUTCHER ☐

MARKET ☐

BOUTIQUE ☐

FISHMONGER ☐

CANDY STORE ☐

BAKERY ☐

TODAY'S GREATEST ACHIEVEMENT

A big smile ☐

A happy mind ☐

A vicious temper ☐

POTATOE OR POTATO?

BROCOLLI

OR

BROCCOLI

Answers to puzzles on the previous page

Learning Lines: Carol Anne (Heather O'Rourke), *Poltergeist* (1982).
Dicey Arithmetic: The signs are times, plus and minus.

Patchwork:

3	4	1	2	5	6	7
4	7	6	3	2	1	5
7	1	2	5	6	3	4
2	6	5	4	3	7	1
6	5	3	7	1	4	2
1	2	4	6	7	5	3
5	3	7	1	4	2	6

WORDSEARCH

Can you find all of the listed motoring words in the grid? Words may run in either a forwards or backwards direction, horizontally, vertically or diagonally, but always in a straight, uninterrupted line.

ACCELERATE

ACCUMULATOR

AMBER

ANTIFREEZE

BRAKES

CARBURETTOR

CARRIAGEWAY

COMBUSTION

CORNER

```
P E Z E E R F I T N A L R
A N D N O I T S U B M O C
S I R O T A L U M U C C A
D L A C C E L E R A T E R
A E C O M Y M I R R O R B
O T R R O T A R E N E G U
R I A N T M I W A M B E R
S H S E K A R B H W V J E
S W H R G G A R A G E L T
O J N E E R C S D N I W T
R E W O P E S R O H B H O
C A D I S T R I B U T O R
Y T F A H S K N A R C E S
```

CRANKSHAFT   GARAGE   HORSEPOWER

CRASH   GENERATOR   MIRROR

CROSSROADS   HIGHWAY   WHITE LINE

DISTRIBUTOR   CODE   WINDSCREEN

STARTING LINE

Which three letter word can be placed at the start, to form three seven-letter words?

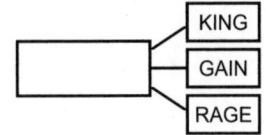

KING
GAIN
RAGE

FILL THE BURGER

HEXAGONY

Can you place the hexagons in the grid, so that where any triangle touches another along a straight line, the contents of both are the same? One triangle is already filled.

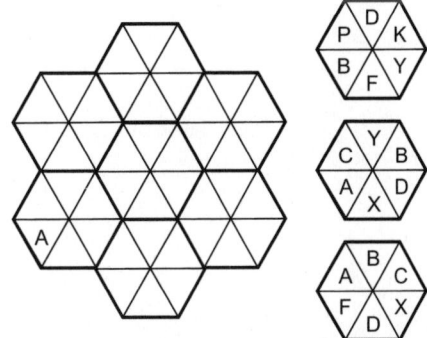

WEATHER for OPTIMISTS

Today the weather will be:

Wet at first, with worse later but your garden needed some water didn't it?

Answers to puzzles on the previous page

A Matching Pair: A and E.
Potatoe or Potato? Broccoli.
On The Cards: 4 –The value of each card when added to the value of the two cards directly below it is 14. The two cards directly below the joker have a total value of 10, so the value of the joker is the difference between 10 and 14, ie 4.

Jigsaw Crossword:

205

WHATEVER NEXT?

Which of the numbered alternatives comes next in this sequence:

| ON | UE | ED | HU | RI | ? |

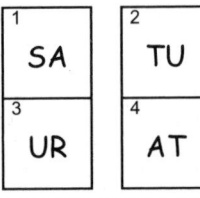

1. SA
2. TU
3. UR
4. AT

DICE-SECTION

Printed onto every one of the six numbered dice below are six letters (one per side), which can be rearranged to form the answer to each clue; however, some sides are invisible to you. Use the clues and write every answer into the grid. When correctly filled, the letters in the shaded squares, reading in the order 1 to 6, will spell out a woman's name.

Item of jewellery — 1

Go after — 2

Small, prawn-like crustacean — 3

Share out, partition — 4

Getting older — 5

Uncultivated field — 6

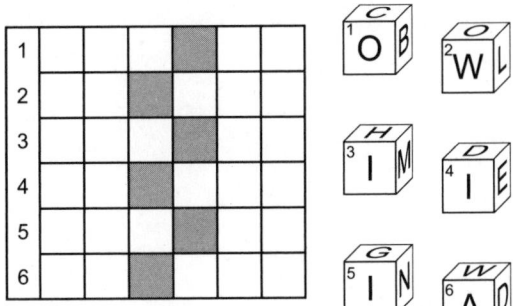

Dice:
1. C, O, B
2. O, W, L
3. H, I, M
4. D, I, E
5. G, I, N
6. W, A, D

TWO DOWN

Fit five of the seven listed words into the Across rows in the grid, so that the other two words read down the shaded columns numbered 2 and 3.

HUMAN   INANE
MAYOR   MELON
QUEEN   SMELT
      THYME

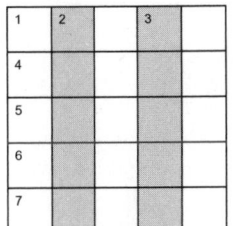

UNLIKELY CANDIDATE

TV AWARDS

_____

DO YOU KNOW…

…what happened on this date?

26 July 1847

WEATHER for PESSIMISTS

Today the weather will be:

A beautiful summer's day with black clouds in the distance.

Answers to puzzles on the previous page

Get The Leader: Hillary Rodham Clinton.
Starting Line: BAR.

Hexagony:

GOOD IMPRESSIONS

Can you pair up these door keys with the impressions of their ends?

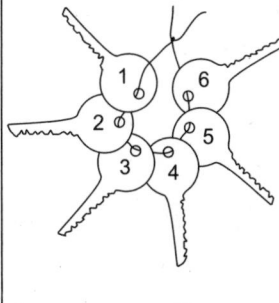

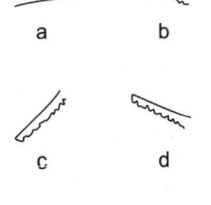

a   b

c   d

e   f

MONEY PROBLEM

Tom and Jerry shared out a certain sum of money in the ration 5:7 respectively; and Tom ended up with £325.00. How much was in the kitty before the share out?

£_____

MY FAVOURITE THINGS

These are a few of my favourite things:

My favourite film star is:

_____

My favourite pastime is:

_____

My favourite drink is:

_____

My favourite make of car is:

_____

BERMUDA TRIANGLE

Travel through the 'Bermuda Triangle' by visiting one room at a time and collecting a letter from each. You can enter the outside passageway as often as you like, but can only visit each room once. When you've completed your tour, rearrange the fifteen letters to spell out a word.

```
          /\
         / C \
        / G  I \
       / A  R  I \
      / T C M V \
     / E  D  U  N  A \
```

JUST A WORD

Can you find 'DAY' hidden in the grid, wordsearch-style?

```
F I O D R S R B N I K D E
I A C F E J N H U O Y A D
C Y H J Y U I A S E A D L
S A H O J D L D Y W S E F
S E D G E M D A T S A A D
D A J I K O S E A D A I P
```

EGG TIMER

Can you complete this puzzle in the time it takes to boil an egg? The answers to the clues are anagrams of the words immediately above and below, plus or minus a letter.

1 Freed from impurities
2 Low metal guard to confine falling coals to a hearth
3 Postpone
4 Antlered animal
5 Avarice
6 Came together
7 Came out

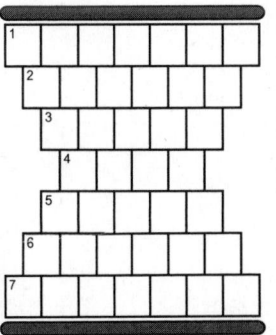

WHERE ON  ?

Where on earth is Arsoli?

Answer: _____

EYE-SPY

I spy with my little eye something beginning with:

FOR SALE

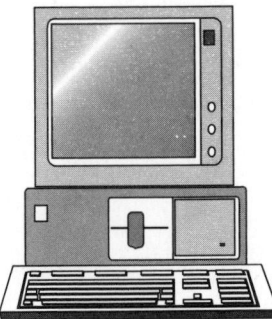

This is worth the asking price

of _____ because it

once belonged to _____

_____,

who used it for _____

_____

WORD LADDER

Change one letter at a time (but not the position of any letter) to make a new word – and move from the word at the top of the ladder to the word at the bottom using the exact number of rungs provided.

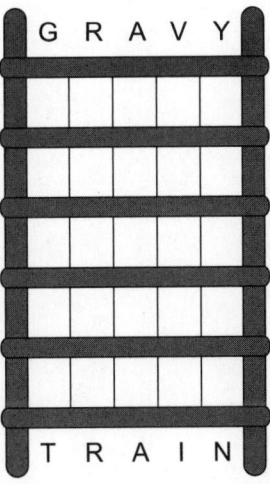

WORDFILLER

Can you place all the listed words into the grid below?

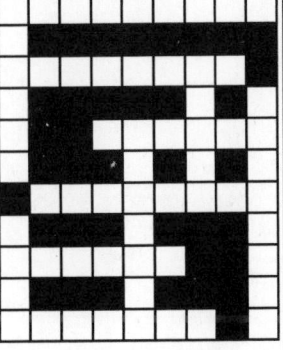

4 letters	7 letters
IOWA	ALABAMA
	ARIZONA
5 letters	8 letters
IDAHO	ILLINOIS
	MISSOURI
	VIRGINIA
6 letters	
HAWAII	9 letters
NEVADA	NEW
OREGON	JERSEY

THOUGHT FOR THE DAY

Some things, such as love or obligation, have meaning only if one stands to lose something by throwing them away.

NAME THAT SONG

We give you the first line, you name the song:

When you're weary, feeling small

Song: _____

Answers to puzzles on the previous page

Where On Earth? Lazio, Italy.
Egg Timer: 1 Refined,
2 Fender, 3 Defer, 4 Deer,
5 Greed, 6 Merged, 7 Emerged.
Bermuda Triangle: The word is
CIRCUMNAVIGATED.
Money Problem: There was £780.00 in the kitty. Tom got five-twelfths of this, so Tom got £325.00 and Jerry got £455.00
Good Impressions: 1c, 2e, 3f, 4a, 5d, 6b.

Just A Word:

F	I	O	D	R	S	R	B	N	I	K	D	E
I	A	C	F	E	J	N	H	U	O	**Y**	**A**	**D**
C	Y	H	J	Y	U	I	A	S	E	A	D	L
S	A	H	O	J	D	L	D	Y	W	S	E	F
S	E	D	G	E	M	D	A	T	S	A	A	D
D	A	J	I	K	O	S	E	A	D	A	I	P

SWEET BAD MUSIC

So who on earth was responsible for this lyric?

Helter skelter in a summer swelter,
The birds flew off with a fallout shelter,
Eight miles high and falling fast.

WORDWHEEL

Using only the letters in the Wordwheel, you have ten minutes to find as many words as possible, none of which may be plurals, foreign words or proper nouns. Each word must be of three letters or more, all must contain the central letter and letters can only be used once in every word. There is at least one nine-letter word in the wheel.

Nine-letter word: _____

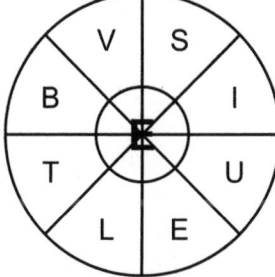

V S B I K T U L E

PROVERBS & SAYINGS

The letters on the tiles were once all in place, but dropped out, falling in a straight line into the lower grid. Some tiles dropped earlier than others, so those on the lowest row aren't all from the same row in the grid above. Can you put them back into position in order to reveal a well-known proverb or saying?

A	N			R		R			A	W		
A	I	V	T	S	A	T			F	I	H	T
H	N	O	T	H	E	N	S	D	A	Y	A	H	T
L	E	D	E	H	U	T	O	F	I	G	G	Y	S

ARRANGING THINGS

If you fit six of these seven words into the grid below, the word left over will appear reading down the shaded squares.

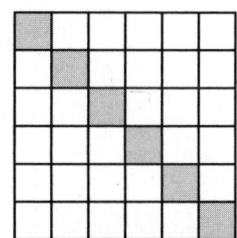

ALBERT   ALFRED
ANDREW   DERMOT
GARETH   HUBERT
        RUPERT

GET THE LOOK

Make the face:

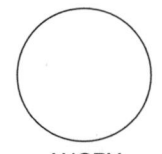

ANGRY

IN YOUR OWN LANGUAGE

Devise an Oriental-looking sign for your home town.

Answers to puzzles on the previous page

Name That Song: *Bridge Over Troubled Water*, Simon and Garfunkel.
Word Ladder: One solution is GRAVY, grave, grace, trace, tract, trait, TRAIN.

Wordfiller:

209

ANTONYM WALL

Pair up these set of letters correctly to spell out two words of the same length but with opposite meanings.

| WLE | ORA | DGE |
| KNO | IGN | NCE |

_____ & _____

DOMINOLOGICAL

What is the value of the question mark?

= 54
= 12
= 16
= ?

TWO-WORD HOROSCOPES

Aries – Bread basket.

Taurus – Insane asylum.

Gemini – Hospital food.

Cancer – It's broken.

Leo – Know it.

Virgo – Destroy it.

Libra – We hear.

Scorpio – Black thoughts.

Sagittarius – Lovely weather.

Capricorn – Please remember.

Aquarius – Boring meeting.

Pisces – Past it.

ON TARGET

The answers to the clues read from the outer circle to the centre, all ending with the same letter. When you've finished, the letters in the shaded ring will give a word.

1 Roman god of love

2 Thick woollen fabric

3 Elected

4 Fathered

5 Deluge

6 Dish of cold vegetables

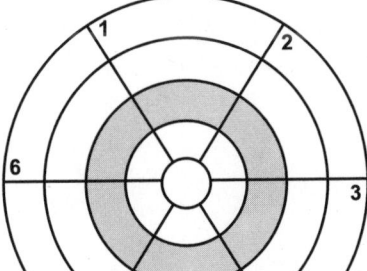

LUCKY NUMBER

Discover your lucky number for today by following these instructions:

1 Think of a number between sixteen and sixty-six;
2 Think of the last two digits of your telephone number;
3 Add the result of 1 above to the result of 2 above;
4 Reverse the digits in this number.

Now you have your lucky number for today. Don't lose it – write it down:

_____

WHO AM I?

Nerd amid late TV

I am:

_____

WHATEVER YOU DO, don't even THINK about…

Wasp stings

Broken mirrors

Missing teeth

Answers to puzzles on the previous page

Sweet Bad Music: Don McLean, *American Pie*.
Arranging Things: Across (from the top): Andrew, Alfred, Hubert, Gareth, Rupert, Dermot. Down: Albert.
Wordwheel: The nine-letter word is VESTIBULE.
Money, Money, Money: Guatemala.
Proverbs & Sayings: He that fights and runs away lives to fight another day.

DOMINADDITION

Can you place the remaining dominoes in their correct positions, so that the total number of spots in each of the four rows and five columns equals the sum at the end of that row or column?

= 18
= 8
= 10
= 21

= 8   = 4   = 15   = 13   = 17

CHARACTER ASSIGNATION

Fill in the answers to the clues, across the grid. Then read down the diagonal line of eight squares, to reveal:
A character from Henry de Vere Stacpoole's *The Blue Lagoon*.

1 Renounce the throne
2 Country, capital Brussels
3 Not very often
4 Joint between leg and foot
5 Cash register
6 Hawaiian garland
7 Symbol for tin
8 First letter of the country of which Cairo is the capital

CHARACTER: _____

THIS WEEK'S PHOBIAS

Sciophobia – Fear of shadows
Ommetaphobia – Fear of eyes
Phengophobia – Fear of daylight

ELIMINATION

Every oval shape contains a different letter from A to K inclusive. Use the clues to determine their locations. Reference in the clues to 'due' means in any location along the same horizontal or vertical line.

1 D is due west of G and due south of H.
2 I is due east of C and due north of A.
3 H is due west of J and due south of F.
4 K is due south of C.
5 G is due west of E and due south of B.

N
W - E
S

NAMED AND SHAMED

Can't act

_____

Can't sing

_____

Can't dance

_____

REAL WORDS

Which is the real word?

SPONDULICKS ☐

SPONDULESTICS ☐

SPONDULICITY ☐

Answers to puzzles on the previous page

Who Am I? David Letterman.
Antonym Wall: Knowledge and Ignorance.
On Target: 1 Cupid, 2 Tweed, 3 Voted, 4 Sired, 5 Flood, 6 Salad. Shaded word: Petrol.
Dominological: 36 – Divide the total number of spots on the first domino by the total number of spots on the second domino, then multiply this by the total number of spots on the third domino.

Begin in the central shaded square and follow a continuous path which will track from square to square, up, down and sideways, but never diagonally.

Your trail should cover every letter once only, in order to find:

Seventeen words relating to astronomy.

U	L	P	R	U	U	T	Y	R	R	E
T	A	R	A	N	R	A	S	O	V	S
O	S	U	N	R	B	I	N	T	A	B
S	L	S	T	E	N	S	O	C	U	O
T	U	P	I	P	O	T	E	L	L	S
A	T	H	J	U	C	E	L	L	A	R
R	R	U	N	R	E	S	E	A	O	N
E	A	S	E	V	T	C	T	T	I	M
E	T	M	Y	C	S	O	E	S	R	A
R	I	E	R	L	U	P	E	P	S	E
O	E	T	U	C	R	E	M	I	L	C

SAY IT, DO IT, BE IT

Your word for today is:

CONTRARY

By what name do we know this famous person?

Steveland Judkins

_____

SHAPE RECOGNITION

Four of these shapes will fit together to produce a bell identical to this one. Can you identify the correct shapes?

A

B

C

D

E

F

G

H

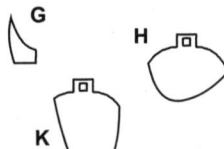

I

J

K

L

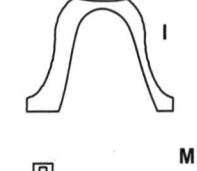

M

WAYS TO PASS THE TIME

Washing ☐

Dirtying ☐

Ironing ☐

PICK 'N' MIX

Choose three words to describe your attitude to drinking alcohol:

Disgust   Outrage
Pickled   Vague
Enjoyment Blurred
Drunken   Eager
Partying   Guzzling

Answers to puzzles on the previous page

Real Words: Spondulicks. Money, cash.
Character Assignation:
1 Abdicate, 2 Belgium, 3 Seldom, 4 Ankle, 5 Till, 6 Lei, 7 Sn, 8 E.
Character: Emmeline.

Elimination:

Dominaddition:

4	3	2	4	5
0	0	5	1	2
1	0	3	2	4
3	1	5	6	6

COUPLINGS

Apart from two, every word listed below can be coupled with one of the others to make another word or phrase. Rearrange the letters of the two which can't be paired together, to form one word, the name of a type of hat.

1 TOM	2 RAZOR
3 ARK	4 DANCING
5 BLADE	6 FISH
7 SLEEK	8 THUMB
9 PLUG	10 SPARK
11 NOAH'S	12 TAP
13 TRADER	14 FINGERS

Answer: _____

MISSING LETTERS

One letter of the alphabet is missing from each box. Find them all and place them in the order of the numbered boxes to reveal a six-letter word.

Word: _____

1	2	3
QVXHA	MYHPF	TKQHD
PFLNJ	SWLUB	OVYGC
RCWGS	OICZG	JBUMF
ODKZI	RXJQD	ZPWAN
UMYET	NTVKA	IXRLE

4	5	6
FTOMC	YISNF	PWSJA
RYUDH	KBOUH	VGZMB
BVZPN	XAPZJ	TQLCI
JKEXG	MTQLC	NKXDH
SAQWL	WRGVE	URYFO

SYMBOLISM

What whole number value between 1 and 9 should be allocated to each different symbol in order to reach the sum totals shown at the end of each row and column?

○	■	■		=11
○		◇	◇	=13
■	△	○		=10
○	◇	△	△	=15
=8	=15	=16	=10	

STARTER LETTER

Write down one each of the listed items, all of which must begin with the starter letter:

D

Country	
Tree	
Boy's name	
Girl's name	
River	
City	
Animal	
Make of car	
Drink	

MISSING LINKS

Which word links the one on the left with the one on the right? We've done the first one, and when you've finished them all, the first letters of the link words will spell the name of a North American lake.

FOOT	**HOLD**	UP
SNOWED		HAND
GUY		LADDER
PASS		BOARD
FOOT		PAPER

PLACE YOUR BETS

Your chair collapsed because:

You're drunk ☐

You've broken it ☐

It had no legs ☐

WHAT DOES IT MEAN?

What is the meaning of the word

SISYPHEAN

Answer: _____

_____

Answers to puzzles on the previous page

Pre-Fame Name Game:
Stevie Wonder.
Letter Tracker: Constellation, Mars, Eclipse, Telescope, Mercury, Cluster, Venus, Meteorite, Earth, Jupiter, Binoculars, Observatory, Saturn, Uranus, Pulsar, Pluto, Star.

Shape Recognition:

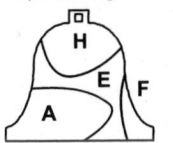

213

PATCHWORK

Fit the numbers 1, 2, 3, 4, 5, 6 and 7 into the grid below, so that every horizontal row, every vertical column and the two long diagonal lines of six smaller squares contain six different numbers. Some are already in place.

	3				6	
7				6		
	5					3
5	6					
1				7		
	2		1			6
		2	5	3		

MIRROR WRITING

Write this word upside down:

ORANGES

_____

BALANCING THE SCALES

Given that scales A and B balance perfectly, how many squares are needed to balance scale C?

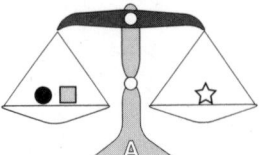

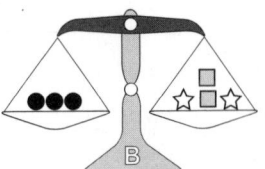

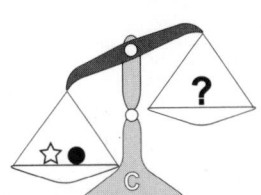

DESIGN YOUR OWN

Car

TOP TEN

CANDLES

LAMPS

STRIP LIGHTING

TORCH

GAS LAMP

OIL LAMP

TEA-LIGHT

CHANDELIER

CEILING LIGHT

WALL LIGHT

DICEY ARITHMETIC

Using three of the arithmetical signs ÷, −, x and +, can you achieve the correct total?

    =

LEARNING LINES

We give you a line, you tell us who said it and the film:

"It's just another Wednesday. The calendar's full of 'em."

DICE-SECTION

Printed onto every one of the six numbered dice below are six letters (one per side), which can be rearranged to form the answer to each clue; however, some sides are invisible to you. Use the clues and write every answer into the grid. When correctly filled, the letters in the shaded squares, reading in the order 1 to 6, will spell out a man's name.

Bovine animals

Towards the rear

Place of learning

Red fruit used in salads

Night-time visions

Reply, response

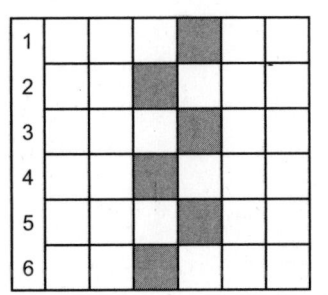

THIN DIVIDING LINES

By using three straight lines, can you divide this grid into four sections, each containing four different arrow symbols?

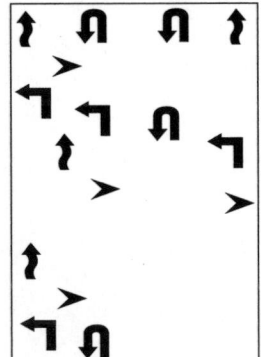

COMPLETE THIS LIMERICK:

A lady whose name we shan't tell

One day climbed down into a well

She said to her daughter:

"I'm now in deep water"

_____

WEATHER for PESSIMISTS

Today the weather will be:

A taste of how terrible life is to become.

UNLIKELY CANDIDATE

ALCOHOLIC

_____

Answers to puzzles on the previous page

Learning Lines: L B "Jeff" Jefferies (Jimmy Stewart), *Rear Window* (1954).
Dicey Arithmetic: The signs are times, minus and plus.
Balancing The Scales: 9.

Patchwork:

2	3	1	4	5	6	7
7	1	3	2	6	4	5
4	5	6	7	1	2	3
5	6	4	3	2	7	1
1	4	5	6	7	3	2
3	2	7	1	4	5	6
6	7	2	5	3	1	4

BROKEN-HEARTED

Don't be half-hearted in your attempts to get these couples back together again! Match both sides of each heart, to reveal their names.

___ & ___   ___ & ___   ___ & ___

___ & ___   ___ & ___   ___ & ___

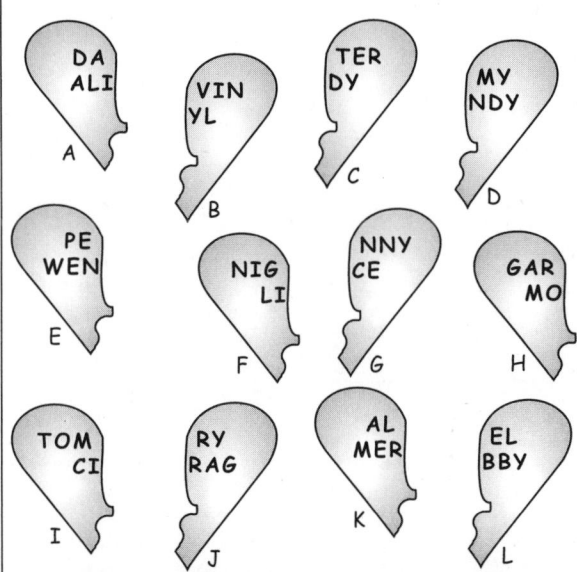

DA ALI — A

VIN YL — B

TER DY — C

MY NDY — D

PE WEN — E

NIG LI — F

NNY CE — G

GAR MO — H

TOM CI — I

RY RAG — J

AL MER — K

EL BBY — L

CLOCKWORDS

It's a race against the clock…
How many common words of three or more different letters can you make from those on the clockface (without using plurals, proper nouns or abbreviations) in ten minutes? All words must contain BOTH the letters indicated by the hands on the clock.

NUMB-SKULL

Fit the listed numbers into the grid, crossword-fashion.

2 digits	673
12	771
25	888
34	
41	**4 digits**
45	2341
56	4605
59	6321
64	7645
65	9871
90	
	5 digits
	44405
3 digits	85647
228	86452
407	
461	**6 digits**
496	355367
512	
624	**7 digits**
654	7654453

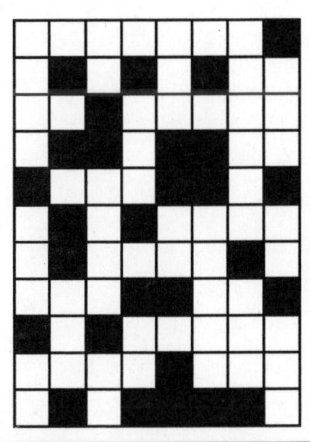

TODAY'S GREATEST ACHIEVEMENT

No accidents ☐

A tidy desk ☐

Saying the right things ☐

BRIEF SURVIVAL GUIDE

STARTING A NEW JOB:

1 Aim to get there on the specified day
2 Try to remember what you are supposed to be doing
3 Don't wear sequins or feathers (unless you are a stripper)

Answers to puzzles on the previous page

Dice-Section:

C	A	T	T	L	E
B	E	H	I	N	D
S	C	H	O	O	L
T	O	M	A	T	O
D	R	E	A	M	S
A	N	S	W	E	R

Thin Dividing Lines:

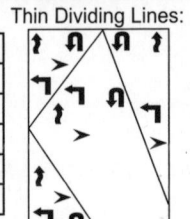

216

TWO DOWN

Fit five of the seven listed words into the Across rows in the grid, so that the other two words read down the shaded columns numbered 2 and 3.

AWARE   BALSA
BREAD   JERKY
STEAK   SWOTS
     TAPER

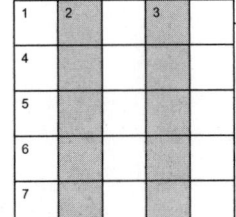

STARTING LINE

Which three letter word can be placed at the start, to form three seven-letter words?

FUME
JURY
USED

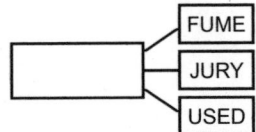

ODD ONE OUT

Which one is different to the rest?

THE TANGLED TRAIL

Which child is holding the string attached to the present?

SECRET MISSION

Your secret mission (should you choose to accept it) is:

To say "Yes!" but look doubtful every time someone asks you for anything.

NAME THAT SONG

We give you the first line, you name the song:

Well, hurry up, hurry up, here we go

Song: _____

Answers to puzzles on the previous page

Broken-Hearted: A and G, E and C, F and L, H and J, I and D, K and B.

Numb-Skull:

7	6	5	4	4	5	3
6		9		9		5	6
4	5		8	6	4	5	2
5			8			3	4
	2	2	8			6	
6		3		9	8	7	1
5		4	6	0	5		2
4	6	1			6	4	
	7		4	4	4	0	5
6	3	2	1		7	7	1
5		5					2

TONGUE TWISTER

Get your tongue around this one, if you can!

You've no need to light a night-light,

On a light night like tonight.

For a night-light's light's a slight light,

And tonight's a night that's light.

When a night's light, like tonight's light,

Then it's really not quite right,

To light night-lights with their slight lights,

On a light night like tonight.

PAIR SHAPES

In the box below there are shapes in three different colours, black, white and grey. Any shape may have been rotated, but can you see which is the only shape to appear exactly twice in exactly the same colour?

THOUGHT FOR THE DAY

Other people are quite dreadful. The only possible society is oneself.

Oscar Wilde

THE WHOLE PICTURE

Can you finish this picture?

MASS HYSTERIAS

Today we are all going to:

Dye our hair a colour from the rainbow spectrum.

JIGSAW CROSSWORD

Fit the blocks into the empty grid to form a complete crossword which, when finished, will be symmetrical, similar to the example seen here:

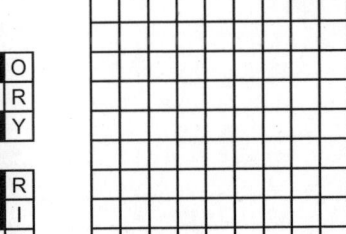

SWEET BAD MUSIC

So who on earth was responsible for this lyric?

Sure as Kilimanjaro rises like Olympus above the Serengeti,
I seek to cure what's deep inside.

Answers to puzzles on the previous page

Name That Song: *Rockin' All Over The World*, Status Quo.
Starting Line: PER.
Two Down: Across: 1 Balsa, 4 Swots, 5 Taper, 6 Bread, 7 Jerky. Down: 2 Aware, 3 Steak.
Odd One Out: E – A spot is missing just below the saddle.
The Tangled Trail: B.

218

WHATEVER NEXT?

Which of the numbered alternatives comes next in this sequence:

A	E	D	H	G	K
J	N	M	Q	P	?

1	2
S	V

3	4
T	U

WORDWHEEL

Using only the letters in the Wordwheel, you have ten minutes to find as many words as possible, none of which may be plurals, foreign words or proper nouns. Each word must be of three letters or more, all must contain the central letter and letters can only be used once in every word. There is at least one nine-letter word in the wheel.

Nine-letter word: _____

Wheel letters: D, C, H, B, A, E, K, O (centre: K)

WAYS TO PASS THE TIME

Copying ☐

Changing ☐

Collecting ☐

PROVERBS & SAYINGS

The letters on the tiles were once all in place, but dropped out, falling in a straight line into the lower grid. Some tiles dropped earlier than others, so those on the lowest row aren't all from the same row in the grid above. Can you put them back into position in order to reveal a well-known proverb or saying?

G	F			H								
I	I	T	C	O	U	T		A			T	H
K	T	A	N	O	E	N	H	E	F	H	O	A	E
S	E	T	Y	D	U	T	C	O	N	N	E	T	T

WHERE ON EARTH?

Where on earth is Dikshit?

Answer: _____

Answers to puzzles on the previous page

Sweet Bad Music: Toto, *Africa.*

Pair Shapes:

Jigsaw Crossword:

P	I	T	C	H		P		S
			E		E	X	A	C	T
E	R	R	O	R		R		U
X		R		O	F	T	E	N
P		I			I			N
E	N	T	E	R		C		E
N		O		O	I	L	E	D
S	C	R	U	B		E		
E		Y		E	A	S	E	L

MATCH THAT

Remove one match to leave a square.

GET THE LOOK

Make the face:

CRAZY

GET THE LEADER

Can you unscramble the anagram to reveal the leader?

Old, CIA frets

Answer: _____

AMAZING

Can you work your way from the entrance at the top to the exit at the bottom of this maze?

WEATHER for OPTIMISTS

Today the weather will be:

Strong winds and cold temperatures make it a perfect day to wrap up warm and take a healthy stroll.

WORDS TO REMEMBER

With which company or organisation or product do you associate this slogan?

"We try harder."

THINK ABOUT IT!

Can you picture this animal?

A dingaroo

JOIN THE DOTS

Answers to puzzles on the previous page

Where On Earth? India.
Wordwheel: The nine-letter word is BLOCKHEAD.
Proverbs & Sayings: If you cannot stand the heat get out of the kitchen.
Whatever Next? 3 – count four places forward in the alphabet, then one place back, then four places forward, then one place back, etc.

GOOD IMPRESSIONS

Can you pair up these door keys with the impressions of their ends?

1 6
2 5
3 4

a   b

c   d

e   f

WORDSEARCH

Can you find all of the listed rivers in the grid below? Words may run in either a forwards or backwards direction, horizontally, vertically or diagonally, but always in a straight, uninterrupted line.

AMAZON
COLORADO
CONGO
DANUBE
DARLING
ELBE
GANGES
HUANG HE
HUDSON
INDUS
JORDAN

```
O G N O C D A L U T S I V
N I A G A R A J D U P Z J
Y Y A N G T Z E D P P E N
Z A U I G J E N I H R B O
M B R L O E I S R N N M S
E F I R U O S S I M S A D
K C D A U I U L O C H Z U
O A W D S M E H G N A U H
N R P S T L A W R E N C E
G E I Z N E K C A M N Z L
T M N A M A Z O N W O D B
F F C O L O R A D O N K E
R E G I N I Z S E M A H T
```

MACKENZIE   NIAGARA
MEKONG   NIGER   ST LAWRENCE
MISSISSIPPI   NILE   THAMES
MISSOURI   RHINE   VISTULA
MURRAY   RIO GRANDE   YANGTZE
               SHANNON   ZAMBEZI

WORD LADDER

Change one letter at a time (but not the position of any letter) to make a new word – and move from the word at the top of the ladder to the word at the bottom using the exact number of rungs provided.

B R O W N

B R E A D

NAMED AND SHAMED

Worst song

_____

Worst book

_____

Worst artwork

REAL WORDS

Which is the real word?

TATTERNASTICY ☐

TATTERMECTIOUS ☐

TATTERDEMALION ☐

Answers to puzzles on the previous page

Get The Leader: Fidel Castro.
Match That: 9 = 3 squared.
Words To Remember: Avis.

Amazing:

221

CHARACTER ASSIGNATION

Fill in the answers to the clues, across the grid. Then read down the diagonal line of eight squares, to reveal:
A character from William Shakespeare's *The Tempest*.

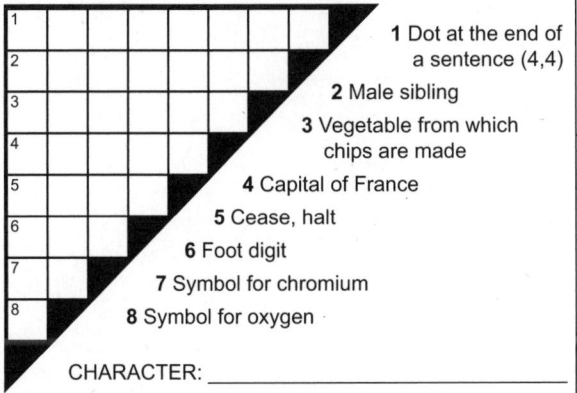

1 Dot at the end of a sentence (4,4)
2 Male sibling
3 Vegetable from which chips are made
4 Capital of France
5 Cease, halt
6 Foot digit
7 Symbol for chromium
8 Symbol for oxygen

CHARACTER: _____

DOMINADDITION

Can you place the remaining dominoes in their correct positions, so that the total number of spots in each of the four rows and five columns equals the sum at the end of that row or column?

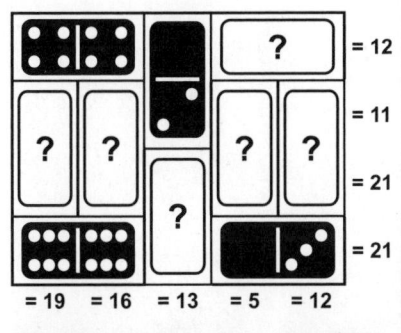

= 12
= 11
= 21
= 21

= 19   = 16   = 13   = 5   = 12

Devise an Oriental-looking sign for your mum.

TOM JONES

-v-

ELVIS PRESLEY

BOX CLEVER

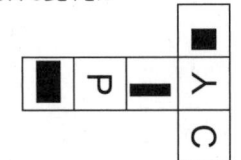
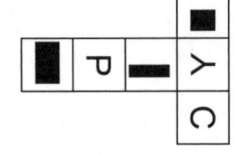

When the above is folded to form a cube, which one of the following can be produced?

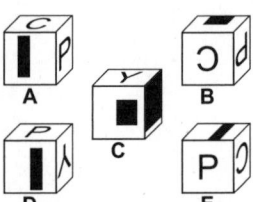

A   B   C   D   E

PICK 'N' MIX

Choose three words to describe your group of friends:

Idiots   Trendy
Mates   Nerds
Spiteful   Laughable
Malicious   Cool
Caring   Supportive

DO YOU KNOW...

...what happened on this date?

25 December 1223

Answers to puzzles on the previous page

Real Words: Tatterdemalion. A tattered or ragged person.
Word Ladder: One solution is BROWN, crown, croon, crook, brook, brood, broad, BREAD.
Good Impressions: 1f, 2d, 3c, 4e, 5a, 6b.

SNAKES & LADDERS

This is a standard game, so when you land at the foot of a ladder, you climb it; and when you land on the head of a snake, you slide down its tail. You need to throw an exact number to land on 100 to win – counting backwards if you don't, eg if you land on 98 and throw a five, you will end up on 97. The dice is thrown for you and always lands in this recurring order: 3, 2, 6, 5, 1, 4, so you can start by immediately placing your counter on square 3. Good luck – hope you win!

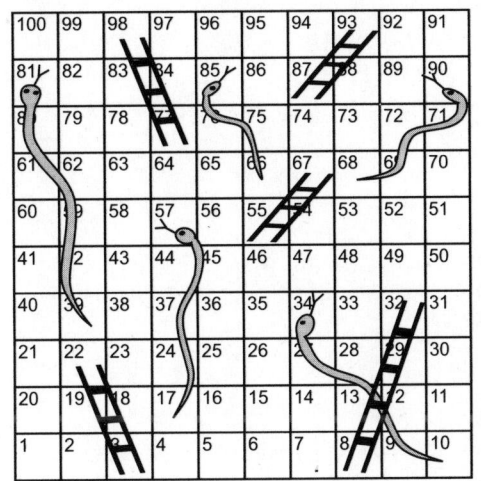

MISSING LETTERS

One letter of the alphabet is missing from each box. Find them all and place them in the order of the numbered boxes to reveal a six-letter word.

Word: _____

1	2	3
KAZVG	JTXAP	HMTYA
SLQFB	YQBLF	GLSEU
JMECP	ZGRMC	PCFIO
DUNXH	DWUSH	ZQDVJ
YTIWO	INKVE	KRWXN

4	5	6
RPCZO	OVCGJ	KYZQB
QHVGL	BPAKF	CPLRJ
DEWXK	LUYZE	SDXHM
YITAN	HMDIR	IOGEW
SBJFM	NWTXQ	NUAFV

USE YOUR IMAGINATION

Can you fill each of these boxes with a different sandwich filling?

PLACE YOUR BETS

_____'s tie today will be:

Multicoloured, crazy-patterned ☐

Possibly pink or yellow ☐

A lovely velvet bow ☐

COUPLINGS

Apart from two, every word listed below can be coupled with one of the others to make another word or phrase. Rearrange the letters of the two which can't be paired together, to form one word, the name of a country.

1 BEEF	2 FORE
3 WHITE	4 SOUR
5 LIGHTER	6 ANGINA
7 HEAD	8 FIRE
9 WEDDING	10 STAGE
11 CENTRE	12 SHAFT
13 BURGER	14 GRAPES

Answer: _____

LETTER TRACKER

Begin in the central shaded square and follow a continuous path which will track from square to square, up, down and sideways, but never diagonally.

Your trail should cover every letter once only, in order to find:

Eighteen calendrical words.

A	D	R	E	T	N	U	S	S	A	M
Y	S	W	E	N	D	A	Y	A	U	T
D	E	N	D	I	W	N	M	U	T	S
E	I	D	A	Y	W	I	N	H	R	I
C	R	F	O	N	D	A	T	C	Y	A
E	R	Y	M	G	S	Y	E	R	T	D
M	A	U	N	N	P	E	T	E	H	S
B	E	R	A	I	R	A	S	R	U	R
T	C	O	J	H	C	R	A	M	J	U
O	R	F	R	U	Y	S	U	R	Y	L
B	E	E	B	A	R	A	T	D	A	Y

WORDFILLER

Can you place all the listed words into the grid below?

3 letters	
ERA	EARLY
HIE	HOURS
NOW	PULSE
	SPEED
4 letters	TODAY
LENT	WEEKS
RATE	
YEAR	6 letters
	ANNUAL
5 letters	DECADE
ALARM	
APRIL	7 letters
	DYNASTY

WEATHER for PESSIMISTS

Today the weather will be:

Hailstones big enough to smash up your house and no sunshine.

WHAT DOES IT MEAN?

What is the meaning of the word

TREGETOUR

Answer: _____

_____

Answers to puzzles on the previous page

Pre-Fame Name Game: Boy George.
Missing Letters: ROBUST.

PYRAMID PLUS

Every brick in this pyramid contains a number which is the sum of the two numbers below it, so that F=A+B, etc. No two bricks contain the same number, or just a zero, so work out the missing numbers!

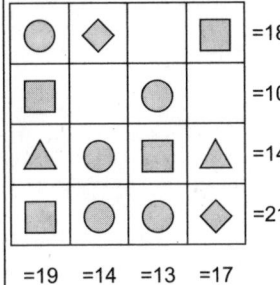

O=120

M=   N=

J=38   K=   L=26

F=   G=   H=7   I=

A=   B=15   C=   D=   E=

SYMBOLISM

What whole number value between 1 and 9 should be allocated to each different symbol in order to reach the sum totals shown at the end of each row and column?

○	◇		■	=18
■		○		=10
△	○	■	△	=14
■	○	○	◇	=21

=19   =14   =13   =17

TODAY'S TEMPERATURE

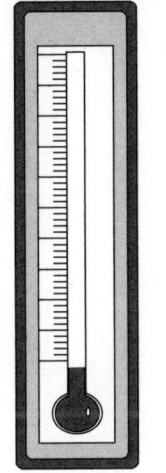

EYE-SPY

I spy with my little eye something beginning with:

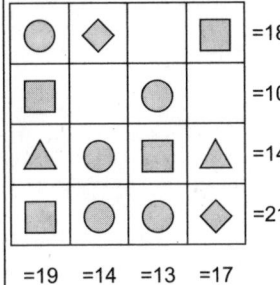

M

DICEY ARITHMETIC

Using three of the arithmetical signs ÷, −, x and +, can you achieve the correct total? Afterwards, see if you can spot an alternative way to do this.

    =

GET THE LOOK

Make the face:

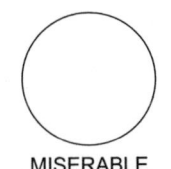

MISERABLE

LEARNING LINES

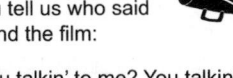

We give you a line, you tell us who said it and the film:

"You talkin' to me? You talkin' to me? You talkin' to me? Then who the hell else are you talkin' to?"

225

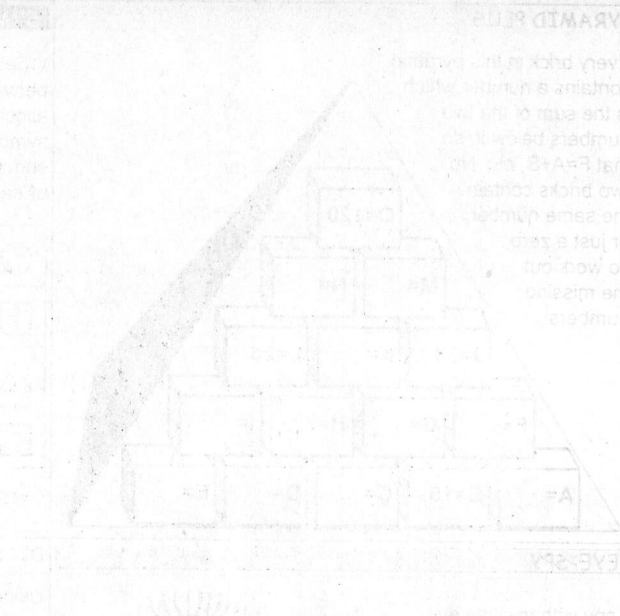

Best songs for relaxing with a bar of chocolate:

1 _____
_____

2 _____
_____

3 _____
_____

4 _____
_____

5 _____
_____

TWO DOWN

Fit five of the seven listed words into the Across rows in the grid, so that the other two words read down the shaded columns numbered 2 and 3.

BRIDE   LABEL
LAURA   NEEDY
PLANE   RULER
    SATYR

1	2		3	
4				
5				
6				
7				

MIRROR WRITING

Write this word upside down:

POSTMAN

_____

FOR SALE

This is worth the asking price

of _____ because it

once belonged to _____

_____,

who used it for _____

_____

WAYS TO PASS THE TIME

Laughing ☐

Crying ☐

Looking ☐

WHATEVER YOU DO, don't even THINK about...

Bare feet on sticky floors

Bad breath

Sunburn

PATCHWORK

Fit the numbers 1, 2, 3, 4, 5, 6 and 7 into the grid below, so that every horizontal row, every vertical column and the two long diagonal lines of six smaller squares contain six different numbers. Some are already in place.

	6		5		2	
3		4				5
				5		
			3	6	4	
		7				
4						1
	7			2	3	

MY FAVOURITE THINGS

These are a few of my favourite things:

My favourite flower is:

_____

My favourite tree is:

_____

My favourite time of day is:

_____

My favourite season of the year is:

_____

Answers to puzzles on the previous page

Learning Lines: Travis Bickle (Robert De Niro), *Taxi Driver* (1976).
Dicey Arithmetic: The signs are times, divide and plus or divide, plus and minus.
Symbolism: Circle=3, Diamond=8, Square=7, Triangle=2.
Pyramid Plus: A=2, B=15, C=6, D=1, E=18, F=17, G=21, H=7, I=19, J=38, K=28, L=26, M=66, N=54, O=120.

WHATEVER NEXT?

Which of the numbered alternatives comes next in this sequence:

A	D	B	F	D	I
G	M	K	R	P	?

1	2
X	U

3	4
V	Q

DICE-SECTION

Printed onto every one of the six numbered dice below are six letters (one per side), which can be rearranged to form the answer to each clue; however, some sides are invisible to you. Use the clues and write every answer into the grid. When correctly filled, the letters in the shaded squares, reading in the order 1 to 6, will spell out a man's name.

Yell, as with fear

Walk like a duck

Pull-out container (for socks, eg)

Dark red wine

Woman in charge of a hospital

Pool of rainwater

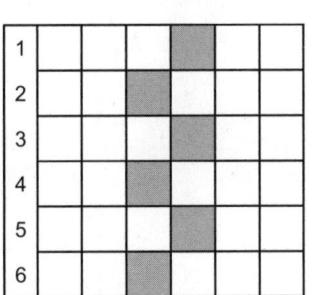

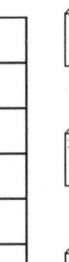

WEATHER for OPTIMISTS

Today the weather will be:

Mist and drizzle later but, before this, plenty of time to throw that barbecue if you hurry!

BRIEF SURVIVAL GUIDE

BUYING CLOTHES:

1 Consider colour
2 Be honest about your size and shape (however hard this may be)
3 Don't listen to shop assistants: they may be money-grabbing and spiteful

Answers to puzzles on the previous page

Two Down: Across: 1 Plane, 4 Label, 5 Ruler, 6 Bride, 7 Satyr. Down: 2 Laura, 3 Needy.

Patchwork:

7	6	3	5	1	2	4
3	1	4	2	7	6	5
6	4	2	1	5	7	3
2	5	1	3	6	4	7
5	3	7	6	4	1	2
4	2	6	7	3	5	1
1	7	5	4	2	3	6

COMPLETE THIS LIMERICK:

When the landlord called out "Come on, TIME!"

Rachel downed her twelfth vodka and lime

Staggered towards the door

But then fell to the floor

_____

CAPITALS

The capital of

AFGHANISTAN

is:

_____

EGG TIMER

Can you complete this puzzle in the time it takes to boil an egg? The answers to the clues are anagrams of the words immediately above and below, plus or minus a letter.

1 Endorse
2 Put forth shoots
3 Athletic game
4 Blemish on the skin
5 Writers of verse
6 Sent by mail
7 Sediment

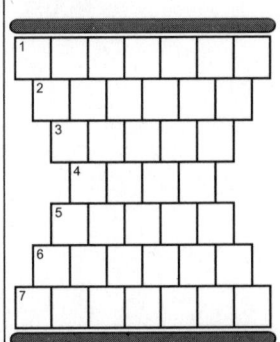

ON TARGET

The answers to the clues read from the outer circle to the centre, all ending with the same letter. When you've finished, the letters in the shaded ring will give a word.

1 Father's brother

2 Orange-yellow colour

3 Military blockade

4 Largest of the Greek islands

5 One of the five senses

6 Portion

TONGUE TWISTER

Get your tongue around this one, if you can!

In sifting a sieve full of unsifted thistles, Theophilus Thistle, the successful thistle-sifter, thrust three thousand thistles through the thick of his thumb. Now if Theophilus Thistle, the successful thistle-sifter, in sifting a sieve full of unsifted thistles, thrust three thousand thistles through the thick of his thumb, see that thou, in sifting a sieve full of unsifted thistles, thrust not three thousand thistles through the thick of thy thumb. Success to the successful thistle-sifter!

MASS HYSTERIAS

Today we are all going to:

Leap over walls rather than use the gates.

SECRET MISSION

Your secret mission (should you choose to accept it) is:

To look at everyone you know as if you've never met them.

Answers to puzzles on the previous page

Whatever Next? 1 – work through the alphabet counting as follows: three places forward (to D), two back (to B), four forward (to F), two back (to D), five forward (to I), two back (to G), six forward (to M), two back (to K), seven forward (to R), two back (to P), then eight forward to X.

Dice-Section:

S	C	R	E	A	M
W	A	D	D	L	E
D	R	A	W	E	R
C	L	A	R	E	T
M	A	T	R	O	N
P	U	D	D	L	E

BERMUDA TRIANGLE

Travel through the 'Bermuda Triangle' by visiting one room at a time and collecting a letter from each. You can enter the outside passageway as often as you like, but can only visit each room once. When you've completed your tour, rearrange the fifteen letters to spell out a word.

DOMINOLOGICAL

What is the value of the question mark?

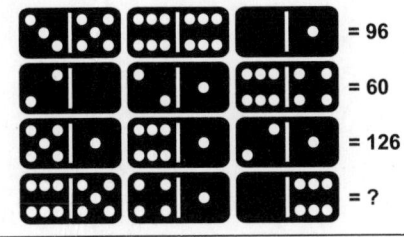

= 96

= 60

= 126

= ?

WORDWHEEL

Using only the letters in the Wordwheel, you have ten minutes to find as many words as possible, none of which may be plurals, foreign words or proper nouns. Each word must be of three letters or more, all must contain the central letter and letters can only be used once in every word. There is at least one nine-letter word in the wheel.

Nine-letter word: _____

G C
R H
N L
E A
(central: A)

TOP TEN

OVERCOAT ☐
JACKET ☐
PONCHO ☐
CLOAK ☐
PARKA ☐
MAC ☐
WINDCHEATER ☐
GILET ☐
ANORAK ☐
CAPE ☐

TODAY'S GREATEST ACHIEVEMENT

Waking before noon ☐

Wearing appropriate footwear ☐

Answers for everything ☐

JIGSAW CROSSWORD

Fit the blocks into the empty grid to form a complete crossword which, when finished, will be symmetrical, similar to the example seen here:

SPOT THE BALL

Place a cross where you imagine the centre of the ball to be.

HEXAGONY

Can you place the hexagons in the grid, so that where any triangle touches another along a straight line, the contents of both are the same? One triangle is already filled.

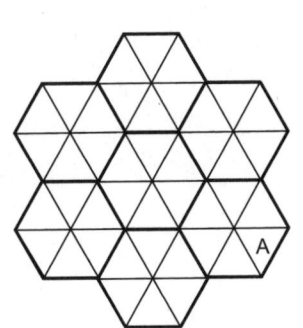

BALANCING THE SCALES

Given that scales A and B balance perfectly, how many squares are needed to balance scale C?

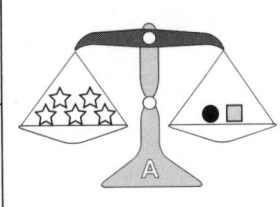

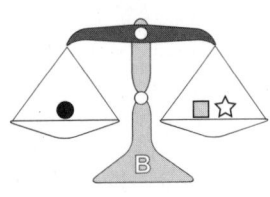

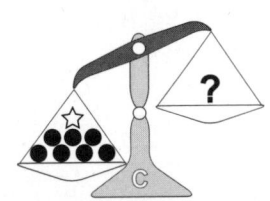

THE TANGLED TRAIL

Which child is holding the string attached to the balloon?

A   B   C

WHERE ON EARTH ?

Where on earth is Dunnydoo?

Answer: _____

EXCUSES FOR

EXCUSES FOR

Children's television:

_____
_____
_____
_____
_____

Answers to puzzles on the previous page

Wordwheel: The nine-letter word is ARCHANGEL.
Bermuda Triangle: The word is HOSPITALISATION.
Dominological: 330 – multiply the total number of spots on the first domino by the total number of spots on the second, then multiply this by the total number of spots on the third domino.

Jigsaw Crossword:

TOTAL CONCENTRATION

Can you fill in the missing numbers so that each row, each column and the two long diagonal lines meet the totals given?

							317
55	44		49	16		73	367
21	14	75		42		25	219
25	11	71		50	55	76	367
78	55		64	73	57	19	357
53	33	72		14	45		288
	3	42	15	63	65		265
		21	62		50	11	224
320	177	334	334	307	401	214	294

DESIGN YOUR OWN

Roof terrace

POTATOE OR POTATO?

PAVILION

OR

PAVILLION

MATCH THAT

Remove two matches and leave one.

STARTING LINE

Which three letter word can be placed at the start, to form three seven-letter words?

RANT

MING

FARE

THIS WEEK'S PHOBIAS

Phronemophobia – Fear of thinking
Siderophobia – Fear of stars
Xanthophobia – Fear of the colour yellow

NAME THAT SONG

We give you the first line, you name the song:

Is it my imagination, or have I finally found something worth living for?

Song: _____

Answers to puzzles on the previous page

Where On Earth?
New South Wales, Australia.
Balancing The Scales: 11.
The Tangled Trail: Child B.

Hexagony:

MISSING LINKS

Which word links the one on the left with the one on the right? We've done the first one, and when you've finished them all, the first letters of the link words will spell the name of a river.

FRUIT	**CAKE**	STAND
MOVE		HEAD
FORE		PLATE
SIDE		WAY
PASS		GOING

MY NEXT MISTAKE

What

Where

Why

WORDSEARCH

Can you find all of the listed volcanoes in the grid below? Words may run in either a forwards or backwards direction, horizontally, vertically or diagonally, but always in a straight, uninterrupted line.

ACATENANGO

BILIRAN

ETNA

FANTALE

FUJI

HARGY

ISABELA

KETOI

KILIMANJARO

```
A C A T E N A N G O I L D
K E T N A L B M I H T L N
E I Q A E I A L C E A O A
T W L B L U O N P S K N L
O S A I N B A E S L T G S
I S R A M I T E E F E V I
I A L O L A N G A O H A E
N O R A C P N N I A S L T
A T D O E A T J R H U L I
S U P A R A U G A U A E H
W O K W L F Y B Y R P Y W
P Z Y E L L O W S T O N E
B O A I R A M A T N A S P
```

LASSEN PEAK	PAUSHETKA	WHITE ISLAND
LONG VALLEY	POPOCATEPETL	WRANGEL
MAUNA LOA	SANTA MARIA	WUDALIANCHI
OAHU	STROMBOLI	YELLOWSTONE

A IS TO B

A is to B

as C is to

D E

F G

PICK 'N' MIX

Choose three words to describe your dress sense:

Criminal	Tarty
Trendy	Inimitable
Ridiculous	Cool
Stylish	Casual
Suspicious	Tasteful

PRE-FAME NAME GAME

By what name do we know this famous person?

Frances Gumm

Answers to puzzles on the previous page	
Name That Song: *Cigarettes And Alcohol*, Oasis. Starting Line: WAR. Total Concentration: From left to right, top to bottom, the missing numbers are: 42, 88, 1, 41, 79, 11, 64, 7, 74, 3, 14, 17 and 49. Potatoe or Potato? Pavilion.	Match That: (one over one)

CODEWORD

This is a crossword puzzle in code. Every number represents a different letter of the alphabet and this number remains the same throughout the puzzle. Use the check-box to keep a track on your progress.

6	19	24	13	21	19	■	10 (A)	■	16
18	■	15	■	13	■	8	4 (N)	22	13	26
26	17	19	10	3	10	4	24 (T)	■	24
10	■	25	■	9	■	24	■	26	19	2
3	8	6	5	8	1	10	24	19	21
3	■	12	■	10	■	4	■	15	■	10
■	1	19	23	12	23	1	13	16	10	12
2	10	21	■	13	■	12	■	19	■	13
■	25	■	10	20	20	13	7	13	4	1
20	8	3	3	18	■	4	■	14	■	4
■	24	■	11	■	23	1	15	19	3	3

1	2	3	4	5	6	7	8	9	10	11	12	13

14	15	16	17	18	19	20	21	22	23	24	25	26

WHO IS HE?

Who is the man in the picture, given that the viewer makes a true statement?

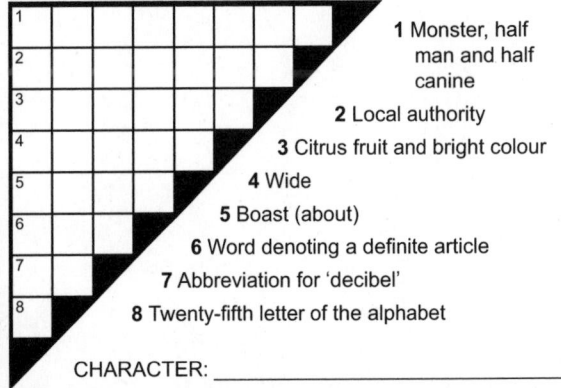

> Brothers and sisters have I none, but that man's father is my father's son.

CHARACTER ASSIGNATION

Fill in the answers to the clues, across the grid. Then read down the diagonal line of eight squares, to reveal:
A character from Charles Dickens' *Our Mutual Friend*.

1 Monster, half man and half canine

2 Local authority

3 Citrus fruit and bright colour

4 Wide

5 Boast (about)

6 Word denoting a definite article

7 Abbreviation for 'decibel'

8 Twenty-fifth letter of the alphabet

CHARACTER: _____

GET THE LOOK

Make the face:

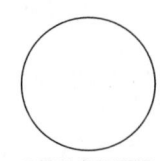

DEVASTATED

WHO AM I?

I lead, sir.

I am:

_____

UNLIKELY CANDIDATES

WEDDING OF THE YEAR

_____

&

_____

OUT OF SIGHT

What is the sum total of the spots on the hidden faces of these three dice?

LETTER TRACKER

Begin in the central shaded square and follow a continuous path which will track from square to square, up, down and sideways, but never diagonally.

Your trail should cover every letter once only, in order to find:

Eighteen fruits and nuts.

N	D	I	N	C	A	E	A	R	Y	R
A	A	R	P	E	N	P	N	A	B	R
M	I	L	O	N	O	M	A	C	H	E
E	V	E	L	O	N	L	N	T	T	N
R	Y	M	O	L	D	A	A	U	R	E
R	E	N	G	A	W	A	L	N	E	C
E	A	I	P	N	Y	F	I	L	B	T
B	P	P	T	B	R	G	N	E	N	A
L	I	L	I	E	R	E	A	H	I	R
E	B	E	U	E	P	G	R	I	C	K
M	I	L	R	F	A	R	O	Y	R	O

STARTER LETTER

Write down one each of the listed items, all of which must begin with the starter letter:

S

Country	
Tree	
Boy's name	
Girl's name	
River	
City	
Animal	
Make of car	
Drink	

MISSING LETTERS

One letter of the alphabet is missing from each box. Find them all and place them in the order of the numbered boxes to reveal a six-letter word.

Word: _____

```
    1          2          3
U Z E I R   H M T E Y   O J A I V
N W T X Q   G L S U B   P B W T F
A C G J V   P C F I O   C X Q K M
O P K Y S   Z Q D V J   G Y N D L
H D B L F   K R W X N   E Z S H U

    4          5          6
D M W H J   K Y Z Q B   Y L P X W
T E P Y B   N U A F V   M Z D G K
G U X F O   C P L R J   F E C J Q
Z V A S N   S D X H M   I O U B V
L Q C R I   I T O G W   N A H S R
```

NAMED AND SHAMED

Biggest ego

_____

Biggest fantasist

_____

Biggest beer goggles

REAL WORDS

Which is the real word?

TERMAGANT ☐

TERMIGENTIOUS ☐

TERMAGENACITY ☐

234

WORD LADDER

Change one letter at a time (but not the position of any letter) to make a new word – and move from the word at the top of the ladder to the word at the bottom using the exact number of rungs provided.

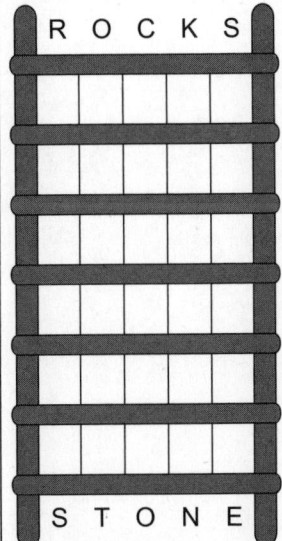

R O C K S

S T O N E

COUPLINGS

Apart from two, every word listed below can be coupled with one of the others to make another word or phrase. Rearrange the letters of the two which can't be paired together, to form one word, the name of a town in Hampshire, England.

1 TAPE	2 ALBERT
3 LAMP	4 KEEPER
5 NURSE	6 BINGO
7 SHADE	8 STEAKS
9 HOSPITAL	10 ZOO
11 DRIER	12 WORM
13 SPIN	14 EINSTEIN

Answer: _____

PROVERBS & SAYINGS

The letters on the tiles were once all in place, but dropped out, falling in a straight line into the lower grid. Some tiles dropped earlier than others, so those on the lowest row aren't all from the same row in the grid above. Can you put them back into position in order to reveal a well-known proverb or saying?

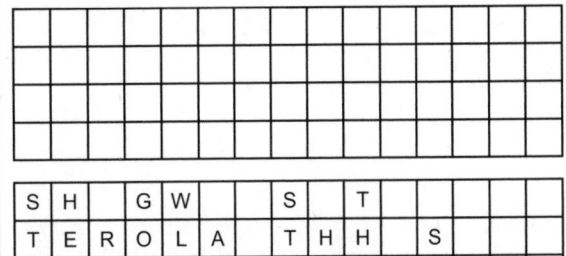

S	H		G	W			S		T		
T	E	R	O	L	A		T	H	H		S
I	N	O	U	L	D	S	N	O	O	E	L	I	E	S
P	H	O	P	L	E	S	W	O	N	O	U	S	V	E

CLOCKWORDS

It's a race against the clock…
How many common words of three or more different letters can you make from those on the clockface (without using plurals, proper nouns or abbreviations) in ten minutes? All words must contain BOTH the letters indicated by the hands on the clock.

TODAY'S GREATEST ACHIEVEMENT

Clean teeth ☐

Clean socks ☐

Clean head ☐

DO YOU KNOW…

…what happened on this date?

1 January 404

Answers to puzzles on the previous page

Real Words: Termagant. A harsh-tempered or overbearing woman.
Out Of Sight: 40.
Letter Tracker: Walnut, Cherry, Banana, Almond, Loganberry, Filbert, Nectarine, Hickory, Orange, Grapefruit, Pineapple, Lime, Bilberry, Melon, Olive, Mandarin, Pecan, Pear.
Missing Letters: MARKET.

A MATCHING PAIR

Mrs Ewers would like a matching pair of vases. Which two should she buy?

 A
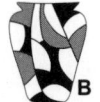 B

 C
 D

 E
 F

DOMINADDITION

Can you place the remaining dominoes in their correct positions, so that the total number of spots in each of the four rows and five columns equals the sum at the end of that row or column?

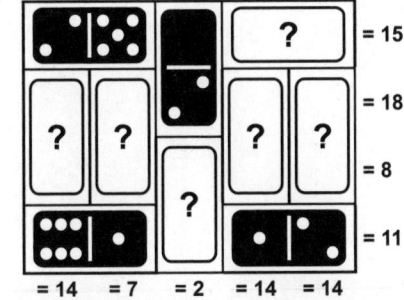

UNFINISHED PICTURE

Can you complete the left half of this picture?

TOP TEN

FOOTBALL

BASEBALL

TENNIS

HOCKEY

SKIING

SWIMMING

ATHLETICS

HORSE-RACING

WRESTLING

BOXING

SWEET BAD MUSIC

So who on earth was responsible for this lyric?

Some call me the gangster of love,
Some people call me Maurice.

DICEY ARITHMETIC

Using three of the arithmetical signs ÷, −, x and +, can you achieve the correct total?

    =

PYRAMID PLUS

Every brick in this pyramid contains a number which is the sum of the two numbers below it, so that F=A+B, etc. No two bricks contain the same number, or just a zero, so work out the missing numbers!

O=90

M=   N=

J=36   K=   L=14

F=   G=12   H=   I=

A=   B=   C=   D=5   E=

WORDS TO REMEMBER

With which company or organisation or product do you associate this slogan?

"The ultimate driving machine."

THINK ABOUT IT!

Can you picture this animal?

A chimpanda

MIRROR WRITING

Write this word upside down:

RAINING

_____

SYMBOLISM

What whole number value between 1 and 9 should be allocated to each different symbol in order to reach the sum totals shown at the end of each row and column?

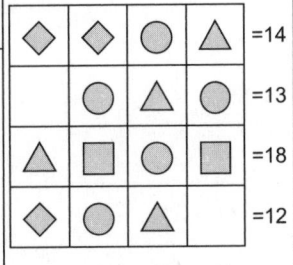

=14
=13
=18
=12

=11 =12 =20 =14

SUM TOTAL

Place the digits 1-9, one per square, so that the sums are correct, according to the totals at the ends of the rows and columns. The calculations should be done in the order in which they appear, for example 6−2x5=20 should be read as 6−2(=4), then 4x5=20.

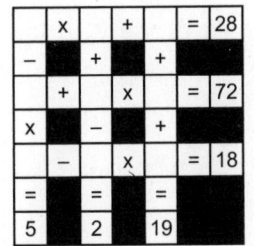

WHAT DOES IT MEAN?

What is the meaning of the word

WIDDERSHINS

Answer: _____

_____

Answers to puzzles on the previous page

Sweet Bad Music: Steve Miller, *The Joker*.
A Matching Pair: C and F.
Dicey Arithmetic: The signs are minus, plus and divide.

Dominaddition:

2	5	0	3	5
5	1	2	6	4
1	0	0	4	3
6	1	0	1	2

PAIR SHAPES

In the box below there are shapes in three different colours, black, white and grey. Any shape may have been rotated, but can you see which is the only shape to appear exactly twice in exactly the same colour?

IN YOUR OWN LANGUAGE

Devise an Oriental-looking sign for your own name.

JOIN THE DOTS

SUDOKU

Each heavily outlined box of nine smaller squares should contain the digits 1-9, as should every row of nine squares and every column of nine squares in the grid below. Only one number should be placed in every smaller square. Can you fill in the missing numbers?

	1			3		4	5	
			4		7			6
2		3			8			7
8					9			1
		4					7	3
7		6		2		5		
			8			6	3	
		1		7		8		
3	5		2		4			

TOP FIVE

Best songs for singing along to:

1 _____
_____

2 _____
_____

3 _____
_____

4 _____
_____

5 _____
_____

THOUGHT FOR THE DAY

One fool may maketh many.

LEARNING LINES

We give you a line, you tell us who said it and the film:

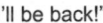

"I'll be back!"

Answers to puzzles on the previous page

What Does It Mean? In the contrary direction; going in the opposite direction to the course of the sun.
Symbolism: Circle=3, Diamond=2, Square=4, Triangle=7.
Words To Remember: BMW.
Pyramid Plus: A=15, B=9, C=3, D=5, E=1, F=24, G=12, H=8, I=6, J=36, K=20, L=14, M=56, N=34, O=90.

Sum Total:

8	x	3	+	4
−		+		+
7	+	1	x	9
x		−		+
5	−	2	x	6

TWO DOWN

Fit five of the seven listed words into the Across rows in the grid, so that the other two words read down the shaded columns numbered 2 and 3.

ARENA EASEL
RURAL SLOTH
TENET TRUTH
TUNER

1	2		3	
4				
5				
6				
7				

WORDWHEEL

Using only the letters in the Wordwheel, you have ten minutes to find as many words as possible, none of which may be plurals, foreign words or proper nouns. Each word must be of three letters or more, all must contain the central letter and letters can only be used once in every word. There is at least one nine-letter word in the wheel.

Nine-letter word: _____

Wheel letters: O, N, R, D, L, C, E, U (centre **S**)

MONEY, MONEY, MONEY

The

OGUIYA

is the currency of

_____

FOR SALE

This is worth the asking price

of _____ because it

once belonged to _____

_____ ,

who used it for _____

_____

WAYS TO PASS THE TIME

Simpering ☐

Smouldering ☐

Smoking ☐

JUST A WORD

Can you find 'JOB' hidden in the grid, wordsearch-style?

```
E J D R E T U B J I K A J
D O I J J O P R E S V O X
J U M V F R E T R J A E W
S C B I J U K M O P J B I
D E B J O M N E F O S I O
A E D Z X U I C B H I J L
```

SAY IT, DO IT, BE IT

Your word for today is:

GIVING

WEATHER for PESSIMISTS

Today the weather will be:

Very hot with cool breezes, stifling air quality and a huge storm to end.

GET THE LEADER

Can you unscramble the anagram to reveal the leader?

Old man, I charm all

Answer: _____

MASS HYSTERIAS

Today we are all going to:

Cut the nails on our left hand very short and grow the nails on our right very long.

BRIEF SURVIVAL GUIDE

DATING:
1 Aim to appear uncomplicated and carefree (at least for now)
2 Aim to appear attentive and interested (at least for now)
3 Aim to please (at least for now)

WATER WAYS

Here's a puzzle to test your skills! Fit the shapes into the grid so that the completed puzzle shows six six-letter rivers. Three letters are already in place, to get you off to a good start…

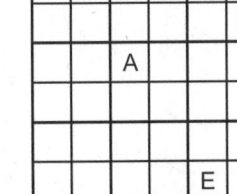

| A | M | | I | S |
| N | U | | E | S |

| E | S | | F | F |
| B | E | | A | Z |

| T | I | | E | Y | | T | H | | L | I | | G | R |
| G | A | | O | N | | D | A | | A | M | | N | G |

(Grid with N, A, E already placed)

ARRANGING THINGS

If you fit six of these seven words into the grid below, the word left over will appear reading down the shaded squares.

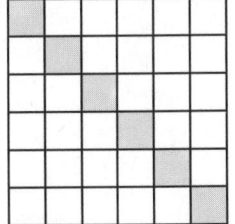

BOSNIA   BRAZIL
FRANCE   JORDAN
RUSSIA   RWANDA
      ZAMBIA

MY FAVOURITE THINGS

These are a few of my favourite things:

My favourite football team is:

_____

My favourite DJ is:

_____

My favourite film is:

_____

My favourite television programme is:

_____

PATCHWORK

Fit the numbers 1, 2, 3, 4, 5, 6 and 7 into the grid below, so that every horizontal row, every vertical column and the two long diagonal lines of six smaller squares contain six different numbers. Some are already in place.

		7			1	
	5		1			
3				6		
		5				2
	7		3			1
			2		6	
5	2			1		

EYE-SPY

I spy with my little eye something beginning with:

SHADOWLAND

Test your skills of observation. Only one of the five shadows is that of the pianist. Which one?

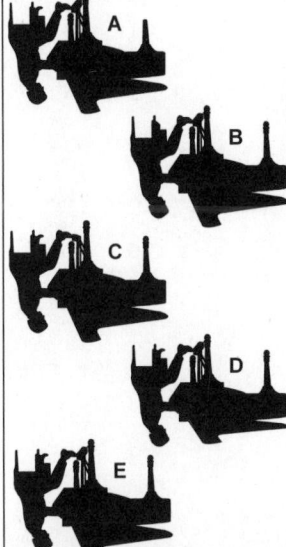

A

B

C

D

E

COMPLETE THIS LIMERICK:

There once was a gardener from Harrow

Who grew a magnificent marrow

He showed it to his wife

But she ran for her life

_____

HEXAGONY

Can you place the hexagons in the grid, so that where any triangle touches another along a straight line, the contents of both are the same? One triangle is already filled.

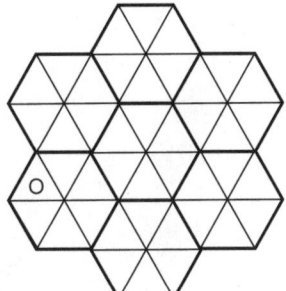

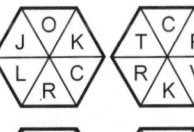

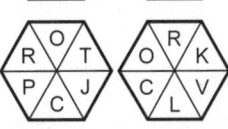

THIN DIVIDING LINES

Can you divide this grid into five sections of different shapes, each containing five different symbols?

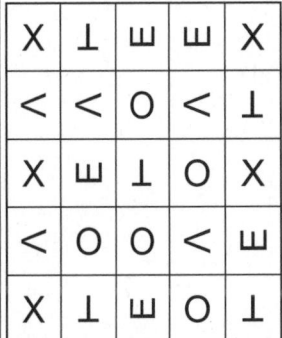

STARTING LINE

Which three letter word can be placed at the start, to form three seven-letter words?

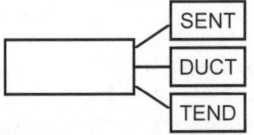

| SENT |
| DUCT |
| TEND |

WHATEVER YOU DO, don't even THINK about...

The smell of strong cheese

Travel sickness

Squeaky gates

WEATHER for OPTIMISTS

Today the weather will be:

Uneventful and grey, but at least it won't rain.

PRE-FAME NAME GAME

By what name do we know this famous person?

Issur Danielovitch Demsky

WORDFILLER

Can you place all the listed words into the grid below?

3 letters	5 letters
APE	CAMEL
CAT	DINGO
COW	
DOE	6 letters
DOG	WOMBAT
EWE	
OWL	7 letters
RAT	MACAQUE
	WALLABY
4 letters	9 letters
STAG	BANDICOOT
WOLF	CHAMELEON

USE YOUR IMAGINATION

Can you fill each of these boxes with a different fruit?

MISSING LETTERS

One letter of the alphabet is missing from each box. Find them all and place them in the order of the numbered boxes to reveal a six-letter word.

Word: _____

1	2	3
RYBLU	TJVAE	OYCGJ
VKQEF	KRUFP	BPKRS
MJGAP	BSLGX	HMDLA
CWHSO	HZOCQ	UZEIF
XIZTN	NYDMW	NWTXQ

4	5	6
JTXAP	HMTYA	OJAIV
YQBLF	GLSUB	PBWTF
ZGRMC	PCFIO	CXQKM
DWUSH	ZQDVJ	GYRDL
NVEKO	EKRWX	NZSHU

EXCUSES FOR

Not telephoning:

_____
_____
_____
_____

THE TANGLED TRAIL

Which of these anglers has landed the fish?

A   B   C

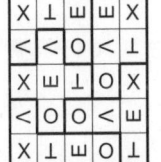

WHATEVER NEXT?

Which of the lettered alternatives comes next in this sequence:

| 14 | 17 | 12 | 15 | 10 | ? |

A	B
8	5

C	D
13	10

DICE-SECTION

Printed onto every one of the six numbered dice below are six letters (one per side), which can be rearranged to form the answer to each clue; however, some sides are invisible to you. Use the clues and write every answer into the grid. When correctly filled, the letters in the shaded squares, reading in the order 1 to 6, will spell out a woman's name.

Glass container

Make very happy

Type of fortified wine

Fold, pleat

Shut

Jacket worn as part of school uniform

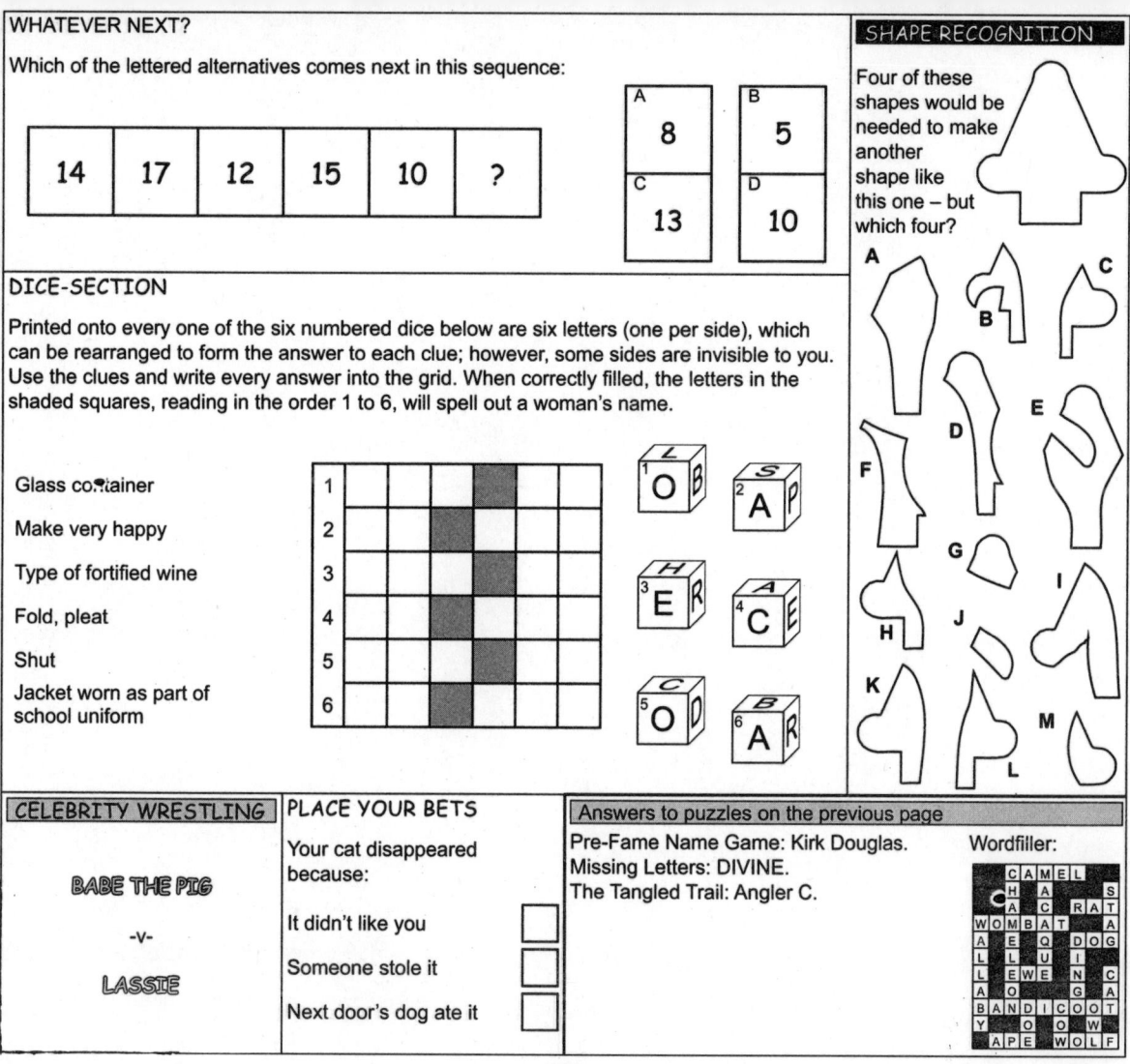

1 — L O B
2 — S A P
3 — H E R
4 — A C E
5 — C O D
6 — B A R

Four of these shapes would be needed to make another shape like this one – but which four?

A B C D E F G H I J K L M

CELEBRITY WRESTLING

BABE THE PIG

-v-

LASSIE

PLACE YOUR BETS

Your cat disappeared because:

It didn't like you ☐

Someone stole it ☐

Next door's dog ate it ☐

Answers to puzzles on the previous page

Pre-Fame Name Game: Kirk Douglas.
Missing Letters: DIVINE.
The Tangled Trail: Angler C.

Wordfiller:

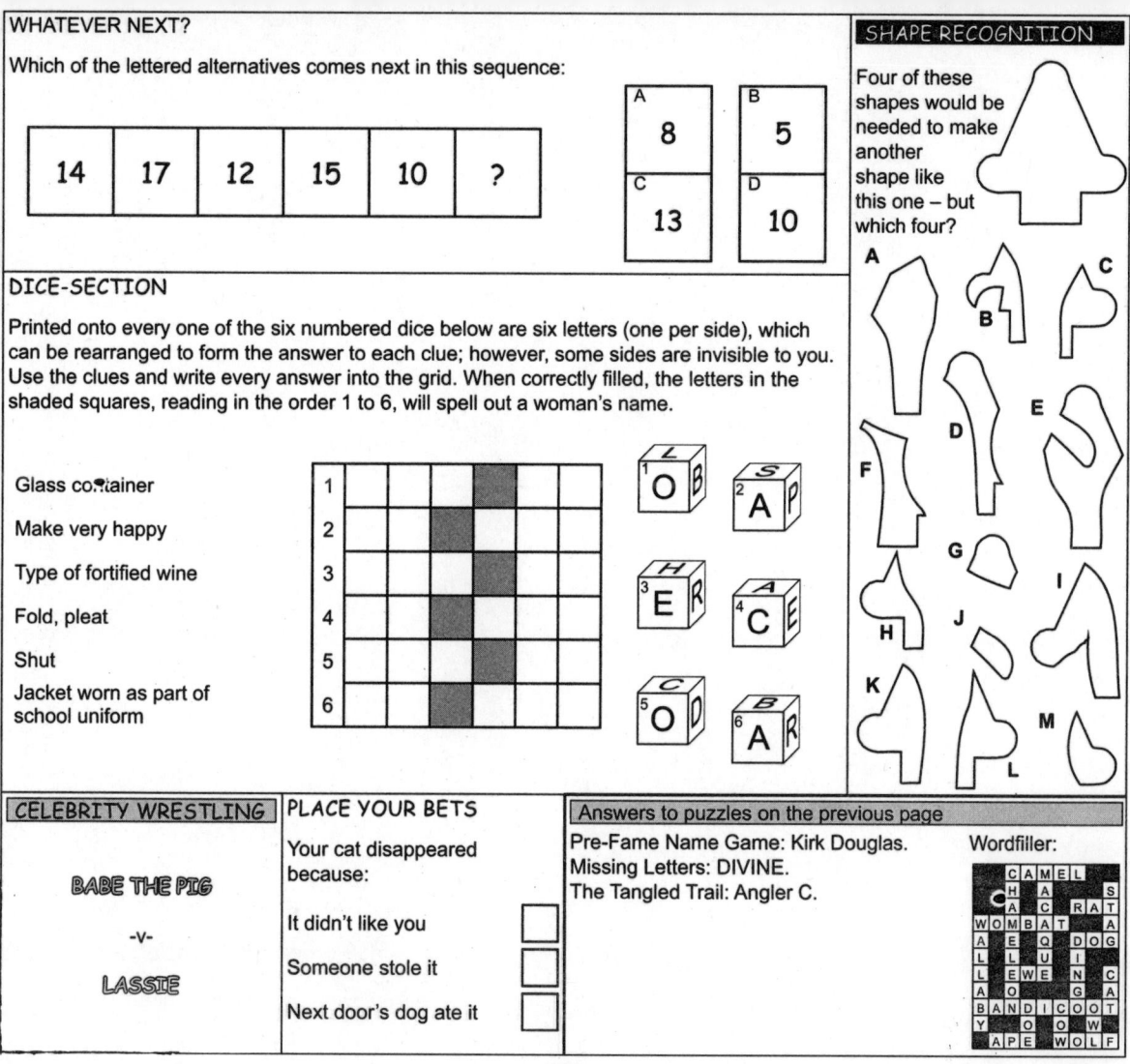

Begin in the central shaded square and follow a continuous path which will track from square to square, up, down and sideways, but never diagonally.

Your trail should cover every letter once only, in order to find:

Eighteen words relating to the weather.

A	H	E	L	O	N	R	A	I	L	B
I	T	E	S	W	S	D	Z	Z	L	E
L	D	W	E	R	S	C	H	A	B	A
W	O	O	C	E	R	R	M	N	G	E
N	S	H	A	S	O	O	L	I	R	E
P	T	U	S	T	F	T	H	G	B	E
O	S	N	N	Y	R	S	T	N	G	Z
U	I	M	H	T	E	D	U	I	N	Y
R	G	Y	U	N	D	Y	O	L	O	T
O	G	O	R	S	A	O	V	C	R	N
F	T	N	F	T	C	R	E	O	D	A

WORDSEARCH

Can you find all of the listed wedding words in the grid? Words may run in either a forwards or backwards direction, horizontally, vertically or diagonally, but always in a straight, uninterrupted line.

AISLE

BETROTHED

BOUQUET

BRIDE

BUTTONHOLE

CARNATION

CARS

CELEBRATE

CHAMPAGNE

ETIQUETTE

FLOWER

FREESIAS

GARTER

```
N B N O O M Y E N O H B T
O Z U T B O U Q U E T E E
I C B T E R U T C I P T N
T Y A S T L F L O W E R G
P A T R A O E P H O T O A
E M O R N I N G S U I T P
C A R S A A S H R R S H M
E L S I A P T E O A K E A
R E T R A G G I E L M D H
T N E S E R P A O R E S C
U A E S S U O R T N F T Q
C E L E B R A T E S A A Y
E T T E U Q I T E D I R B
```

HONEYMOON

MORNING SUIT   RECEPTION

PHOTO   STAG PARTY

PICTURE   TELEGRAMS

PRESENT   TROUSSEAU

Can you finish this picture?

PICK 'N' MIX

Choose three words to describe your home:

Minimal	Poor
Exclusive	Crazy
Filthy	Arty
Designer	Untidy
Disaster	Beautiful

Answers to puzzles on the previous page

Whatever Next?
C – add three to the first number, then take five from the next, add three to the next, take five from the next, etc.

Shape Recognition:

J
H E C

Dice-Section:

B	O	T	T	L	E
P	L	E	A	S	E
S	H	E	R	R	Y
C	R	E	A	S	E
C	L	O	S	E	D
B	L	A	Z	E	R

MIRROR WRITING

Write this word upside down:

TUESDAY

_____

MATCH THAT

Remove four matches to leave four equally-sized triangles – and no loose ends!

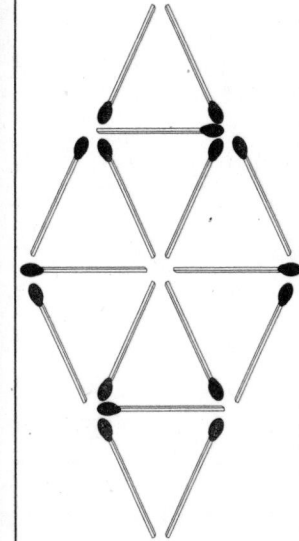

BOX CLEVER

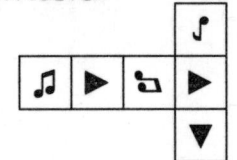

When the above is folded to form a cube, which one of the following can be produced?

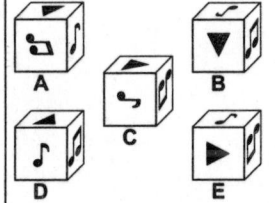

ON TARGET

The answers to the clues read from the outer circle to the centre, all ending with the same letter. When you've finished, the letters in the shaded ring will give a word.

1 Dreadful, shocking
2 Dog's warning sound
3 Source of danger
4 Written slander
5 Artistry
6 Lever operated with the foot

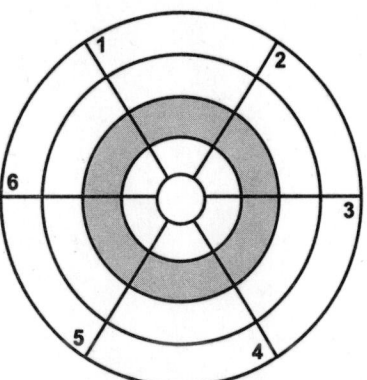

DOMINO PUZZLE

Which domino (A, B, C, D or E) should fill the empty space?

NAME THAT SONG

We give you the first line, you name the song:

Mother, mother, there's too many of you crying

Song: _____

MY NEXT AWARD

What

_____

Presented by

_____

Where

_____

Answers to puzzles on the previous page

Letter Tracker: Forecast, Sunny, Thunderstorm, Lightning, Breezy, Tornado, Cloudy, Overcast, Front, Foggy, Mist, Showers, Changeable, Blizzard, Snow, Sleet, Hail, Downpour.

CHARACTER ASSIGNATION

Fill in the answers to the clues, across the grid. Then read down the diagonal line of eight squares, to reveal:
A character from George Eliot's *Middlemarch*.

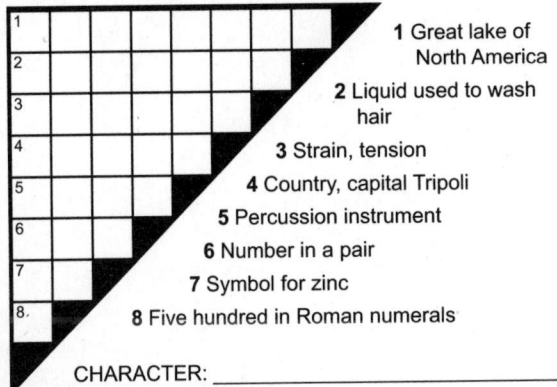

1 Great lake of North America
2 Liquid used to wash hair
3 Strain, tension
4 Country, capital Tripoli
5 Percussion instrument
6 Number in a pair
7 Symbol for zinc
8 Five hundred in Roman numerals

CHARACTER: _____

LOOSE LETTERS

Someone has taken twenty-six different letters of the alphabet from what was once a completed crossword. Can you put them all back in again?

A B C D E F G H I
J K L M N O P Q R
S T U V W X Y Z

TWO-WORD HOROSCOPES

Aries – Read on…

Taurus – Clean up.

Gemini – Bossy animals.

Cancer – Last chance.

Leo – Loveable stories.

Virgo – Great legs!

Libra – Grubby business.

Scorpio – Hopeless ideas.

Sagittarius – Greater patience.

Capricorn – You'll win.

Aquarius – Good hunting.

Pisces – Noodle soup.

EXCUSES FOR

Wasps:

_____
_____
_____
_____
_____

WHERE ON EARTH?

Where on earth is Twatt?

Answer: _____

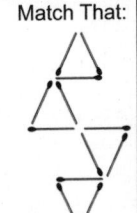

SNAKES & LADDERS

This is a standard game, so when you land at the foot of a ladder, you climb it; and when you land on the head of a snake, you slide down its tail. You need to throw an exact number to land on 100 to win – counting backwards if you don't, eg if you land on 98 and throw a five, you will end up on 97. The dice is thrown for you and always lands in this recurring order: 3, 1, 5, 6, 4, 2, so you can start by immediately placing your counter on square 3. Good luck – hope you win!

DESIGN YOUR OWN

Wilderness

DICEY ARITHMETIC

Using three of the arithmetical signs +, −, x and ÷, can you achieve the correct total? Afterwards, see if you can spot an alternative way to do this.

BERMUDA TRIANGLE

Travel through the 'Bermuda Triangle' by visiting one room at a time and collecting a letter from each. You can enter the outside passageway as often as you like, but can only visit each room once. When you've completed your tour, rearrange the fifteen letters to spell out a word.

L
Y O
D U P
E R N A
T A U S T

TOP TEN

HOUSE ☐

APARTMENT ☐

HOTEL ☐

CABIN ☐

TRAILER ☐

TENT ☐

BEACH-HOUSE ☐

PENTHOUSE ☐

TENEMENT ☐

MANSION ☐

TWO DOWN

Fit five of the seven listed words into the Across rows in the grid, so that the other two words read down the shaded columns numbered 2 and 3.

CORAL   DRUNK
IMPLY   LANCE
MATCH   MORAL
       SLEEK

1	2		3	
4				
5				
6				
7				

THIS WEEK'S PHOBIAS

Selenophobia – Fear of the moon
Sophophobia – Fear of learning
Verbophobia – Fear of words

WHAT DOES IT MEAN?

What is the meaning of the word

VILLIPEND

Answer: _____

_____

CLOCKWORDS

It's a race against the clock…
How many common words of three or more different letters can you make from those on the clockface (without using plurals, proper nouns or abbreviations) in ten minutes? All words must contain BOTH the letters indicated by the hands on the clock.

R I U P T
N G
E A
L W S

NUMB-SKULL

Fit the listed numbers into the grid, crossword-fashion.

2 digits
12
23
29
34
45
56
64
76
91

3 digits
111
323
444
496
541
946

4 digits
1827
1965
7333

5 digits
13144
54312
75352

6 digits
235546
369015

7 digits
1124532
7564453

Answers to puzzles on the previous page

Dicey Arithmetic: The signs are times, plus and minus or minus, times and plus.

WORDWHEEL

Using only the letters in the Wordwheel, you have ten minutes to find as many words as possible, none of which may be plurals, foreign words or proper nouns. Each word must be of three letters or more, all must contain the central letter and letters can only be used once in every word. There is at least one nine-letter word in the wheel.

Nine-letter word: _____

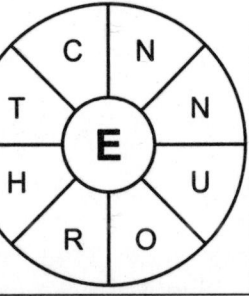

TODAY'S GREATEST ACHIEVEMENT

Sabotage ☐

Subterfuge ☐

Subordination ☐

LEARNING LINES

We give you a line, you tell us who said it and the film:

"You know how to whistle, don't you, Steve? You just put your lips together and blow."

JUST IN CASE

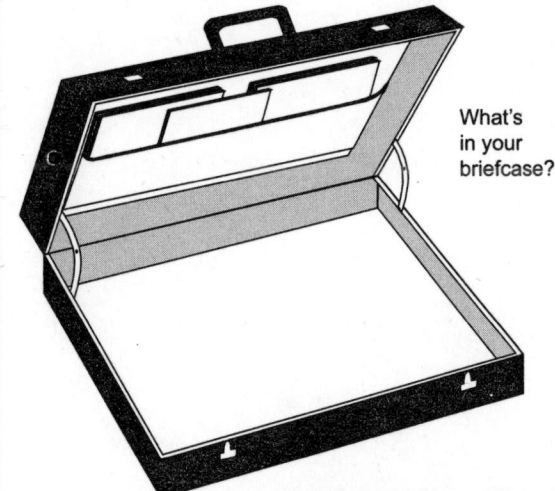

What's in your briefcase?

FOR SALE

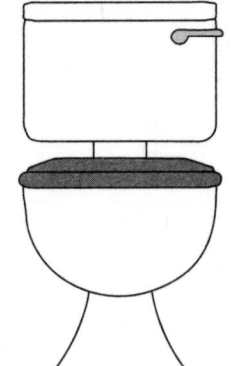

This is worth the asking price

of _____ because it

once belonged to _____

_____,

who used it for _____

_____

ANTONYM WALL

Pair up these set of letters correctly to spell out two words of the same length but with opposite meanings.

TI	NE	VE	PO
TI	SI	VE	GA

_____ & _____

DOMINADDITION

Can you place the remaining dominoes in their correct positions, so that the total number of spots in each of the four rows and five columns equals the sum at the end of that row or column?

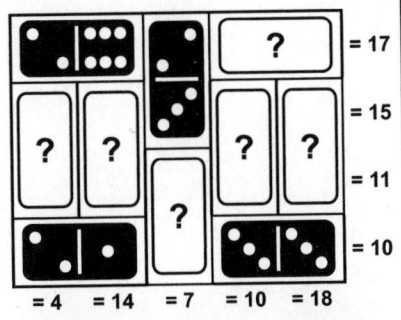

= 17
= 15
= 11
= 10

= 4   = 14   = 7   = 10   = 18

JIGSAW CROSSWORD

Fit the blocks into the empty grid to form a complete crossword which, when finished, will be symmetrical, similar to the example seen here:

 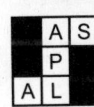  

EGG TIMER

Can you complete this puzzle in the time it takes to boil an egg? The answers to the clues are anagrams of the words immediately above and below, plus or minus a letter.

1 Less exposed to the sun
2 Pungent salad vegetable
3 Splinter (eg of glass)
4 Foolhardy
5 Apportion, dole out
6 Look high and low
7 Bank teller

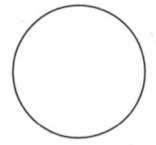
NAMED AND SHAMED

No brains

No sense

No idea

WHO AM I?

Dare that ex-general

I am:

Broken furniture

A sticking plaster which has become too firmly attached to the hair on your leg

Loose floorboards

MISSING LETTERS

One letter of the alphabet is missing from each box. Find them all and place them in the order of the numbered boxes to reveal a six-letter word.

Word: _____

1	2	3
JTXAP	HMTYA	KYZQB
YQBLF	GLSCB	ICPLJ
ZGRMC	PEFIO	SDXHM
KWUDH	ZQDVJ	TOGEW
INVEO	KRWXN	NUAFV

4	5	6
DMWHJ	KZCPG	JQWGA
TPYKB	LQWDI	NROCK
GUXFO	JAVHN	LUXSD
ZVASN	BUFXO	TZMEI
LQCRI	RESYM	BPVFH

CODEWORD

This is a crossword puzzle in code. Every number represents a different letter of the alphabet and this number remains the same throughout the puzzle. Use the check-box to keep a track on your progress.

The grid contains the clue letters A N D at position 1-2-12.

1	2	3	4	5	6	7	8	9	10	11	12	13

14	15	16	17	18	19	20	21	22	23	24	25	26

COUPLINGS

Apart from two, every word listed below can be coupled with one of the others to make another word or phrase. Rearrange the letters of the two which can't be paired together, to form a further TWO WORDS, the name of a body of water.

1 FARM	2 COCK
3 ALARM	4 NARCOTIC
5 ACE	6 ANIMALS
7 WASHING	8 WATER
9 CLOCK	10 MACHINE
11 WHEEL	12 HANGER
13 TURKEY	14 COAT

Answer: _____

REAL WORDS

Which is the real word?

WHILONASTIC ☐

WHILONOBULIST ☐

WHILOM ☐

MASS HYSTERIAS

Today we are all going to:

Abandon the washing up and let mice lick our plates clean instead.

Answers to puzzles on the previous page

Who Am I? Alexander the Great.
Egg Timer: 1 Shadier, 2 Radish, 3 Shard, 4 Rash, 5 Share, 6 Search, 7 Cashier.

Dominaddition:

2	6	2	3	4
0	5	3	2	5
0	2	1	2	6
2	1	1	3	3

Jigsaw Crossword:

I		D	R	E	A	M	S
S	O	F	A		Y		E
S		I	M	M	E	N	S	E
U	B		A	S	I	A	
E	A	R		P		G	Y	M
	R	E	A	L		H		E
D	E	S	S	E	R	T		L
E		K		O	S	L	O
N	U	R	S	E	D		

SWEET BAD MUSIC

So who on earth was responsible for this lyric?

And your loving is satisfying.
Love you such a sweeping –
 good enough to weeping,
And the sweeping that ain't
 fine.

WEATHER for PESSIMISTS

Today the weather will be:

Endless rain, dreary conditions and wet shoes. You will catch a cold.

WORD LADDER

Change one letter at a time (but not the position of any letter) to make a new word – and move from the word at the top of the ladder to the word at the bottom using the exact number of rungs provided.

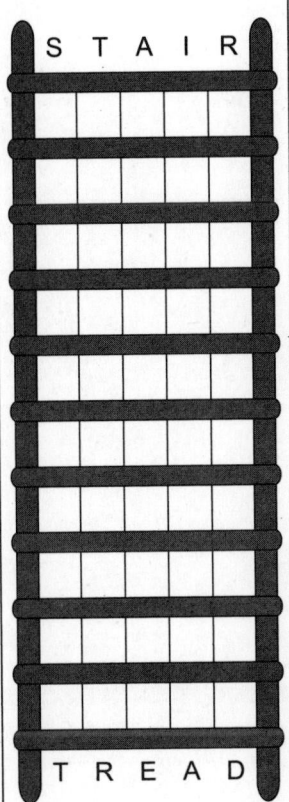

S T A I R

T R E A D

A MATCHING PAIR

Two of these frogs are identical – which two?

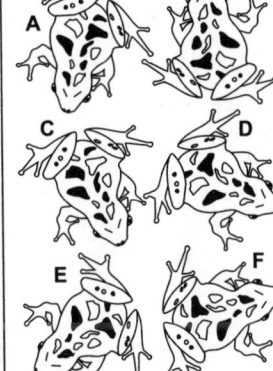

A B C D E F

THOUGHT FOR THE DAY

The enemy of your enemy is your friend.

SYMBOLISM

What whole number value between 1 and 9 should be allocated to each different symbol in order to reach the sum totals shown at the end of each row and column?

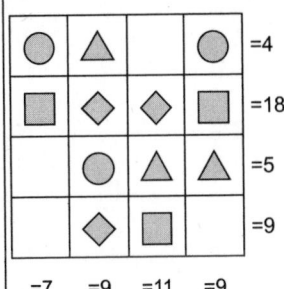

○	△		○	=4
▢	◇	◇	▢	=18
○	△	△		=5
◇	▢			=9
=7	=9	=11	=9	

STARTING LINE

Which three letter word can be placed at the start, to form three seven-letter words?

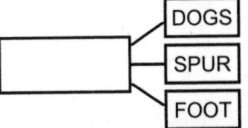

DOGS
SPUR
FOOT

Answers to puzzles on the previous page

Real Words: Whilom. An adjective meaning former.
Couplings: 1/6, 3/9, 7/10, 8/11, 13/2, 14/12. The letters of 4 and 5 can be rearranged to form ARCTIC OCEAN.
Missing Letters: SURETY.

Codeword:

WEATHER for OPTIMISTS

Today the weather will be:

Torrential rain giving your flowers a nice long drink and cleaning your car as well. Perfect.

UNLIKELY CANDIDATE

POP STAR

_____

WAYS TO PASS THE TIME

Wailing ☐

Whimpering ☐

Whispering ☐

PLACE YOUR BETS

In your garden there is/are:

Beautiful flowers and shrubs ☐

An old sofa and a couple of baths ☐

God knows, you haven't been in it this year ☐

SHADY BUSINESS

Shade in these shapes, using different shades where they overlap.

BRIEF SURVIVAL GUIDE

DIETING:
1 Put a lock on the fridge/ cupboards
2 Put a clothes peg on your nose to prevent any sense of smell and taste
3 Buy clothing two sizes too small: you can't leave the house until you lose weight

JOIN THE DOTS

GET IT WRITE

Write these letters upside down, like a mirror image:

A K Q R

THE WHOLE PICTURE

Can you complete the picture?

SECRET MISSION

Your secret mission (should you choose to accept it) is:

To say "What?" happily to every question, as if you haven't understood a word.

Answers to puzzles on the previous page

Sweet Bad Music: Ohio Express, _Yummy Yummy Yummy_.
Pre-Fame Name Game: Sigourney Weaver.
A Matching Pair: E and F.
Starting Line: HOT.
Word Ladder: One solution is STAIR, stain, swain, twain, train, grain, groin, groan, groat, great, treat, TREAD.
Symbolism: Circle=1, Diamond=3, Square=6, Triangle=2.